Mar
a Millionaire

These lucky ladies can't resist their
millionaire's touch…

Three passionate novels!

In July 2007 Mills & Boon bring back
two of their classic collections, each
featuring three favourite romances
by our bestselling authors...

MARRIED TO A MILLIONAIRE

The Millionaire's Marriage Demand
by Sandra Field
At the Millionaire's Bidding
by Lee Wilkinson
Surrender to the Millionaire
by Margaret Mayo

SECRET PASSIONS

The Greek's Secret Passion
by Sharon Kendrick
A Shocking Passion
by Amanda Browning
Passion in Secret by Catherine Spencer

Married to a Millionaire

THE MILLIONAIRE'S MARRIAGE DEMAND
by
Sandra Field

AT THE MILLIONAIRE'S BIDDING
by
Lee Wilkinson

SURRENDER TO THE MILLIONAIRE
by
Margaret Mayo

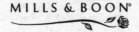
MILLS & BOON®

MILLS & BOON and MILLS & BOON with the Rose Device are registered trademarks of the publisher.
Harlequin Mills & Boon Limited,
Eton House, 18-24 Paradise Road, Richmond, Surrey, TW9 1SR

MARRIED TO A MILLIONAIRE
© by Harlequin Enterprises II B.V./S.à.r.l 2007

The Millionaire's Marriage Demand, At the Millionaire's Bidding and Surrender to the Millionaire were first published in Great Britain by Harlequin Mills & Boon Limited in separate, single volumes.

The Millionaire's Marriage Demand © Sandra Field 2003
At the Millionaire's Bidding © Lee Wilkinson 2003
Surrender to the Millionaire © Margaret Mayo 2003

ISBN: 978 0 263 85520 3

05-0707

Printed and bound in Spain
by Litografia Rosés S.A., Barcelona

THE MILLIONAIRE'S MARRIAGE DEMAND

by

Sandra Field

Although born in England, **Sandra Field** has lived most of her life in Canada; she says the silence and emptiness of the north speaks to her particularly. While she enjoys travelling and passing on her sense of a new place, she often chooses to write about the city which is now her home. Sandra says, 'I write out of my experience; I have learned that love with its joys and its pains is all-important. I hope this knowledge enriches my writing and touches a chord in you, the reader.'

CHAPTER ONE

SHE had the place to herself.

Heaven, Julie thought blissfully. The rocks and salt spray of the coastline where she'd grown up were what she missed most of all when she was overseas.

The tide was lapping at the wharf. She slipped her feet out of her sandals and with scant regard for her pretty summer dress sat down on the rough wood, dangling her legs over the edge. A wave grabbed at her bare toes. She gave a laugh of mingled shock and dismay; the water was icy cold.

What did she expect? After all, this was Maine and it was still June. She splashed her feet vigorously, watching how the golden light of early evening tangled itself in the foam. She was home again. Temporarily, to be sure, and not for the happiest of reasons. But home, nevertheless.

The wharf was at the end of a dirt road. To her ears wafted the sigh of wind through the pines and the chirping of sparrows in the underbrush; overlying everything was the steady hiss of surf against the shore of the nearest island.

Her destination was further out. She was spending the weekend on Manatuck Island, owned by Charles Strathern, whose son Brent had invited her to Charles's sixtieth birthday party tomorrow.

She'd been late leaving work this afternoon. By the time she'd driven from her apartment in Portland to this isolated shoreline, she'd missed the launch that was to have taken her and some of the caterers to the party. Now the launch had to make a return trip just for her.

She should be feeling guilty. But she wasn't. She splashed her feet again, hoping Charles Strathern had a heated swimming pool at Castlereigh, his estate on Manatuck. One thing Brent had made clear was that his father was very rich; the inference being that Brent, also, was more than comfortably off.

Julie sighed. Brent was handsome, charming and out for a good time. This meant, no doubt, that sooner or later she'd be fighting him off. Her spirit of adventure, that had caused her to live for the last few years in faraway places not always known for comfort or safety, didn't extend to sex. Or marriage, for that matter.

But for the space of a weekend, surrounded by Brent's family, she'd be safe enough.

Abruptly she turned her head, straining her ears. What had she just heard? A vehicle coming down the road? She didn't want company. Not right now. Oliver, captain of the launch, had been quite explicit that she was the only guest expected this Friday evening.

The unmistakable crunch of tires on gravel grew louder and louder. Julie scowled at the gold-tinted trees, inwardly urging the unknown interloper to stop at the last cottage a quarter of a mile from the wharf. To stop anywhere but here.

To leave her alone.

As the tires of his sleek black Porsche skidded in the gravel, Travis eased his foot off the accelerator. He was driving too fast. Partly, of course, because he was later than he'd wanted to be. He'd been doing fine until that emergency in intensive care, which had ended very satisfactorily for the patient but had put him way behind schedule.

Lateness wasn't the only reason he was driving fast. Gut-wrenching anxiety was the other reason. His lips stretched in a humorless smile. On a beautiful Friday evening in

June, when he could have been sailing on Penobscot Bay or going to the local opera with that nurse with the come-hither eyes, he was traveling to the one place in the world where he was guaranteed to get the cold shoulder.

Another quarter mile to the wharf. He'd use the phone on the dock there, contact Oliver and ask for the launch to be sent over. Once he was on the island, they couldn't very well send him back. Or if they tried, he'd put up one hell of a fight.

Through the open window he caught the scent of spruce resin mixed with the sharp tang of the ocean; he breathed deeply, filling his lungs, and for an instant was a little boy again, roaming the cliffs and rocky shoreline of Manatuck Island. Happy. Secure. With no inkling of what was to come.

It wasn't just the family he was returning to. It was the island as well. Of the two, he wasn't sure which had the greater potential for damage.

Probably the island.

Insanity to come back. Pure insanity.

The car swung around the last corner, and from the rise Travis saw the bay spread in front of him, its velvet-green islands sprinkling the deep blue waters, foam edging them like white ruffs. His throat tightened. One reason he'd driven himself so hard the last few years was to bury the blend of yearning and emptiness that was popularly called homesickness.

He jammed his foot on the brake. Someone was sitting on the wharf.

His gaze narrowed. Was it a teenager from one of the cottages up the road? Dammit, he didn't need company. If there was one time in his life he needed to be alone, it was right now, while he was waiting for the launch.

It wasn't a kid. It was a woman. She must be the driver

of the blue car that was parked by the side of the road above the wharf.

Travis swung the wheel, his tires grabbing at the gravel, and parked behind the blue sedan. It had a rental sign on the back bumper, he noticed absently. He got out of his car, slammed the door and strode down the slope toward the dock; as he did so, the woman stood up.

He'd get rid of her as fast as he could and then he'd contact Oliver.

Because the sun was behind him, she was bathed in soft light. His footsteps slowed. How could he ever have mistaken her for a young girl? Her flowered dress was full-skirted with a bodice that clung to her breasts and bared her shoulders and arms; her ankles and feet were soaking wet. Her hair was cut short, a gleaming dark cap that emphasized the slim line of her throat and her winged brows.

She was exquisitely, unbelievably beautiful.

She also, he realized, looked as displeased to see him as he'd been to see her. She said coolly, taking the initiative in a way that irked him, "Hello. Are you lost?" Giving him a quick survey that no doubt took in all six feet of him in his faded jeans and casual open-necked shirt, she added politely, "The road, as you see, comes to an end here. Perhaps you were looking for Bartlett Cove? The turnoff's about a half a mile back."

"No," Travis said brusquely, "I'm not lost—but you're trespassing. This wharf is on private property. It belongs to the owner of Manatuck Island."

"That's where I'm going."

"Oh? The party's not until tomorrow—did you get the timing wrong?"

"No, I didn't," she replied crisply.

His eyes clashed with her green ones. They couldn't really be that color, he thought. Eyes of a deep true green were very rare, and made comparisons with emeralds in-

evitable. Hers, at the moment, certainly looked as unyielding as emeralds. She was several inches shorter than he;
why, when his normal fancy was for laughing blondes who
were nearly his height, was he lusting after a brunette who
looked about as warm as the ocean in January?

Light played across her high cheekbones, making him
itch to stroke them; it took an actual physical effort to keep
his hands at his sides. And all the while he was forcing
himself to keep his gaze well above the entrancing shadow
of her cleavage. What the devil was wrong with him?

Think, Travis. Use your much-vaunted brains. "Let me
guess," he said softly. "You're arriving early on the island
because you're Brent's date."

She bit one delectable lip. "How did you know?"

"Brent's always had a weakness for females with great
bodies and more than passably pretty faces."

"When you've just complimented me twice over, why
do I feel as though I've been thoroughly insulted?"

The wind suddenly seized her skirt, flattening it to her
legs, then tugging it free to briefly bare her thighs. As she
clutched at the brilliantly flowered fabric, thrusting it down
to cover herself, Travis said hoarsely, "Your eyes—you
must be wearing colored contacts?"

He'd had no intention of asking anything so personal;
and was nevertheless furious when she disregarded his
question. "Are you going to Manatuck as well?" she said
bluntly.

"I am."

"And whose date are you?"

"Oh, I'm on my own," Travis said, giving her a smile
that in no way touched his eyes. Eyes that could look
through you as though you weren't there, Julie thought edgily, and heard him add, "I don't belong to anyone, it's
against my principles."

"A principle I happen to share."

"I doubt that. Not if you're Brent's date."

The slight emphasis he put on the word *date* brought a flush to her cheeks. "His date is precisely—" she began, then broke off. Why was she defending her morals to a complete stranger?

He gave a short laugh. "I'm glad you didn't bother finishing your sentence. Brent's reputation precedes him."

"I won't ask if you're a friend of his. Obviously you're not."

"You got that right."

There was a depth of bitterness to his words that shocked Julie; she was suddenly aware of how tightly strung he was. As though he could explode any moment, she thought uneasily, and for the first time wished the wharf wasn't quite so isolated. Not another person in sight, and the nearest house a quarter of a mile up the road.

Normally she wasn't easily scared. She'd had too many close calls for that, too many times when she'd had to depend on her own resourcefulness to get her out of threatening situations. And this was Maine. Not Lima, or Dares-Salaam, or Calcutta.

When he'd walked down the slope toward her, he'd moved with the unconscious grace of the tiger she'd been lucky enough to sight in the mangrove swamps of West Bengal. Tigers might be graceful. They were also dangerous and had very sharp teeth.

Get a grip, Julie scolded herself. She had a trick or two up her sleeve when it came to self-defense. And so what if he was the kind of man who'd guarantee that any woman worthy of the name would be chomping at the bit? She said with a valiant attempt at friendliness, holding out her hand, "My name's Julie Renshaw."

With huge reluctance Travis clasped her hand, then dropped it as fast as he decently could. "Travis Strathern," he said.

She frowned. "Are you a cousin of Brent's?"

"No."

She flushed again at a reply whose brevity verged on rudeness. "Let me be honest," she said pleasantly. "I was really enjoying being alone until you came along, and it's pretty clear you're not craving my company. But we have to wait here for the launch and share the trip to the island. Couldn't we at least talk about the weather? Which, you must admit, is perfectly glorious."

Travis was known in some circles as a diplomat for his ability to smooth ruffled feathers under difficult circumstances; why had this ability been turned on its head by a pair of emerald eyes? He said incautiously, "If you think sunset's beautiful, wait until you see the sun rise through a mist lying low on the water…"

For a moment his gaze was lost in the past. Julie said curiously, "You've obviously been here before. If your last name's Strathern, I'm surprised they don't know you're coming—Oliver said I was the only guest arriving today."

They didn't know he was coming because he hadn't told them. Simple. Restlessly moving his shoulders, Travis said, "There must have been a mix-up."

He was, Julie thought, a very bad liar. But why would he bother lying to a complete stranger? Intent upon learning more about him, she said easily, "Have you visited Manatuck often?

"Not for years," he said shortly. "How did you meet Brent?"

"Through mutual friends. We've only had a couple of dates. But I've always wanted to stay on one of the islands, so I must admit I jumped at the chance of this weekend."

To his horror, Travis heard himself say, "So you're not Brent's lover?"

His question hung in the air. Julie said coolly, "You didn't mean to ask that, did you?"

She was much too astute for his own liking. "You're right—it was the wrong question," he said. "I should have asked if your eyes are really that green?"

If her eyes were green, Julie thought furiously, his were a startling blue. Yet close up, they yielded as little information about what lay below the surface as did the ocean. "Why do you care what color my eyes are?"

"Put it down to idle curiosity."

"I don't think anything's idle where you're concerned," she said dryly. "So if you're not Brent's cousin, who are you?"

His eyes narrowed. "What if I'm his elder brother?"

"What if the launch is docking right now?" she replied with gentle mockery. "He's never mentioned a brother to me."

"I'm sure he hasn't. What if you tell me the real color of your eyes?"

Thoughtfully Julie gazed up at him. She was realistic enough to know that her eyes were her best feature. Her creamy skin she was apt to curse in these days of high UV and sunscreen; her body had gotten her into hot water too many times to be considered a desirable asset. As for her hair, she'd cut it short several years ago, partly because Africa and India were hot countries, partly because she'd read somewhere that waist-length hair turned men into lustful idiots. Quite suddenly she began to laugh. "I'm not wearing contacts at all, bright green or otherwise—I have twenty-twenty vision. Do you want to know something else? My mother always said I was stubborn. But compared to you, I'm a rank amateur."

Although his own smile was reluctant, it changed his face immeasurably. The strong nose, firmly carved lips and hewn chin were still the same, as was the unruly hair, so dark as to be almost black; but the smile brought his features to life in a way that was wholly masculine and incredibly, compellingly sexy. Male energy, Julie thought dazedly, that's what powers him. Forceful, formidable and hugely charismatic energy. It enveloped her, almost as if he'd put his arms around her.

She took an unconscious step backward, saying breathlessly, "I've met a lot of men the last few years, many of them very attractive. But you, I have to say, take the cake."

His lashes flickered. Then he said ironically, "Good line. Now are you going to ask for my phone number? Brent won't like that."

"Don't tell me you're not fighting the women off. Because I won't believe you."

"Yeah," he drawled, "I fight 'em off. Like I said, I don't belong to anyone."

"Neither do I," she said softly. "And that includes Brent."

A flicker of rage removed any vestige of Travis's smile; Brent, unless Travis was very much mistaken, was the one who'd sealed his exile from Manatuck and from his father all those years ago. Was that why he couldn't bear the thought of Julie Renshaw as his brother's lover? But he'd only just met the woman. Why should he care what she did, or with whom? "Let me give you a word of advice," he said curtly. "Keep your distance from Brent this weekend. For your own good."

She blinked. "You hate him, don't you?" she said slowly.

"No! But I wouldn't want to see you out of your depth."

Too late, she thought with a flash of humor. Ten minutes of Travis's company and she was seriously out of her depth. She said, "I'm not going to—oh, there's the launch."

A sleek powerboat had just appeared from behind the nearest island. Travis's head swung around, his whole body taut with tension. Julie gaped up at him, quite sure he'd instantly and completely forgotten her presence. It was as though he were steeling himself for an ordeal, she thought wildly. As though whatever had brought him here would require all the courage and endurance he possessed.

He possessed a good deal. Intuitively she knew that.

Her gaze dropped. His fists were clenched at his sides, the knuckles white. With a compassion that had gotten her into trouble before, she rested a hand on his bare arm. "There's something really wrong here, isn't there?" she said. "Won't you tell me what it is? Maybe I can help."

Travis dragged his eyes away from the launch: the same launch on which, at the age of sixteen, he'd fled the island. He said with icy precision, "Why don't you mind your own business?"

She flinched, snatching her hand back. "Fine. Forget I asked."

In a whirl of skirts she ran away from him, along the length of the wharf and up the slope, her sandals scrabbling in the loose dirt. Once she reached her vehicle, she unlocked the trunk and took out a bag. Then she leaned against the side of the car, ostentatiously staring into the woods as though the pine trees were the most fascinating sight she'd ever seen.

Travis's jaw tightened. He didn't need her help. He didn't need anyone's. Ever since he'd first been banished from the island at the age of six, he'd managed on his own. And no woman, no matter how beautiful, was going to change that.

CHAPTER TWO

MOODILY Travis stared out to sea, where the setting sun was glancing off the polished bow of the launch. Unimaginatively, she was named *Manatuck,* after the island. A boat named after a woman was not for Charles; despite his two marriages, Charles Strathern didn't have much use for women.

Even less use for his elder son.

Or for his only daughter. Travis already knew that Jenessa wouldn't be on Manatuck for her father's birthday.

The launch was close enough that he could see Oliver's stout figure at the wheel; the bow wave curved backward in two white arcs. Slowly Travis turned and walked up the slope. He had to pass Julie's car to get to his. "Time to go down to the wharf," he said.

She nodded and headed down the hill. Her hips swung gracefully; her narrow shoulders filled him with passionate yearning. For what? For Brent's leftovers?

It was eighteen years since he'd laid eyes on Brent. Twice, in the early years, he'd made an effort to see his brother. But both times Brent had canceled their meeting at the last minute, and so Travis had stopped trying. Through mutual acquaintances he'd heard news over the years, mostly about Brent's profligate spending and strings of women.

Of which Julie Renshaw was the latest.

Cursing under his breath, Travis hefted his bag from the back seat. He dumped it on the wharf a few moments later and stationed himself by the rubber tires tied to the pilings to protect *Manatuck's* hull. Oliver cut the engine and with a grappling hook latched onto one of the metal rungs bolted to the wharf. Then he looked up at the tall, dark-haired man on the dock. "Master Travis? Is that really you?"

The old name took Travis aback. He said, emotion roughening his voice, "Oliver…how are you? It's great to see you. But none of that master stuff—Travis is good enough."

"They didn't tell me you were coming," Oliver said gruffly, shoving his greasy cap further back on his head. "Darned if it's not good to see you, boy."

Oliver was almost bald, Travis noticed, and must have gained thirty pounds in the intervening years. "They don't know I'm coming—it's a surprise," he said dryly. "Isn't that the same shirt you were wearing the day I left?"

Oliver glanced down dubiously. "Can't be. Would have wore out by now. Looks like I spilled my dinner on it, though."

Forgetting his tension in a surge of affection, Travis said, "*Manatuck* looks good." The decks were shiny, the brass polished to a high luster, and the paintwork immaculate.

"She's aging better than I am," Oliver said. "Come on aboard, it'll be like old times."

No, it won't, Travis thought. You can't go back, he'd learned that the hard way. He said, indicating the woman standing silently beside him, "This is Julie Renshaw. Brent's date."

"Ah, yes," Oliver said, his faded blue eyes assessing her shrewdly. "Hand her bag down, Mr. Travis, and we'll get going. The tide'll be turning soon, and I'd just as soon be clear of the channel."

Julie picked up her bag. "I can manage," she announced, and passed it down to Oliver. Then she clambered down the metal rungs and jumped lightly onto the deck. "Hi, Oliver…I'm pleased to meet you."

Oliver grinned, baring the gap in his teeth that had been

there for as long as Travis could remember. "Master Brent arrived yesterday," he said. "Aren't you the pretty one, now."

Julie blushed. "Thank you."

Travis had also descended the ladder. The deck swayed gently beneath his feet. As Oliver dropped the grappling hook, Travis pushed off; with a sweet purr of her engines, *Manatuck* left the dock. Julie had stationed herself against the railing, where she could see where they were headed, but also keep Travis and Oliver in view. If Oliver liked Travis, then Travis couldn't be all bad, she thought. But there was a mystery attached to his return; the family didn't know about it, and she'd have sworn when she'd asked Brent about any siblings, he'd said no.

It looked like her weekend was shaping up to be more interesting than she'd expected. Rather too interesting. Travis had planted his feet on the deck, the wind ruffling his thick hair; his physique, broad-shouldered and slim-hipped, made her feel weak at the knees. Brent, technically the more handsome of the two men, and certainly friendlier, didn't have that effect at all.

Not that it mattered. She wasn't in the market for a lover, and definitely not for a husband.

The bay was choppy. She moved forward, clutching the railing, and wondered which of the islands was their destination. Fifteen minutes later, she was in no doubt. On the most rugged island in the bay, four stone turrets pierced the jagged outline of the spruce trees; Castlereigh, she thought with a quiver of inner laughter, and watched it come closer. A stone boathouse, twice the size of her parents' bungalow, anchored a long wharf which jutted out from the island; there was also a raked sand beach, and a vast expanse of manicured lawn.

Skillfully Oliver steered the launch to nudge the dock; Travis jumped ashore and fastened the lines. Then he reached down a hand to Julie. His face was inscrutable; his eyes didn't meet hers.

He lifted her to the dock as easily as if she were a child. Oliver slung their bags up. "See you tomorrow, Mr. Travis. Right glad you're back where you belong."

Although Travis had no idea where he belonged, he was almost sure it wasn't here. "Thanks, Oliver," he said, and picked up the two bags. "Let's go," he said to Julie.

He was striding up a long wooden stairway as though pursued by the hounds of hell. She jogged after him, past a thicket of rhododendrons and azaleas, followed by an enormous formal rose garden that would have graced the grounds of Versailles but was definitely out of place here. Then they rounded a copse of birch trees and she stopped dead in her tracks. "Well," she said inadequately.

For a moment Travis stopped, too. "It does kind of take your breath away, doesn't it?" he said wryly.

An array of crenellations, archways, porticos and buttresses was crowned by the four soaring turrets she'd seen from the launch. There was even a partial moat. She said faintly, "It's certainly imposing."

"It's a godawful monument to the triumph of money and egotism over taste," Travis said succinctly. "And you've only seen the outside."

"You mean there's more?"

"All that the almighty dollar can buy."

He looked fractionally less tense, Julie was glad to see. Although why his emotional state should matter to her, she didn't have a clue. He hadn't exactly been friendly to her; she'd better keep that in mind. "Is there a front door?" she asked. "Shouldn't I be mounted on a snow-white charger?"

"A suit of armor's not a bad idea," he said with a touch of grimness. "Follow me."

A massive bell pull dangled by twin doors that were

ornately spiked with wrought iron. Travis pulled the bell and pushed one door open. An aged butler was crossing the entrance hall. "Master Travis," he said, clutching his tailored black jacket in the vicinity of his heart. "Oh, Master Travis...how wonderful to see you, sir. It's been a long time."

"Hello, Bertram," Travis said, shaking the old man's hand. "Thought I'd surprise the family. How's your family, by the way?"

"Very well indeed. Peg will be so happy to know you're here. Cocktails are being served in the drawing room, sir. Shall I announce you?"

"Why don't you do that? This is Julie Renshaw, Brent's date."

Bertram gave her a courtly nod. In a procession of three they marched past a bloodthirsty display of medieval weapons, then down an imposing corridor checkered with portraits; not one of the painted faces, Julie noticed, looked at all happy to be hanging on the walls of Castlereigh. Travis didn't look very happy to be here, either.

As Bertram ushered them through a wide doorway, Travis took her by the hand. His fingers were cold; not for anything would she have let go of them. Bertram quavered, "Miss Julie Renshaw and Mr. Travis Strathern."

Three people were seated on overstuffed leather chesterfields in a room that dwarfed them with its dimensions. Quantities of marble and velvet, and carpets as big as playing fields were Julie's first impressions; her second the reaction of each of the three people to Travis's presence.

Brent leaped to his feet, turning to face the door. Hatred, raw and implacable, scored his face. He looked so unlike his usual handsome, carefree self that the hair rose on the back of Julie's neck. The older man, who must be Charles Strathern, looked terrified out of his wits; while the woman, impeccably dressed in linen and pearls, projected a well-bred mixture of dismay and distaste. Brent's stepmother, Julie decided, and watched as polite masks replaced all these initial, instinctive reactions.

Then Brent walked over to her, the lamplight shining in his golden hair, his perfect teeth stretched in a smile she would have sworn was genuine. She hadn't imagined the hatred, though. She knew she hadn't. "Julie!" he said, taking her by the shoulders. "How lovely you look." Before she could duck, he kissed her hard and thoroughly on the mouth.

Squirming free of Brent, suppressing the instinct to wipe her mouth with the back of her hand, she sputtered, "Hello, Brent. Sorry I'm late. But luckily Travis and I were able to get the launch together."

"Ah yes...my long-lost brother," Brent said. "A surprise birthday present, Travis. Is that what you are?"

His hazel eyes were entirely unamused; he was balancing lightly on the balls of his feet. Travis said easily, "Yes, I thought I'd surprise you all."

"How gratifying to have had such instant success," Brent said smoothly. "Be sure and tell Dad he hasn't aged," he added, swinging around to include Charles in his brilliant smile.

Why had it never struck her before how aggressive that smile was? Julie wondered. Or was she simply seeing for the first time what lay beneath the charm? She hadn't liked being kissed by him. Hadn't liked it at all. By kissing her, Brent had been getting at Travis, she'd swear to it; in that sense, it had been nothing to do with her.

Charles Strathern stepped forward. He was a tall man with iron-grey hair rigidly combed across his scalp, his chin stubborn rather than strong; he was wearing a tailored business suit. If he had been frightened earlier, he now had himself firmly under control. Making no effort to hug his son, or even shake his hand, he looked Travis up and down. "You'll just have time to change for dinner."

"I'll have a Scotch on the rocks first," Travis said calmly, yet with a note in his voice that caused his father's eyes to drop.

"Fine," Charles said. "Help yourself. But kindly say hello to your stepmother."

"Corinne," Travis said, crossing the room with that economical grace Julie had noticed earlier. He bent and brushed her perfectly made-up cheek with his lips. "You look very well."

"Thank you, Travis," she said coolly, without reciprocating his gesture. "Get your drink and I'll ring for Bertram to set another place for dinner."

Brent pulled Julie forward. "Dad, Corinne, this is Julie Renshaw. Julie, my father Charles Strathern, and my stepmother, Corinne Strathern."

Julie shook hands, murmured the usual inanities, and was offered an array of drinks. She chose vodka and orange, and heard herself chatting on about the boat trip and the rose garden. Corinne offered her a tour of the garden in the morning, then Charles led her to the far wall to show her an oil painting of *Manatuck's* predecessor. Travis said nothing.

Half an hour later, having been shown to her room, Julie closed the door and leaned back against the panels. She had fifteen minutes until dinner. Her sole desire was to run down the slope and beg Oliver to take her back to the mainland. Pronto.

What on earth had Travis done to make his return so little a cause for rejoicing? While Oliver and Bertram had been genuinely pleased to see him, his family was acting as if a viper had dropped into their midst. No one had welcomed him, or asked him how he was. Or why he was back.

The other glaringly obvious question was why he'd left. Why, when, and how.

She could always ask. Right, she thought ironically. A sure way to commit social suicide.

Her bag had been unpacked, and her clothes pressed and hung in a cavernous walk-in cupboard. Quickly Julie showered and changed into white silk pants with a long tunic, jade earrings that she'd bought at a bazaar in Tanzania dangling from her lobes, and jade-green sandals on her feet. Makeup, a quick brush through her hair and she was ready.

It was going to be a long evening.

As she walked down the hallway toward the magnificent curved staircase, another door opened. Travis said, "Wait, Julie, we'll go down together. Otherwise you'll get lost."

She turned. He was wearing a dark grey suit with a thin-striped shirt and silk tie; but his hair was still unruly, and his eyes remained that burning and unrevealing blue. Her heart quickened. Had she called him attractive? What a wishy-washy word for a man who exuded such a powerful combination of intelligence, willpower and animal grace. A man who pulled her toward him with every breath he took.

Which certainly made him unique. Normally she was immune to sexy, charismatic men. Avoided them like the plague.

He stopped a foot away from her, giving her a leisurely survey. "Very elegant—less is always more, isn't it? Something neither Charles nor Corinne has ever learned."

"I'm to take that as a compliment?"

"Don't fish, Julie."

"How else am I to find out what you're thinking?"

"You can take it as read that you're the most beautiful woman I've ever seen."

Her jaw dropped inelegantly. *"Me?"*

"Come on—you've looked in the mirror."

"My mouth is too wide and my nose is off-center."

"Only slightly. I never did have much use for perfection." Deliberately he reached out and ran his finger across the curve of her cheekbone to the corner of her mouth, where it lingered for a moment. "I've been wanting to do that since we met," he said thickly.

Warm color flooded her cheeks. "Come off it. You wanted the wharf to yourself when we met," she retorted. "Which, after that scene in the drawing room, I can fully understand. So please don't pretend you were overcome by the sight of me."

"You need to know two things about me. I don't pretend. And I'm capable of holding more than one emotion at once."

Wasn't she the same? If fury and lust could be called emotions, she was certainly swamped by both right now. Not that she was going to tell him that. She said lamely, "We're going to be late for dinner. Punishable by confinement in the dungeon."

"In irons." Travis held out his arm. "Let's go."

It was a challenge. He was daring her, Brent's date, to walk into the dining room on his arm. "Don't use me to get at your younger brother," she flared.

"Don't drag me down to his level."

He was saying, indirectly, that he wanted to take her arm for his own sake. Subduing a treacherous thrill of pleasure, she said, "Does anyone ever win an argument with you?"

He said dryly, "I have a feeling you could."

"I wish I shared that feeling," she said, and slid her fingers through the crook of his elbow, searingly aware of the taut muscles of his forearm under the expensive cloth. "Why are you here, Travis?" she blurted.

He said flatly, "It's time I made peace with my father. His sixtieth birthday seemed as good a time as any to start."

She looked straight up at him. "If peace is what you want, wouldn't you have been better to let him know you were coming? He looked scared out of his wits when he saw you."

"So you noticed that as well." Travis frowned. "Anger I'd have understood. But not fear."

"What if he doesn't want to make peace with you?"

"Then I'll just have to find a way to make it happen, won't I? And don't ask why I left, because I won't tell you."

"Well, that's straightforward enough." She gave him an impish grin. "This conversation will, I'm sure, be the only real one of the whole evening."

"What would you do if I kissed you right now?"

She blinked, swallowing hard. "Scream for help? Haul you into the nearest bedroom? How do I know?"

"Then we'd better postpone it until we have the time to find out," Travis said, and set off down the corridor as imperturbably as if they'd been discussing the weather.

Julie scurried along beside him, her head buzzing with questions, her body, regrettably, aching with a hunger that had nothing to do with dinner. When would she ever learn to keep a guard on her tongue?

How could she have said that about hauling him into the nearest bedroom? She'd never hauled a man into a bedroom in her life; and she wasn't going to start with Travis Strathern.

CHAPTER THREE

DINNER was an interminable, exquisitely prepared meal during which Brent flirted with Julie unrelentingly, Corinne talked at great length about gardens of the eighteenth century, and Charles and Travis said very little. Julie did learn two things. Travis was a doctor, and he'd left home eighteen years ago.

It didn't seem like much for the better part of two long hours, every minute of which seethed with the undercurrents of things unsaid. Just like home, Julie thought with a touch of panic. When had her parents ever voiced an honest emotion or spoken out of a genuine need? Never. Excruciating politeness was the way they operated, too, just like the Stratherns. And it was from that deadly politeness that she herself had run away from home at the age of seventeen and a half.

By ten o'clock Julie had the beginnings of a headache, which she used as the excuse to beg off after-dinner drinks on the stone patio that led from the dining room. As Brent accompanied her to the dining-room doorway, she managed to turn her head so that his good-night kiss hit her cheek rather than her mouth. His fingers digging into her arm with punitive strength, he said in a voice laden with innuendo, "Sleep well, darling."

"Thank you...good night, everyone."

She almost ran up the stairs to her room. Once inside, after a moment's thought, she locked the door, using the heavy brass key. Brent hadn't liked her entering the dining room arm in arm with Travis. Brent might possibly be planning a middle-of-the-night revenge. Well, she'd foiled that, she thought smugly, and stripped off her clothes.

Accepting Brent's invitation for the weekend hadn't been the smartest move of her life. But she'd had two fun-filled dates with him, the first a seafood dinner followed by a movie, the other sailing with two other couples in the bay; so it had seemed safe enough to come to Manatuck. It might well have been safe if only Travis hadn't shown up.

Travis wasn't safe.

She pulled on her nightgown and prowled around the room, picking up some of the heavy marble statuettes and putting them down again. Why was a bedroom in a fake medieval castle decorated with naked Greek goddesses, an Elizabethan four-poster and imitation Louis XIV chairs? Travis was right. Too much hard cash and too little restraint.

She was thinking about Travis again. As the soft fabric of her gown brushed her nipples, she shivered, wondering what it would be like were he to touch her breasts. His fingers were long and lean, and his strength and lightning-swift reactions she'd already experienced. When had she ever felt such helpless and overwhelming hunger for a man's touch?

Never. She'd been too busy keeping each and every man she met at a distance. So why didn't that work with Travis?

With an impatient sigh, Julie put a simpering marble nymph back on the mantel of the Victorian tile fireplace. She'd eaten too much, that was her problem; and her brain was as restless as a squirrel in a cage. She carefully opened the glass doors to the balcony, which was screened with lush Virginia creeper and scented with the climbing roses espaliered below her window. What had Corinne called them? Evangeline?

The soft swish of waves on the shore soothed her ears; a delicate crescent moon was couched on an array of sparkling stars. And then she heard something else: the scrape of chairs on flagstone, and voices. All too familiar voices coming from the patio two stories down. Her body tensed.

"I fail to understand why you didn't warn us you were coming," Charles said furiously.

"Because I knew you'd tell me to stay away," Travis said.

"You'd have been right. Don't you realize that tomorrow night all my friends will be here? That we'll have to make up some kind of story to account for your presence?"

"Tell them the truth, Dad. That I've come home to make peace with you."

"You must see that your father couldn't possibly do that," Corinne interposed. "You abandoned us all eighteen years ago, Travis. You can't expect to walk in as though nothing's happened."

"Abandonment can go two ways, Corinne."

"Nonsense! You always had a home here."

"The minute my mother died, I was parceled off to boarding school. I wasn't even allowed back on the island the first two summers."

"That was before my time," Corinne said fastidiously.

"Boarding school was the best place for you," Charles snapped. "You never liked the Boston house. And out here you were running wild. Spending day after day on the cliffs watching seagulls when you should have been playing football."

"Stick to the facts. You didn't want me around."

"Boarding school made a man out of you."

"Was that what it did? So why did you kick me out of the house when I turned sixteen?"

"You know the answer to that—you'd smeared my name in all the papers, made a laughingstock out of me. And then to cap it all you stole the family ring." Charles's voice roughened. "Where is that ring, Travis? Did you sell it?"

"I never took it."

"It disappeared the same night you did…I've never forgiven you for stealing it like a common thief."

"If you knew me at all, Dad, you'd know that I might stab you in the chest, but never in the back. It's not the way I operate."

Brent said smoothly, "So your opportune arrival this evening doesn't have anything to do with the lawyers who are going to rewrite Dad's will in the next couple of weeks?"

There was a small, deadly silence. Julie held herself painfully still, knowing she shouldn't be listening, afraid that if she retreated to her room, they'd hear her. "No," Travis rapped. "This is the first I've heard of it. I don't need Dad's money, I've got my own."

"What you earn as a doctor?" Brent mocked. "Come off it, brother dear—we're talking big bucks here."

"Are you forgetting I inherited my share of Grandad's money when I turned thirty? You'll do the same, Brent. Or can't you wait that long?"

Corinne said sharply, "Stop it, you two! This has gone on long enough. You've come back, Travis, but in view of all you've done, reconciliation is impossible. You must leave in the morning. I'll order the launch first thing after breakfast."

"No, Corinne," Travis said, so quietly Julie had to strain to hear him.

"Of course you must leave!" Charles blustered.

"I'll make that unanimous," Brent said lazily.

Travis said evenly, "I left when I was just a kid. Barely sixteen. I'm thirty-four now, and I've changed. I don't want your money, Dad, I never did. But I do want my family back. You back. It's that simple."

"You ran away," Charles fumed. "For six weeks we

didn't even know if you were alive or dead. And you took the ring with you.''

"I'm sorry I didn't get in touch. But I was young, and just as headstrong as my father. As for the ring, all I can say is that I never touched it. For heaven's sake, Dad, I knew what that ring meant to you.''

"You trashed me in the press.''

"You were hiring illegal immigrants in your factories and paying them a pittance,'' Travis said, exasperated. "I spoke to you about it, begged you to increase their wages and approach immigration so they could get their papers. But you refused. So yes, I went to the press. I didn't know what else to do.''

"You'd do it again, wouldn't you?''

"I'd find some other way of dealing with it now.''

"You haven't really changed,'' Charles said in a hard voice.

"The past is the past. Can't we let it go?''

"Corinne's right…you must leave in the morning.''

"Unless you're prepared to set Bertram and Oliver on me, I'm staying,'' Travis said with a lightness that didn't quite ring true.

A chair was pushed back. Corinne said briskly, "Why don't we all sleep on it? I'm sure in the morning you'll have reconsidered, Travis, and see our point of view. Are you coming, Charles? Bertram will clean up. Good night, Brent.''

"Good night, Dad,'' Travis said.

"Humph,'' said Charles. The patio door closed with a decisive click.

"In disgrace again, Travis,'' Brent said lightly. "Just like old times.''

"What did you do with the ring, Brent?''

Brent hesitated just too long. "Nothing!''

"Somebody took the ring, and it wasn't me. That leaves

you. Did you hide it somewhere? Come on, you were only ten. No one's going to hold it against you after all these years.''

"It won't wash, Travis. Why don't you just confess? Who knows, Dad might even forgive you.''

"He loved that ring. Tell me where it is.''

"Lay off,'' Brent said in a furious whisper. "And lay off Julie as well. She's my date, not yours.''

"I don't know Julie very well, but I do know one thing— she's got a mind of her own. Why don't we let her decide whose date she is?''

"Stay out of my way—I'm telling you!''

"I don't take orders kindly. Especially from you…good night, Brent.''

Again Julie heard the soft swish of the patio door. Then, making her jump, a glass suddenly shattered, as though Brent had hurled it against the stone wall. A chair clattered to the floor. Once again, the door clicked shut.

She took a long, shaky breath. How was she ever going to behave tomorrow as though ignorant of all she'd overheard? No wonder eavesdropping wasn't recommended.

She now knew why Travis had left the island, and why he hadn't been welcomed home. After the public exposure of his father's labor practices and a stolen heirloom ring it was little wonder his family wasn't embracing him.

But her mind seethed with other images: a tousle-haired boy watching the gulls soar by the cliffs. The same boy exiled to boarding school and not allowed back to his island home for two long years. Tears pricked at the back of her eyes.

Oliver and Bertram, she'd be willing to bet, didn't believe Travis had stolen the family ring. But if he hadn't, who had? Brent?

She gave a heavy sigh. Bed. That's what she needed. Bed and a good night's sleep.

Would she wake in the morning to find that Travis had reconsidered? And once again had left the island?

Eventually Julie did fall asleep. She dreamed about Travis, first that they were driving full speed on a gravel road to an island where they would dig for hidden treasure, gold rings and rusty, iron-studded suits of armor; and then, abruptly, that they were making impassioned love on a blanket of roses called Evangeline. The dream slid into wakefulness, into a flicker of candlelight and a man's hand fumbling for her breast. Travis, she thought in a flood of delight, and turned to face him, opening her eyes.

Travis didn't have blond hair.

It wasn't Travis. It was Brent.

She shoved herself backward in the bed, hit her wrist on one of the four posts and tumbled off the edge in a welter of sheets. Frantically she struggled to extricate herself. "For Pete's sake, Julie," Brent hissed, "what are you trying to do? Wake the entire household?"

She tugged at her nightgown, covering her breasts. "Get out of here—right now."

He rolled off the other side of the bed as she scrambled to her feet; he was bare-chested, she noticed with the small part of her brain that appeared to be working. "How did you get in?" she demanded. "I locked the door."

"Bertram keeps a set of spare keys in the pantry."

"I locked it for a reason," she blazed; after all the stresses of the evening before, it felt very liberating to lose her temper. "I'm not your lover. I never have been and I never will be."

"You're old enough to know the score, Julie. Why do you think I invited you here for the weekend?"

Travis's reasoning exactly. She told the exact truth. "Because I'd told you how homesick I get for the ocean."

"Sure," he jeered, "your little miss naive act."

"It's no act. I don't do casual sex. Maybe you should have checked that out before inviting me out here."

"So you're all come-on and no delivery."

In a cold fury she said, "I haven't encouraged you in any way to think that I'd get into bed with you."

"That dress you had on when you got here, all bare shoulders and cleavage—you don't call that a come-on?"

"It's a perfectly ordinary sundress and why are we standing here in the middle of the night discussing my wardrobe?" She grabbed the nearest marble statue, a particularly nubile Aphrodite. "Get out of here, Brent, or I'll scream the place down. I have very good lungs, believe me."

"So is it Travis you want?"

"I don't want either one of you! Head for the door."

For a moment he hesitated, the muscles bunched in his arms. She tensed, wondering if she'd have the nerve to hit him with a solid marble goddess; to her great relief, he took a couple of steps away from the bed. "What a little Puritan you are."

"Out," she said.

He sauntered over to the chair, picked up his shirt and crossed the room. "Just stay out of my way for the rest of the weekend," he said.

"You haven't got a worry in the world." All she could think of was how he'd entered her room while she was asleep and watched her, leisurely taking off his shirt in the meantime. It made her feel dirty all over.

As the door closed softly behind him, Julie let out her breath in a ragged sigh. There was no point in locking it. Grunting with effort, she dragged the cedar chest from the foot of her bed until it was lodged against the panels, and sat down hard. Now that Brent was gone, she was trembling with delayed reaction.

She'd find Oliver in the morning and go back to the

mainland with him on his first crossing. She'd had her fill of the Strathern family. And that included Travis just as much as the rest of them.

She didn't need seducing, even in her dreams.

CHAPTER FOUR

TRAVIS was wide-awake at 5:00 a.m. He hadn't been given his old room up in the tower, but rather one of the guest suites. Another message that he wasn't welcome here, he thought with a wry twist of his lips. And another reason why he'd had one of the worst night's sleep in his life.

But not the main reason. Not if he were honest.

His room was down the hall from Julie's. He'd sat on a rock by the shore for a long time after that scene on the patio, then come up the back stairs to go to bed. In consequence, he'd had a ringside view of Brent leaving Julie's bedroom in the middle of the night. His brother's shirt had been casually looped over his arm, the night-lights gleaming on his bare chest.

Even now, several hours later, Travis's gut clenched at the memory. Julie had been lying to him all along. Swearing that she belonged to herself, not to Brent. It had been an act. An impressively credible one, moreover. Her big green eyes had been so full of sincerity, had met his so unflinchingly...but she'd been deceiving him from the beginning.

He sat up in bed, running his fingers through his hair. Twenty-four hours ago he hadn't even met Julie. Hadn't known she existed. So why did it matter so much that she'd lied to him?

The thought of her in Brent's arms, making love, was more than he could stomach. Jealousy, hot and lethal, surged through his veins. He wanted her for himself. Himself alone.

Not likely. If he didn't believe in casual sex, even less did he believe in sharing his lover with another man.

Particularly when the man was his brother.

Corinne was right, Travis thought sickly. There was no point in him staying here. Charles still resented him for going to the media, an action Travis had regretted as he'd aged and gathered experience; there must have been a better way of dealing with that situation. But he'd been young and hotheaded and deeply angry with the man who'd exiled a little boy from the island he'd loved, and so he'd acted without thought of the consequences.

What really hurt was that Charles still thought him capable of stealing the family ring.

He'd take Corinne's advice, and leave on the first boat this morning. Reconciliation was impossible, a pipe dream. He'd been a fool to come here, stirring up all the old animosities.

Restlessly Travis got up from the bed and stared out the window. The launch wouldn't be leaving for another four hours. He could at least walk along the cliffs to the lighthouse before he left. Feeling minimally better for this decision, Travis hauled on his jeans and a T-shirt, and padded down the corridor in his socked feet, his sneakers in his hand. He let himself out the west door, taking a deep breath of the cool morning air. The grass was wet with dew, the birds singing as though this was the first morning of creation. After doing up his laces, Travis set off.

It took a full five minutes to get clear of the painstakingly tended gardens and lawns, another five to cross the equally artful natural garden, the trees carefully placed, the stream rerouted beneath a whimsical bridge. But finally he reached the edge of the forest, and the track that he'd blazed himself many years ago. Although it had grown over considerably, it was still passable.

When a redstart flitted through the maples, he stopped to

admire its black and orange plumage. Next he startled a rabbit, then a red squirrel dropped a pinecone on his head. Laughing, he tossed it back up the tree. The squirrel scolded him indignantly; for the first time in hours, Travis felt like a human being. Shutting his mind to family and Julie alike, he strode on, feeling his muscles loosen and watching the rising sun spear through the thick spruce boughs.

A perfect day for his father's party. Even if he himself wouldn't be in attendance.

Fifteen minutes later Travis emerged at the brink of the granite cliffs on the offshore side of Manatuck. Bear Island, the next island beyond Manatuck, belonged to him, willed to him by his grandfather. It, too, was very beautiful.

He might just build a cabin on it. Use it as a getaway when his job got too much for him. If he placed the cabin carefully, he wouldn't even have to see Castlereigh.

He tramped along, gulls and kittiwakes swirling like tossed white papers over the turquoise sea. At the foot of the lighthouse that warned of the reefs further east, he threw himself down on the wet grass. How often had he lain here as a young boy, listening to the thunder of the surf?

He laced his fingers behind his head and closed his eyes. It wouldn't have to be a very big cabin. A wharf would be essential; but there was a perfect natural harbour at the southwest end of the island, so that wouldn't be a problem...mentally he started cataloging all the birdcalls he could hear, amused to discover that he hadn't lost his old talent. Gradually his mind quietened. He was almost asleep when a new noise startled him, the snapping of twigs along the path. Remembering that occasionally a deer would land on Manatuck after swimming the channel, Travis twisted over onto his stomach.

It wasn't a white-tailed deer that emerged into the clearing behind the lighthouse; it was Julie.

She was wearing bright pink shorts and a white shirt; she hadn't seen him. As Travis surged to his feet, he watched her whirl, as startled as any deer. "Travis, you frightened me—I wasn't expecting to see anyone." Then she smiled at him, a generous smile full of delight. "Isn't it a glorious morning?"

All the emotions of the last twelve hours coalesced into a flame of rage. Travis crossed the wet grass, standing very close to her. "I'm surprised you're up so early," he grated. "After making love to Brent half the night."

Her smile was wiped from her face; he could almost see her brain working. "You saw him leave my room," she said in an unreadable voice.

"Yes, I did. Not that you're sleeping with him, of course."

Refusing to drop her eyes, Julie said, "I didn't make love with Brent. Nor did I, in the literal sense of the words, sleep with him."

"Why don't you tell the truth for once?"

"Why don't you listen when I do?"

"I believe what I see. And what I saw was my brother leaving your room at two-thirty in the morning, in his bare feet and carrying his shirt over his arm."

"Too bad you hadn't seen me threatening him with a marble statue of Aphrodite and then dragging a cedar chest across the door so he couldn't get in again!"

"Didn't you like him as a lover?" Travis snarled.

Hands on her hips, she railed, "You listen to me—I locked my bedroom door last night when I went to bed because the thought crossed my mind that Brent might try some funny business in the middle of the night. But Bertram, bless his doddery old soul, keeps a spare set of keys in the pantry where everyone can help themselves. Did I know that? No, I did not!"

As she briefly paused for breath, Travis said nastily, "If

you had, you'd have done the cedar chest routine when you went to bed. I bet.''

As quickly as it had flared to life, Julie's temper died, leaving her with a horrible emptiness in her belly. She dropped her hands to her sides. ''You won't believe me whatever I say, will you, Travis? You made your mind up about me the first moment you saw me on the wharf. Fine, believe what you like. See if I care.''

She sounded like a kid in kindergarten, she thought in despair, and pivoted so she could hurry back down the path. Anywhere, just as long as she could run from the contempt in Travis's face. Tears blurring her vision, she stumbled over a rock.

Travis grabbed her around the waist. She flailed out at him, striking him on the wrist. ''Take your hands off me!''

Instead he pulled her to face him, lifted her chin and kissed her full on the mouth. For Julie, this was the last straw. She wrenched her mouth free, the tears now streaming down her cheeks. *''Don't!* You're no better than he is.''

Travis stared at her, appalled. She thought he was like Brent. That was what she was saying. According to her, first Brent had attacked her, and now he, Travis, was doing the same thing. Acting instinctively, he smoothed away the tears that were dribbling down to her chin. ''Don't cry, Julie,'' he said in a raw voice. ''Please don't cry.''

She pulled a crumpled tissue from her pocket and blew her nose. ''I'm not crying,'' she said defiantly. ''I never cry over men, they're not worth it.''

Her eyes were still shimmering with tears; he could feel them drying on his palm, in a way that seemed incredibly intimate. But before he could think of anything else to say, she hiccuped, ''Do you know what was worst about last night? He let himself into my room while I was asleep and then he just sat there, watching me.'' Her breath caught on another sob. "I hate the thought of him doing that. Besides, I was d-dreaming about you."

"About me?" Travis repeated stupidly.

"Oh God, I shouldn't have told you that. My tongue's always running away with me, my mother says it's one of my worst faults and she's right. Forget I ever mentioned it. I'm going back to my room to pack, I'm going to eat a huge breakfast and then I'm going right back to the mainland with Oliver. I've had enough of you and your family and that horrible Disneyland heap of stone."

Travis said, a quiver of laughter in his voice, "I was planning to do exactly the same."

She gave him a look that was far from friendly. "You can go on a later boat. Not on mine."

"Surely there's room on the launch for both of us."

"There wouldn't be room on the *Titanic* for you and me. Besides, you came here to make peace with your father, that's what you told me. So do it. And good luck to you."

Travis said carefully, "So you didn't make love with Brent last night? You've never made love with him?"

"Two brilliant deductions. You can add something else. I never will make love with Brent."

Could he believe her? Going to her room in the dead of night would be the sort of stunt Brent would pull. Travis said sharply, "Did he hurt you?"

"He did not. Although I broke two fingernails on one corner of the cedar chest."

His breath escaped from his lungs in a small whoosh. But he had one more question. "What kind of dream was it? The one about me, I mean."

"Never you mind."

"Unprintable?"

Hurriedly she changed the subject. "Did you spend much time here as a boy?"

"Until I was six, yes," he said shortly. "Then I was sent to boarding school."

"Which, by the look of you, you hated."

"Yeah," he said dismissively. "Although later on I made a good friend there—we still keep in touch. Bryce was as big a rebel as I was." He gave a reminiscent smile. "Once we took all the masters' black gowns and draped them around the cows in a nearby field. They were Jersey cows, the ones with the big eyelashes, they looked very sweet. We nearly got expelled for that."

"I put banana peels in the church organ when I was nine. But I didn't get caught."

As mischief danced in her eyes, Travis laughed. "Does that mean you're smarter or sneakier?" Then, suddenly intent, he added, "Why don't you cry about men, Julie? And how many men are we talking about here?"

She put her head to one side, her amusement fading. "You and I are going our separate ways today. I don't really think my romantic past, such as it is, is any of your business."

"Where do you live?"

"Portland. For now."

"So do I. It's a small place—we'll probably bump into each other."

"I doubt it—I won't be there long."

She'd retreated from him in a way he couldn't fathom, and that at some deep level angered him intensely. "What are you running away from?"

"You're a fine one to talk. You're giving up on your father without a fight."

"You know nothing about my father and me. So lay off," Travis said softly.

She knew quite a bit; but she wasn't about to reveal she'd eavesdropped on an acrimonious family discussion. By the look of him, he'd bite her head off. She said flatly, "I'm going to walk back along the cliffs. Goodbye, Travis. It's been interesting meeting you."

Not so fast, he thought, and said with a lazy grin, "I'll stay for the party if you will."

"That's boarding school talk!"

"Scared to stay, Julie? Surely you're not scared of me?"

One of the several ways she'd rebelled against the sterility of her upbringing had been to accept any dare that came her way; she still had the scars where she'd fallen off the high brick wall that surrounded her elementary school. Hadn't every job she'd ever taken been a continuation of that dare?

Travis was just a man. She'd been exaggerating her response to him; she'd never had any trouble handling men before. And despite what she'd said to him about going back to the mainland, she was intensely curious to learn more about the Stratherns and their tangled family history. "If you stay, you have to make an effort to reconcile with your father," she said, tossing her head.

"If you stay, you have to keep your distance from Brent."

"No problem," she said fervently.

"Done," Travis said, took her in his arms and kissed her.

He'd intended it as a joke, a way of sealing their bargain. But as her body stiffened in his embrace, her palms pushing against his chest, it very soon changed into something else. Fire streaking through his belly. A searching for a response he wanted more than he'd ever wanted anything before. He moved his lips over hers, one hand stroking her spine, the other moving lower to clasp her by the hips.

With a suddenness that jolted through his body, Julie kissed him back. The resistance melted from her frame; her hands moved up his shoulders to lace themselves behind his head, her fingers tangling in his hair. In a surge of heat he felt the softness of her breasts against his chest, and deepened his kiss, easing her lips apart, drinking deeply of their sweetness.

His groin hardened. But instead of moving away, she leaned into him, her hips pressed to his. "Julie," he muttered, "beautiful Julie," and thrust with his tongue. His whole body was aflame with need. And what better place to make love with her than here, his favorite haunt since he was a small boy?

She was willing. He was in no doubt of that.

He fumbled for the hem of her shirt, easing his hand beneath it to find the silky smoothness of her back, the curved ridges of her ribs. With another of those disorienting jolts he realized she wasn't wearing a bra; as his fingers slid around her ribs to cup the soft swell of her breast, she whimpered with pleasure.

Her nipple hardened beneath his thumb. He plundered her mouth, desperate for her, and felt her tug his T-shirt free of his jeans. Then her palm glided from his navel up to the tangle of dark hair on his chest. He freed his mouth long enough to mutter, "We're wearing far too many clothes." Easing her away, he reached for the top button on her shirt. "I want to see you. All of you. Lie down with me, Julie…"

Her eyes were dazzled, her skin delicately flushed; her mouth was swollen from his kisses. He nibbled gently at her lower lip, murmuring between kisses, "I want you so much, you're so lovely, so generous." With a husky laugh he added, "But the buttons on your shirt are much too small…can you help me?"

Taking her consent as a given, he hauled his shirt over his head. She was standing very still, watching him, her eyes glued to the taut lines of his body. Her face convulsed, and briefly she pressed her hands to her cheeks. She looked stunned, he thought. Stunned and frightened out of her wits. Frightened? Of him? "You don't need—"

She said faintly, as though he hadn't spoken, "Travis, we can't! We can't make love like this. We don't know the first thing about each other, and all we've done is fight ever since we met." Her breath caught in a little sob. "It would be madness."

Her distress was all too evident; it was no act. Even so, he was almost sure that if he kissed her, he could change her mind. But did he want to make love with her and then have her regret it afterward? He said hoarsely, "Let me tell you this much—I've never wanted anyone the way I want you. And that's the God's truth."

She bit her lip. "You terrify me," she whispered. "You make me into a stranger, a woman I don't even know. I never behave like this. Never!"

The tumult in his body was slowly subsiding. Travis said roughly, "Stay, Julie. Stay the whole weekend. At least do that."

"I don't know. I just don't know!"

She was like a hare cornered by wolves, he thought, with the same desperate need for escape. He'd been a fool to kiss her so passionately, frightening her away.

What scared him was how little choice he'd had; how something about her called to him in the most primitive way possible. And explain that if you can, Travis Strathern.

He should be begging her to leave, not to stay. He had enough on his plate right now without adding to the mix a woman as complex and desirable as Julie.

"I've got to get out of here," she muttered. "I can find my own way back— I'll see you at breakfast."

In full view of the family. He said, making no attempt to hide his frustration, "I don't know the first thing about you—where you live in Portland, whether you're working there, where you're from."

She looked straight at him. "You know something about me I didn't even know myself," she whispered. Then, before he could respond, she'd turned and was running down the path. The shrubs closed over her passage, the leaves swaying and then still. As though he'd dreamed her, Travis thought. As though she didn't really exist.

CHAPTER FIVE

BY THE time Julie had crossed the ornately carved bridge over the stream, she was panting for breath. She'd run hard all the way from the cliffs; and it had helped her make up her mind. She'd go straight to her room to pack. Then she'd go in search of Oliver to find out what time he was leaving for the mainland; she could always tell Corinne and Charles that her headache was worse, not better.

Running away, Julie?

You're darn right, she thought, bursting out of the woods, then stopping dead in her tracks. Corinne, tastefully dressed in tailored trousers and a pale pink sweater, was clipping roses in the garden, laying them in a basket that could have come out of a Jane Austen novel. She raised her head when she saw Julie. "Good morning," she said cordially. "How are you feeling, Julie? Better, I gather?"

Julie swallowed a tremor of laughter. She could hardly say her headache was worse, not when she'd been pounding through the woods as though she were training for a marathon. "It's fine, thank you. What beautiful colors!"

"I want them for decorating the buffet table tonight." Corinne started naming the different varieties, giving Julie a brief history of each as she went. Julie listened with half her attention, wondering why Corinne couldn't be as interested in her stepson's welfare as she was in her roses. Then Corinne broke off to ask, "Have you seen Travis this morning by any chance?"

"He's out at the lighthouse."

"I should have guessed that's where he'd be." Rather too casually, Corinne added, "He did say last night that he may not stay for the party. Oliver could take him back around nine.''

Julie didn't know if Travis was going to stay. Even less did she know her own decision. She stared down at the petals of a rose called Ferdinand Pichard, its petals striped deep pink and white. Passion and purity, she thought, and forced down the memory of Travis's devastatingly passionate kisses, and her own equally ardent response.

Stay or go. Which was it to be?

''Are you sure you're all right?'' Corinne asked.

''I'm fine.'' Julie gulped, and added impulsively, ''I hope Travis will stay. He mentioned something about making peace with his father. Life's too short for families to be estranged, wouldn't you agree, Corinne?''

Corinne snipped off a spray of creamy floribundas. ''Travis isn't easy to get along with. Nor do I want anything to spoil Charles's party—we've gone to far too much trouble and expense for that.'' Reaching for a delicate pale yellow rose centered with pink, she added, ''Have you known Brent long?''

''Long enough,'' Julie said dryly, not really caring how Corinne interpreted that. ''I'm going to have a shower, I'll see you at breakfast.''

She marched across the grass. Huge tents with striped awnings were being erected near the main door; baskets of blue and pink hydrangeas flanked the stone walls. It would be a beautiful party, she thought irritably. Appearance over substance. Just like her entire life with her parents.

Would Travis stay? Or would he leave?

When Travis entered the dining room, where breakfast was always served buffet style on the vast mahogany sideboard, Charles and Corinne were already there. ''Good morning,'' he said pleasantly. ''No sign of Brent?''

''Brent rarely eats breakfast,'' Charles said shortly.

"Did you sleep well?" Corinne asked with punctilious good manners.

"About as badly as a man can sleep," Travis said. "I'm staying, Dad. I'll tell everyone tonight that I just got in from Angola, that's why they haven't seen me around. And before that it was Tanzania and Laos. Apart from anything else, it happens to be the truth."

"And when are you returning to Angola?" Charles rapped.

"I've taken over a private practice in Portland for the summer, because the resident doctor wanted to go to Scotland with his family. So I'll be heading out early in the fall. Although probably not back to Angola."

"All summer?" Charles croaked.

Travis's voice sharpened. "What's the matter?"

"You're spending the whole summer in Portland?"

"That's right." Trying to ignore the fact that his father looked aghast, Travis gave him a crooked smile. "Maybe you'll invite me out to the island in a couple of weeks, when we'll have more time to talk."

Charles took a big gulp of coffee. "I want to talk to you now, Travis. Or at least right after breakfast. Corinne, would you pass the marmalade, please?"

Travis poured a large glass of freshly squeezed orange juice. He had no idea what was going on. But at least Charles wanted to talk to him. That was a hopeful sign.

Why hadn't Julie arrived for breakfast? Had she already left? The launch had still been at the dock when he'd walked back from the lighthouse, and there'd been no sign of Oliver. How would he feel if he never saw her again?

Then footsteps tapped across the oak floor and Julie walked through the door. She was wearing her flowered sundress with scarlet flat-heeled sandals; her hair was damp from the shower. Travis's fingers tightened around his glass. What had happened out at the lighthouse had been no aberration; he wanted her now just as much as then.

With old-fashioned courtesy Charles got to his feet. "Good morning, Julie. Did you sleep well?"

"I woke up early," she said truthfully, "so I went out to the lighthouse." She smiled at Charles. "I can see why Travis loves Manatuck—it's so beautiful out there."

Travis swallowed a smile. Charles said manfully, "I'm glad you're having a good time. I hope you'll join me in a game of tennis later this morning?"

There was a fractional hesitation; Travis held his breath. Then Julie said, "That'd be lovely. Although I haven't played for quite a while."

She was staying. Travis turned back to the sideboard, staring at a platter of sliced fruit as if he'd never seen melons and strawberries before. So the die was cast. For the next twenty-four hours the two of them would be together on the island.

Julie started asking questions about the history of Manatuck, a subject dear to Charles's heart. Travis helped himself to bacon and eggs, sat down and began eating. The legal complications of purchasing the island, and the logistical complications of erecting a castle on it, happily occupied Charles for the next half hour. Then he pushed back his chair. "Finished, Travis?" he asked. "Why don't we go to the library? Julie, I'll meet you at the courts in about an hour. The rackets are kept in the club house."

"I'll look forward to it," Julie said.

After refilling his coffee cup, Travis followed Charles to the library. His father closed the door, then took up a position in front of the hearth. He looked extremely ill at ease. Was he about to discuss changes in his will, changes that possibly disinherited his elder son? Financially Travis couldn't care less; emotionally he cared quite a lot.

He leaned against a leather wing chair. Nothing in the

library had changed. The same prints on the walls, the same array of leatherbound and doubtless unread classics. He himself had discovered Kipling here, C.S. Lewis and Tolkien, all the heroes who had peopled his childhood. He said casually, "What's on your mind, Dad?"

Charles said pompously, "You must understand that your arrival last night was a shock to us all."

"I hope the shock wasn't too unpleasant."

"I possibly said things I shouldn't have, on the patio after dinner," Charles labored on. "I apologize for that."

It was more than Travis had expected. He said warmly, more than willing to meet his father half way, "You're forgiven."

Staring fixedly at the door behind his son's back, Charles said, "A reconciliation is, of course, what we all want. You're right, the past is the past and should be forgotten. Bygones be bygones. The hatchet buried."

Charles had always favored clichés. "I'm very willing to do that," Travis said, trying to disguise the fact that he was inwardly puzzled. This was all too easy. Had Charles really had such a huge change of heart overnight?

"That disgraceful media attack, the ring…water under the bridge."

"I've often regretted that I went to the papers. It was the action of an adolescent, that's all I can say. I wouldn't handle it that way now."

"Yes, yes," Charles said impatiently.

But Travis hadn't finished. His voice rough with the intensity of his feelings, he said, "As for the ring, I swear I didn't take it."

"Never mind the ring, I don't really miss it anymore. So everything's forgiven and forgotten and now you can leave Portland right away. No reason to hang around. You've done what you set out to do."

Looking rather pleased with himself, Charles bounced up

and down on the soles of his handmade Italian loafers. "Leave Portland?" Travis repeated.

"Well yes. Of course. Why would you stay in a little backwater town like Portland?" Charles said bluffly. "I'm sure you've got bigger fish to fry. I've read about you over the years, some of your successes in establishing new hospitals and revitalizing old ones in all those third world countries. Very important work, Travis. Vital. I'm sure you're anxious to get back to it. I can understand you might have thought it would take all summer to soften my attitude, and that's why you allowed two months." He gave a hearty laugh. "I've taken you by surprise, haven't I? You thought I'd be much more adamant."

"I did, yes." Thinking furiously, Travis said, "I'm very glad we're having this conversation, and I look forward to many more. But I can't leave Portland right away—I made a commitment to Mark and his family."

"You can't leave? Of course you can."

Julie was also living in Portland, at least temporarily. Julie and he had some unfinished business. Travis said easily, "I'll be gone by the first of September."

"Get someone else to fill in for your friend!"

"What's the rush, Dad? If you've really forgiven me, why wouldn't you want to spend some time with me?"

"Your stepmother and I are going to be exceptionally busy this summer. We may even go away for a month or more...perhaps you could come to Boston for Christmas."

"Perhaps I could." Although he'd long hated the luxurious mansion in Back Bay. "Let's play it by ear...there's been a big gap in our relationship, and we can't patch it up overnight."

"So you'll leave Portland?" Charles said eagerly.

"I've explained why I can't do that right away."

Charles pursed his lips. "I'm asking a favor of you, Travis. Surely after all these years, you can do one small thing for me. Find a substitute—there must be lots of doctors who'd be happy to spend the rest of the summer in Maine.''

''If I understood why you want me to leave, I might be more open to doing so.''

With vicious emphasis, Charles said, ''Why was your favorite word as a little boy. You could never accept anything at face value, you always had to be poking and prying for reasons. You haven't changed, Travis, you're just the same as you always were.''

So the forgiveness was only skin deep. Travis said carefully, ''I'll be talking to Mark next week, I'll see what he says. It's the best I can do.''

''It's little enough,'' Charles huffed. ''And now I must go and change if I'm to meet Julie.'' He gave his son a sharp nod. ''Take my advice—call Mark as soon as possible.''

He marched past Travis and shut the door behind him with unnecessary force. Travis gazed after him unseeingly. What was going on? And what was he missing? Had that been Charles's inept attempt at a genuine reconciliation? Or had it been fake from the start?

But why?

Which was indeed one of his favorite words, he thought wryly. Why would Charles want him to leave Portland tomorrow?

And why was Julie the main reason he didn't want to?

CHAPTER SIX

AT SEVEN-THIRTY that evening, Travis straightened his tie in the bathroom mirror, adjusted his tuxedo jacket and knew he couldn't delay going downstairs any longer. He'd faced guerillas, epidemics, droughts and floods the last few years. And now he was scared of a crowd of his father's friends?

Put it any way you like, he wasn't looking forward to the evening. Too many people, too many of whom would be less than delighted to see him, coupled with the necessity to behave as though there really had been a reconciliation between himself and his father.

If he'd wanted to be an actor, he wouldn't have gone to medical school.

Not for the first time, he wished his sister Jenessa was here as well. Although he hadn't seen a lot of her since he'd turned sixteen, he'd made a point of staying in touch with her. Beautiful, wayward and artistic, Jenessa was gradually making a name for herself among the galleries and collectors that mattered; Travis had always admired her fierce determination to go her own way. Right now, he could have done with her moral support.

Resolutely Travis left his room and ran down the curved staircase. All afternoon the guests had been arriving in their yachts, cabin cruisers and private seaplanes. Now the party eddied among the tents set up on the lawn, each lit by tiny white lights that glimmered like fireflies. There were enough potted plants to stock every flower shop in New York, and enough jewels on the women to buy the White House. He made his way to the main tent, stopping to talk to people on the way, ironically amused to note those of his father's friends who turned their backs before he could speak to them.

Bankers and stockbrokers tended to have long memories: they wouldn't have forgotten or forgiven that long-ago newspaper article. He sighted Brent at the bar with a blond in a dress that highlighted at least two of her obvious assets, and looked around for Julie. His gaze sharpened as he saw her among a crowd of younger guests at the far end of the lawn, as far from Brent as she could get. She hadn't seen him. He moved closer, his heart thudding over the sound of the band.

Her dress was of raw Thai silk, slit to the knee, its simple lines and thin straps elegant rather than overtly provocative, its subtle blending of blues and greens emphasizing her eyes. A delicate gauze scarf floated from the neckline, her shoulders gleaming through its soft folds. Brazilian crystal shimmered around her throat and at her lobes.

He had to have her. He had to.

But not here. Not now. Later.

The words had come unbidden. But every nerve in Travis's body told him they were true. He'd never in his life desired a woman so imperatively, with such fierce impatience.

He turned away, going back to the main tent, where he joined Charles and Corinne for a celebratory glass of champagne, danced with Corinne and a couple of her friends, and ate supper with the old family doctor and his wife, long allies of his. It was dark by the time he went in search of Julie.

She was dancing to some raucous rock and roll in the tent closest to the water. Slim and lissome, her hips moving with a sensuality that caught at his throat, she looked as though she was having a wonderful time. Her partner was a tall, bearded young man. Not for long, Travis thought, waiting until the song ended before heading for the dance floor. He came up behind her and looped an arm around her waist. "Hello, Julie."

A tremor ran through her body; she froze in the circle of his arm. Then she turned as awkwardly as a puppet. "Travis," she mumbled. With an obvious effort she added, "Do you know these people?"

The tall young man's name was Michael, and his plump pretty wife was called Kathy. "The next dance is mine," Travis said.

The music had started again. Under cover of the bass Julie hissed, "Are you asking me or telling me?"

She hadn't meant her ill temper to show. But all evening she'd been waiting for him to find her, catching occasional glimpses of him, furious that he should so cavalierly ignore her. Travis said abruptly, "You're right, we don't need to dance. Do you want something to eat?"

"I've already eaten."

"Let's go for a walk down by the water."

"You ignore me all evening and now I'm supposed to jump ten feet high the minute you say so? I don't think so."

"Julie," he said, "I've danced with Corinne, I made a speech that was a miracle of diplomacy when they toasted my father, I've been snubbed by two-thirds of his friends, and I need ten minutes away from it all." He'd also been publicly hugged by Charles, briefly, but nonetheless an embrace. One Brent had witnessed, he thought with a quiver of unease.

Julie looked up at him more closely. There were lines of strain bracketing his mouth and his eyes looked dark and depthless. Suddenly she was tired of deception. "Last night I was on my balcony when you and your family came out on the patio. I overheard everything that was said, from the

death of your mother to the disappearance of the family
ring.''

Travis looked down at her, his jawline hard with tension.
He'd always guarded his privacy: a strategy that had served
him well over the years. He didn't like Julie knowing all
the Strathern secrets; other than Bryce, no one knew about
his past. ''Do you make a habit of listening to other people's conversations?'' he rasped.

She tilted her chin. ''Sure...it's how I get my kicks.''

Travis disliked subservient women; he didn't have a
worry in the world about Julie. ''My father, for some unknown reason, wants me to leave Portland within the
week.''

''Are you going to?''

''No,'' Travis said. ''I'm not much good at doing what
I'm told. I'll stay until the end of the summer.''

Julie looked at him in silence. Portland was a small city.
Too small for both of them; she herself had signed a three-
month contract. She said, ''I can't go for a walk with you
right now. I promised Kathy and Michael I'd go with them
when she feeds the baby...I went to school with her and
Michael, and she's dying to show off her daughter. Oh,
she's waving at me now.''

''I'll come with you,'' Travis said.

''I don't think—''

''Hey, Julie,'' Kathy said. ''The sitter just called on the
cell phone, Andrea's awake. Travis, do you want to see our
new addition? Three months old tomorrow.''

''Sure,'' he said easily, and tucked Julie's hand in his
arm. ''Let's go.''

Julie's feet were killing her in her new silver sandals,
and she felt thoroughly out of sorts. She also felt as lustful
as a stray cat under a full moon. She walked across the
grass toward the castle, trying to keep as far from Travis
as she could, every fiber in her body aware of his long,

easy stride. If only he wasn't so tall, so male, so damnably handsome. When she added to that a velvet-soft evening filled with the scent of roses and the tumble of waves on the beach, she was done for.

The baby was in a crib in a bedroom on the ground floor, where a lamp threw golden light over the furniture. Kathy picked her daughter up, while Michael went with the sitter to the nearby kitchen to heat a bottle. "Here, Julie, hold Andrea for a minute," Kathy said. "I've got to dig out a clean diaper."

The baby was thrust into Julie's arms. Instinctively she cupped the little head with its dark fuzz of hair to her shoulder, supporting the baby's spine with her other hand. The warmth of the small body, and Andrea's fretful whimpering filled her with a deep tenderness.

Travis had stationed himself by the door, his eyes glued to the woman holding the baby, his heart beating like a triphammer. If he'd had a camera, he'd have taken a photo of her: Woman with Child. But why did he need a camera? Wasn't her image engraved on his mind?

How little he really knew about her! About her dreams and desires, the betrayals of her past and her needs. He'd always thought of himself as reasonably astute. But she was an enigma.

As though the intensity of Travis's gaze was a pull she couldn't gainsay, Julie glanced up. His eyes seemed to see right into her soul. She held Andrea a little more tightly, trying desperately to look anywhere but at him. And failed.

"Put her down on the bed, Julie," Kathy said. "What's up? Are you okay?"

"Oh...yes, I'm fine," Julie stumbled, and laid the baby on the flannel blanket. Her arms felt empty, her body cold. Warm me, Travis, she thought, warm me.

Knowing she had no choice, she crossed the room toward him. As he put an arm around her shoulders, she leaned into his body, into its solidity and heat, closing her eyes. She couldn't cry. Not here. Not now.

Why would she want to cry? Travis was a stranger, chance-met, soon to be gone from her life.

Travis said softly, "Hold still, the baby dribbled on your shoulder." Gently he started scrubbing at her gauze scarf where it rested on her bare skin, using a tissue he'd taken from his pocket.

Why couldn't she have him? What was to stop her?

The thought had dropped into her mind without any warning. Calling on every ounce of her resolve, Julie straightened, pulling away from him. "Thanks," she said briefly. "Kathy, we'll leave you to it. I'm so glad we met this evening, let's get together in the next couple of weeks."

"Our number's in the book. Give us a call." Kathy chuckled. "Just not too early in the morning."

"She's a lovely baby," Julie said sincerely. "Ready, Travis?"

She walked out of the room ahead of him, her spine very straight. She had no idea how to find her room from here. But find it she had to. And alone.

As they walked back out into the garden, Travis said, "So what was that all about?"

"What do you mean?"

"You almost ran into my arms. Then you backed off as if I were the devil himself."

"You see too much," she said in an unfriendly voice. "I'm tired, and I've had more than enough of this party— I'm going to my room. I'll see you tomorrow."

They were standing in the shadows of the lilac bushes that, long ago, his mother had adored for their scent. One of his earliest memories was of her carrying an armload of purple blooms into the living room and arranging them in a deep copper bowl. Her long black hair had been pinned to her head in lustrous waves; as a little boy he'd likened them to the black sheen of the sea on a winter's evening.

With an effort Travis wrenched himself back to the present. He'd lost his mother. But he was damned if he was going to let Julie walk away from him as if he were nothing but a stick of furniture.

He put his arms around her, pulling her into his body, and lowered his head to her shoulder, smoothing it with his mouth. Her skin was delicately scented; her response quivered through her. He traced the rise of her shoulder to her neck, then dropped to find the pulse at the base of her throat: a pulse racing like that of a bird. And all the while his hands were molding the long curve of her spine all the way to the flare of her hips, learning her, memorizing her. Desire engulfed him, fierce and imperative.

He raised his head to kiss her, unerringly finding her lips in the dark, teasing them open and plunging with his tongue. She was trembling very lightly in his embrace. Slow down, he thought, and with all his willpower gentled his kiss, searching out the sweetness of her mouth.

She arched against him with a moan of surrender that filled Travis with exultation. Her hands were under his jacket, roaming the flat plane of his chest, fitting themselves to his rib cage, then pulling him closer until he was unutterably frustrated by the layers of clothing between his flesh and hers. "Julie," he muttered against her mouth, "let's go to my room. I want you in my bed."

She heard him from a long way away, through a haze of passion as vivid as sunset, as compelling as the tides of the sea. Compelling. Irresistible. She herself out of control in a way that was foreign to her.

Out of control.

She reared back, panic-stricken. She'd never felt this way with a man before; she'd always been able to call the shots. If she made love with Travis, all that would change. He'd have power over her. She knew it in her bones. Power over her forever.

Joke, Julie. Make a joke of it. She said breathlessly, "Are you the college chemistry course that I missed? Your body plus my body, a good dose of lilacs as the catalyst, and an explosion's guaranteed?"

Travis cupped her face in his palms, his forefingers molding her cheekbones. "You can skip the lilacs."

"Lilacs or not, I'm out of here, Travis," she gasped. "You're too much for me."

"Scared, Julie?"

"Chemistry never was my strong point."

He said softly, running his hands over the silken darkness of her hair, "Did you like biology better?"

She managed a credible laugh, forcing herself to step backward from the heat of his body. "Physics was my forte," she said, and abandoned any attempt at humor. "Travis, I'm not looking for an affair. Whether it's just this weekend, or the rest of the summer, it's not in my plans."

"Didn't your chemistry professor ever tell you about spontaneous combustion?"

"I must have missed that lecture."

"We don't need a lecture. Just you and me under the stars."

She was suddenly exhausted. She couldn't take anymore. "I don't want to do something we'd both regret," she said sharply.

"Don't speak for me, Julie...I wouldn't regret it. Some guy must have hurt you really badly, am I right?"

If only it were that simple. But if that's what he wanted to think, let him. "Good night," she said, "I'll see you tomorrow." Then she picked up her skirts and ran away from him across the grass.

Travis watched her go. He could easily have caught up with her, and certainly he could have physically overpowered her. But was that what he wanted? Or did he want Julie to walk into his arms of her own volition? Clear-eyed and willing.

He had at the most two months in which to achieve that aim. But he'd never backed down from a challenge in his life, and he wasn't going to start now. Not when the prize was a woman whose body called to his in the most powerful way possible.

He had to possess her. And he would.

CHAPTER SEVEN

THE woods were lush and green, her feet sinking into a thick carpet of sphagnum moss, ferns brushing her bare knees. As Julie stood still, relishing the silence and peace, a bright yellow warbler landed on a branch just above her, looking at her with its dark eye.

Once again, she'd slept badly. And once again, she'd dreamed about Travis. Unrepeatable dreams. X-rated. No one under the age of eighteen admitted.

But at least she'd had the sense to run away from him last night in the shadow of the lilacs.

Julie sighed. Hadn't her expedition this morning also been related to Travis? Another attempt to put distance between him and her? She was on the island offshore to Manatuck, the kayak she'd borrowed from the boathouse pulled up on the shale beach. As far as she could tell, this island was completely unspoiled. No one living on it, and certainly no stone castles. It had a serenity Manatuck lacked; idly she found herself wondering who was lucky enough to own it.

With a quiver of unease she wondered if her wandering lifestyle was starting to pall. Certainly she missed the rocky shores and crisp blue waves of home more and more with each departure.

Settle in Portland? No way.

She'd explore for a few minutes, then head back to Castlereigh in lots of time for breakfast. Quite a few of the guests had stayed overnight; breakfast would be a very sociable affair. Again, all the better to hide from Travis. And

61

then she'd leave Manatuck on the launch, and go back to her daily life.

She wished Travis was leaving Portland this week, as his father wanted him to.

Her illusory peace shattered, Julie wandered back down the slope, picking her footholds with care, because the rocks among the moss were wet with dew. As she emerged from the trees, she saw with an unpleasant tightening of her nerves that a second kayak had been pulled up on the beach. Brent was striding up the shale toward the trees.

Brent. Not Travis.

"Good morning," she called. "You're up early."

He didn't bother answering, too intent on closing the distance between them. She stationed herself beside a fallen log, feeling her heartbeat quicken. There wasn't another soul on this island other than herself and Brent. She didn't like Brent, nor did she trust him.

He stopped two feet away from her. "This island belongs to Travis," he said. "Did you know that?"

"No."

"Yeah...our grandfather left it to him. Along with a big bundle of money."

She stated the obvious. "You hate your brother."

"Did you see him and Dad last night? A touching little display of filial love. Of course Travis wants a reconciliation, he knows which side his bread's buttered on."

Julie might be terrified of making love with Travis; but she wasn't blind to his character, and somehow she doubted that he was driven by mercenary motives. "You're judging him by your own standards," she said with more truth than wisdom.

"Clever little Julie...you dropped me as soon as you saw him, didn't you?"

"I dropped you when you forced your way into my room."

"You should have thought twice before coming out to this island all by yourself."

"Come off it, Brent," she said sharply. "Strong-arm stuff is punishable by law, or hadn't you noticed? And just to keep the record straight, I'm no more interested in having an affair with Travis than I am with you. I told him so last night."

"You expect me to believe that? I wasn't born yesterday."

"If you weren't born yesterday, then use your common sense and go back to Manatuck. I'll be along in time for breakfast."

"I don't think so," he said.

As his eyes narrowed and his muscles tensed, Julie had a split-second to react. Pivoting, she raced for the shelter of the woods. Brent wasn't in good shape like Travis; she was almost certain she could outrun him. She could hear him close behind her, too close, swearing in a steady monotone that raised the hairs on the back of her neck. She leaped a fallen trunk, slipped on a rock, regained her balance and dashed between two trees. A snag tore at her arm; all she could hear was the drumming of her heart in her ears, and Brent's harsh breathing.

Still too close. And she dared not look back.

Fear lending her wings, she took what looked like a pathway through the trees straight up the slope, still trusting that she could outlast him. Inwardly giving thanks that she'd attended her fitness club so faithfully, she ran hard for several minutes. Then, her lungs heaving for air, she dodged some shrubs, ducked under a couple of low branches and scrambled up a sheer face of granite with an agility that, even in the moment, amused her. She couldn't have done it in cold blood; she'd never liked heights. Darting through some pines, their soft needles giving her a better foothold, she ran on.

She didn't even see the hollow in the ground, burrow of some unknown animal. One foot went down the hole, throwing her off balance. By flinging herself sideways, Julie managed to avoid twisting her ankle. But she landed hard, a broken branch ripping at her leg. With a gasp of pain, she struggled to her feet and staggered on.

But there was no heavy breathing behind her. Had she, despite her fall, outrun Brent?

She threw a glance over her shoulder. Boughs gently waving in the breeze, ferns and rusted needles on the forest floor, and no sign of her pursuer. She was alone in the woods. More slowly, she went further into the pines, then changed direction to throw Brent off in case he was still following her. When she was certain she really was alone, Julie sank down on a granite boulder, her eyes still darting this way and that.

Her leg was bleeding very messily, she'd scraped her palm when she landed, and her cheekbone was bruised and sore. But at least, she thought, cheering up, she hadn't twisted or broken her ankle. All she had to do was wait for a while, then creep back down to the shore. If there was only one kayak left on the beach, then Brent was gone.

Taking her time, limping slightly, Julie put this plan into action twenty minutes later. But when she finally emerged from the trees, she saw to her dismay that both kayaks were gone.

Wrong beach. It must be.

It wasn't. She recognized the reef that she'd rounded to approach the beach. Brent had towed her kayak away.

She said every swearword that she knew, in every language she'd ever been exposed to. While this made her feel better, it didn't produce a second kayak. The tide had turned, the current streaming past the rocks. She couldn't swim back to Manatuck, she'd be swept out to sea.

Great, she thought. Just great. Now what should she do?

Her mad dash through the trees had made her thirsty and given her an appetite; but her water bottle and trail mix were tucked down beside the seat of her kayak. Her only option was to swim back once the tidal rip subsided. In three or four hours, she thought glumly.

How long before she was missed? Would Travis notice she was gone? Or would he assume she'd already left on the launch without saying goodbye? Which, after the way she'd run away from him last night, he'd be entirely justified in doing.

Maybe he'd already left Manatuck himself.

One thing was sure. Brent wouldn't tell anyone where she was.

Travis, unusually for him, slept late that morning, so it was well past nine when he went down for breakfast. He hesitated outside Julie's bedroom door, tapped on the panels, and knew intuitively from the silence that the room was empty. So she must be downstairs.

He ran down to the dining room, crowded with those guests who had spent the night rather than be ferried out to their yachts at two in the morning. Tables and chairs had been set out on the patio, overflowing onto the lawn. Julie was nowhere to be seen. He cornered Charles by the coffeepot. "Have you seen Julie?"

"No, come to think of it, I haven't." Charles chuckled. "I showed her a new spin on her serve, maybe she's practising."

Corinne hadn't seen her, either. She said coolly, "Brent left for the mainland an hour ago with Oliver. Maybe she went with him."

His gut lurched. "Did she say goodbye to you?"

"No. But there's been such a crush of people...oh, there are the Hallidays, I must speak to them. Excuse me, Travis."

Travis stared after her, fighting down a confusion of emotion. Would Julie have left with Brent, without saying goodbye to her host and hostess? He didn't think so; but then, what did he really know about her?

The key question was whether she'd left with Brent. She'd promised to stay away from him; but was she trustworthy?

If she hadn't left with Brent, where was she?

He checked the tennis courts and the pool, without any luck. Then he hurried down to the boathouse. Alongside a small powerboat, four kayaks were moored. A pair of dark glasses was tucked under the bungee cords of the red one. Julie's glasses. She'd been wearing them yesterday afternoon.

A water bottle and a bag of nuts and raisins lay on the seat. His head swiveled around as the door creaked open. But it was one of the groundsmen, not Julie. He said urgently, "Did anyone go kayaking this morning, Russell?"

"I saw Mr. Brent about an hour ago, towing a second kayak from Bear Island. I thought it was kinda funny at the time."

"Towing it—empty?"

"Yep. Just him. Then he took off in the launch with Oliver."

"By himself?"

Russell kept his face expressionless. "Him and a blond lady, sir."

That would be the blonde who'd been wrapped around Brent most of last night. So Julie hadn't left with Brent. "Thanks, Russell," Travis said and knew exactly what he was going to do.

Twenty minutes later, Travis was paddling around the northeast shoals of Manatuck, Bear Island now in sight. Brent was smart enough to know that he couldn't get away with violence. He wouldn't have hurt Julie and left her on the island. Would he?

If he had, there'd be hell to pay, Travis thought grimly. There was a cold lump of dread lodged in his gut; it was taking a huge effort to prevent that dread from turning into outright terror. What had Brent done to Julie? Why had he towed an empty kayak back to Manatuck? Julie was no pushover, she wouldn't have sat by meekly and allowed his brother to leave her stranded on an uninhabited island.

He'd gone far enough north for the tide to carry him toward the beach on the island that he owned. Steering with all his strength, because he was alone in a double kayak, he passed the reefs and saw the long stretch of shale in front of him. Using rudder and paddle, he headed straight for it, jamming the prow of the kayak up onto the rocks. Swiftly he climbed out and hauled his craft out of reach of the tide.

Then he looked up. A woman was walking from the shade of the trees onto the sun-drenched shale. She was limping.

His first reaction was a relief so overpowering that he felt almost dizzy. Julie was safe. Alive and well. It wasn't until now that he could admit to himself how terrified he'd been of the alternative, despite his inner conviction that Brent was too self-serving to do real harm.

His second reaction, predictably, was anger. He strode across the beach toward her, his soft-soled sneakers crunching the shale. "Are you okay?" he rapped.

Julie nodded. "I'm glad to see you," she said with a small smile.

He didn't smile back. "Did Brent leave you here?"

"Yes."

"If he laid as much as a finger on you, I'll have his hide for a floor mat."

"He didn't. I ran away," she said economically.

"Your leg's bleeding."

"I tripped and fell. Can we go back, Travis? I'm hungry, thirsty, and in dire need of a shower."

"We'll go back in a minute," he said, each word dropping like a stone. "Will you kindly explain to me what you and Brent were doing out here in the first place? You promised to stay away from him."

Her chin snapped up. "Are you insinuating I came out here with him?"

"The thought had occurred to me, yes."

"And why would I have done that?"

"You tell me."

"I came out here by myself to get some peace and quiet before breakfast. Brent must have seen me and followed me. Although why I'm bothering to explain this to you when you persist in thinking the worst of me, I have no idea. Take me back to Manatuck, Travis—now. And spare me the sermons, I don't need them."

"If you'd stayed away from Brent in the first place, you wouldn't be in this mess," Travis said furiously.

"And I wouldn't have met you. Which certainly would be a bonus."

"Your cheek—did he hit you?"

"I told you—he didn't as much as touch me!"

"Dammit, Julie, ever since I saw your dark glasses on the kayak in the boathouse, I've been picturing you drowned, raped and murdered," Travis said in a voice raw with emotion.

Too much emotion, he thought distantly. Far too much. But it was too late to take it back.

She let out her breath in a long sigh. "I'm hungry, thirsty and sore. Not drowned, raped or murdered. So why are we standing here yelling at each other?"

"Because I was worried sick about you."

"I get the message." She scowled at him. "I bet all the bacon and eggs will be gone by the time we get back."

"I'll have Bertram order you a breakfast all of your own. He owes you, after leaving the room keys hanging in the pantry."

Looking somewhat more cheerful, Julie said, "You'd do that for me?"

"I'd do a lot more than that for you," Travis said harshly; and listened to the words echo in his head.

"Bacon and eggs would be plenty, thank you."

"Are you warning me off?"

"I don't know!"

Travis took a step back. "Let's go."

"I've hurt you, haven't I?" she whispered. "I'm sorry, Travis, I—"

"Your imagination's working overtime."

"So you don't hurt, like ordinary people?" she lashed.

"I quit that a long time ago."

"I don't believe you!"

"That's your choice," he said curtly. "In the meantime, we can argue half the morning, or we can paddle back to Manatuck."

"Arguing with you is a lost cause," Julie snapped, and turned away, marching down the shore toward the kayak.

Travis stayed where he was. He hated how easily she could get to him. On top of that, he wanted to kiss her so badly he could taste the sweetness of her lips against his. He didn't want to think what he might have done had Brent harmed her. He was a doctor, for God's sake. He was supposed to heal, not hurt.

Raking his fingers through his hair, his footsteps crunching on the barnacles, Travis followed Julie down to the kayak. Once there, he passed her the water bottle and trail mix, watching the movements of her throat as she swallowed. Added to the terror and rage he'd felt earlier was another, disturbingly new emotion: a fierce instinct to protect her from further harm.

Coupled with, of course, the ever-present gnawing of desire. Not that yelling at her on a lonely beach was the way to entice her into his bed. He had to come up with a better strategy than that.

Julie took a handful of nuts from the bag. "Nothing like a few raisins and almonds for making life worth living. Want some?"

Desire wasn't on her mind. For sure.

Travis chewed a few peanuts that might as well have been wood chips and said abruptly, "We'd better get going. We'll follow the beach and the reefs north, then cut across the channel above Manatuck."

Which is what they did. Julie was an adept and strong kayaker, their paddles flashing in unison; Travis knew better than to see this as a metaphor.

They docked in the boathouse, then Travis led the way through the trees to a side door where they'd be unlikely to meet any of his father's guests. The back stairs took them to the far end of the wing where their bedrooms were located. Outside her door he said, "I'll wait for you while you shower. Then I want to check that gash in your leg, you don't want to risk infection."

"I can look after it."

"Julie, I'm a doctor," he said coldly. "This isn't a come-on."

She flushed. "You've got a practice in Portland?"

"Just for the summer. Filling in for Mark MacDonald."

"I'm a physiotherapist," she said rapidly. "So I know enough first aid to look after myself."

This was new information to Travis. Ever since he'd met Julie, he'd been so off balance he'd never thought to ask the ordinary questions, like her age or what she did to earn her living. "Do you work in the hospital? Why haven't I seen you there?"

If she answered him, Julie thought, he'd know where to find her. With huge reluctance she said, "I've got a temporary contract at Silversides, the clinic just out of town."

She knew as well as he that Silversides was a retreat for the very rich; just as she knew Dr. MacDonald's practice was almost exclusively white-collar. She could have told him about her real work overseas; but why bother? After today, she wasn't going to see him again.

"I'll get my bag," he said. "I always travel with it."

"You're like a nor'easter," she said irritably, "there's no stopping you."

"And you don't have to worry about Brent, he left on the launch. With a blonde."

"It isn't Brent I'm worrying about," Julie said unwisely and shut the door in Travis's face.

The hot water stung her various cuts and scrapes; she was going to have a few choice bruises when she went back to work tomorrow. She pulled on her sundress, brushed her hair and left the bathroom.

Travis was sitting on the bed, looking very much at home. He'd changed into cotton trousers and a blue shirt open at the neck, the sleeves rolled up. Suppressing the urge to jump him, Julie said, "Make it fast, I'm hungry."

Recklessly she plunked herself down beside him on the bed, hauling her skirt above her knees. She wasn't going to jump him. She knew better than to do that.

So she was quite safe.

CHAPTER EIGHT

THE scrape on Julie's knee was picturesque and hurt like crazy; but it wasn't overly deep. Travis knelt in front of her, extracting a few specks of bark with sterile tweezers, then smoothing on antibiotic ointment and applying a light bandage. Julie watched him, fascinated by the skill of his long fingers, so deft and gentle. He'd be a very good doctor.

He'd be a very good lover.

Desire washed over her, so strongly that it was as much as she could do to keep her hands at her sides. "Keep an eye on it," Travis said, getting to his feet.

Her face must have been an open book. With a strangled sound in his throat, Travis pushed her back on the bed, threw himself down beside her and began kissing her, fiercely possessive kisses that sang along her veins until the beat of her blood was like a primitive drum. She kissed him back, running her hands through the thick silkiness of his hair, stroking his nape, roaming his muscled shoulders. As he tugged at the hem of his shirt, she went lower, desperate to feel skin and flesh. The rough hair on his belly tangled her fingers; and then she found his nipple, hard as a pebble.

His tongue twined with hers in an intimacy that served only to increase her hunger. She opened to him, whimpering with need; and felt him slide the straps from her shoulders, pulling her dress down to bare her breasts. As he cupped them in his palms, she arched toward him, aching for more, maddened by sensations that were building as inexorably as a storm at sea.

His head dropped to her breast, his mouth taking one tip

then the other, laving them until she was moaning with pleasure. When he raised his head to kiss her mouth again, she tore at the buttons on his shirt; then she pulled him down to lie on her, the roughness of his body hair abrading her breasts.

Her skirt was above her thighs. At the first touch of his fingers between her legs, she gave a strangled cry. All the barriers were down; as the hardness of his erection dug into her thigh, she knew she couldn't rest until he was inside her. Where he belonged.

But even as she fumbled to remove the scrap of lace that was keeping him from her, Travis reared up, his eyes fastened on her face. "Julie," he said hoarsely, "in a moment I won't be able to stop. Is this what you want?"

She looked at him blankly, trying to find her voice. "Of course it is," she gasped, "can't you tell?"

"A summer affair."

It was as though he were trying the words out, she thought, listening to see how they sounded. Only last night she'd told him an affair was the last thing she was looking for; and she'd meant it. But now, crazed by passion, she was just about begging him to take her.

In a cracked voice she said, "I want you so much that I forgot all the reasons we shouldn't be doing this."

Pushing him off, she sat up; as she dragged at her dress to hide her breasts, the words came tumbling from her lips. "I thought I knew myself until you came along. I'm no virgin, Travis—when I was twenty I went to bed with my physics partner, because I figured it was time I found out what sex was all about. Nothing much, that's what I discovered. No big deal. So I got on with my life. And that was fine with me, I didn't want to fall in love back then and I still don't. And I sure don't want to get married."

She paused for breath, her hands clasped in her lap. "I've dated since then, of course I have. Nice men, attractive men, many of whom would have been happy to have an affair with no strings attached. But I never did. Not one of them swept me off my feet. Until you came along.'' She bit her lip. ''I don't understand why you're so different. When you kiss me, I forget everything except you. You saw how I behaved a moment ago, I was like a wild woman. That's not me! I've never been like that.''

''You think I come on to women I've only just met?''

''How would I know?''

He said with vicious truth, ''Whatever's swept you off your feet has knocked the feet right out from under me.''

''And how you hate me for doing that to you!''

''Why don't you want to fall in love or get married?''

He'd gone right to the crux. ''Two reasons,'' she said with an unhappy laugh. ''My father and my mother. And that's all you're getting out of me.'' In a flurry of skirts, she stood up. ''I'm sorry if I seemed to be leading you on, I couldn't help myself. I'm going downstairs for breakfast and then I'll leave with Oliver.''

''I was a damn fool to ask if you really wanted to make love,'' Travis said harshly. ''If we'd just gone ahead and done it, you wouldn't be in such a rush to get on the boat.''

Her knee was hurting, her whole body was a huge ache of sexual frustration, and all she wanted to do was curl up on the bed and sob her heart out. ''I'm glad you did ask. It's better for both of us this way.''

He pushed himself to his feet. ''We'll be in Portland for the summer, you and I. We're bound to meet up with each other.''

''I'll do my best to see that doesn't happen.''

''So this is goodbye,'' he said in an unreadable voice.

She gave him the faintest of smiles. ''You'll have forgotten me in a couple of days, you'll see.''

''Don't judge me by your own standards!''

Flinching from the fury in his face, Julie shoved her feet

into her sandals and ran for the door. But his voice stopped her, pinioning her to the white-painted panels. "You're planning on forgetting me. On forgetting what happens every time we get within ten feet of each other. Aren't you?"

"I've got to!"

"Maybe it's time you started behaving like an adult instead of jerking me around like a puppet on a string. On one minute, off the next. Or are you going to let your parents run your life for the rest of your days?"

"You didn't have to kiss me, Travis."

"You know what I really hate? That I didn't have a choice," he said savagely.

"We all have choices," she retorted. "And I'm choosing to get out of here before we do any more damage."

"I wouldn't have called you a coward," he jeered. "Goodbye, Julie...have a nice life."

She made a sound expressive of fury and frustration, whirled and banged the door shut behind her. Impossible man. Infuriating, arrogant and irresistibly sexy man. Scowling prodigiously, wincing at the pain in her knee, Julie went downstairs and hurried across the hall. She stopped short at the dining-room door, pasted a smile on her face and pushed it open. The huge table was spread with ample bacon and eggs, along with a gorgeous array of fruit, freshly baked croissants and coffee cakes. She stood still in the doorway; her appetite had completely forsaken her.

Forcing herself to calm down, she went in search of Charles and Corinne. They were outside on the patio. Calling on all her good manners, she thanked them for a wonderful stay and made her escape. When she went back to her room to get her bag, there was no sign of Travis. Nor was he, to her infinite relief, on the dock by the boathouse. Oliver was leaving in five minutes, he told her. She waited in an agony of impatience, making conversation with four other guests who were also leaving Manatuck. They all climbed aboard, and the launch pulled away from the dock.

She went to stand by the bow. As the island receded, she stole one last glance at it. But it wasn't the crenellated towers and absurd turrets, or the bannered tents on the lawn that held her attention. It was the lighthouse at the northeast tip of the island, where a dark-haired man had kissed her on the grass, turning her into a woman she didn't even recognize.

A woman of passion, who was afraid of that passion. More afraid than she'd ever been of anything in her life.

Left alone in Julie's bedroom, Travis stared unseeingly out of the window. He'd made a fool of himself. A total and unmitigated fool. Telling her she'd knocked him off his feet. Rambling on about having no choice.

He'd been on the brink of begging her to go to bed with him. Begging? Him?

Thank heavens he hadn't sunk that low.

But how was he ever going to forget the sweet rise of her breast, the racing of her pulse against his palm, the delicate scent of her skin? Or the brilliant green of her irises when he'd kissed her, their depths shot with fire? Why in hell had he blabbed on about summer affairs, giving her the time to think?

If he hadn't, she'd have been his.

He banged his fist hard on the sill, almost relishing the pain. If he'd been all kinds of a fool, at least he wasn't going to repeat his mistakes. He'd make sure of that by never seeing her again. He only rarely went to the clinic, and by the sound of it she wouldn't come near the hospital; plus he had no intention of finding out her phone number.

What did he need her phone number for when he wasn't going to see her again?

Goodbye meant just that. Goodbye.

He was well rid of Julie Renshaw.

Travis stayed on Manatuck until the last of the guests had gone. He, Corinne and Charles ate an informal supper on the patio, Travis doing his best to sound more at ease than he felt. Then he got up. "I'll get my bag, I told Oliver I'd be leaving in a few minutes."

"Fine, fine," Charles said. "Glad you could make it for the party, Travis. You remember what I said...Portland's too small for you, you'd be better off heading overseas where there's more scope for your talents."

"I hear you, Dad." One more person who didn't want to see him again, he thought with an inward wince. "Goodbye, Corinne," he added, "thanks for everything."

She offered him the same cool cheek as when he'd arrived, just as though the intervening two days hadn't happened. It was left for Oliver to say at the wharf on the mainland, "You come back soon, Mr. Travis. Manatuck ain't the same without you."

"Thanks, Oliver. Take care."

Julie's blue car was, of course, gone. Travis drove back to Portland, parking his car and going upstairs to the condo that belonged to Mark MacDonald and that he was renting for the summer. It was a very desirable condo built on one of the wharves on the waterfront, in sight of yachts and ferries and lobster boats. He'd made very little attempt to imprint his personality on it; as he entered, its impersonality struck him like a blow.

He wanted Julie here with him. That's what he wanted.

Dammit, he didn't. He was tired, that's all.

He poured himself a drink. Night was already falling over the harbor, the lights on the marina glittering like earthbound stars. Where did she live? In Old Port, with its handsome brick buildings and cobblestone streets? Or west of here, nearer to the clinic?

Was she thinking about him? Or had she already put him out of her mind, an incident that had happened and wouldn't be repeated?

He loathed the thought of being so summarily dismissed. Forgotten, like a garment she'd discarded.

Travis went to bed early, slept badly for the third night in a row and did a ten-hour shift at the hospital the next day. Afterward, changed into jeans and a T-shirt, he went to the grocery store nearest the medical center. He could have eaten out; but he'd tired of that in his first month here, and now preferred to cook something back at the condo. He was frowning at the array of steaks, wondering if he'd barbecue on the balcony, when a woman's voice said, "Travis? It is you, isn't it?"

He turned, recognizing the voice almost immediately. "Trish," he said warmly, "how are you? Long time no see."

"Eleven or twelve years," she said, shifting the carton of milk she was carrying to shake his hand.

She'd changed very little in those years, her long blond hair still in an untidy knot on her head, her eyes the same warm brown. Travis had been engaged to her his final year at medical school; for a moment he felt like that young man again, head stuffed with knowledge, wanderlust tugging him like a magnet even as he was pulled toward the more ordinary longings for home and a family. He said impulsively, "Have you got time for a drink? Or dinner?"

She consulted her watch. "A drink. I'm going to my in-laws for dinner, my husband's out of town and they've been looking after the children for me. Let me just pay for this."

He grabbed a steak, a few onions and some broccoli, and followed her. Ten minutes later they were seated in a booth in a nearby pub. "To chance meetings," Travis said, raising his glass. "Tell me about your husband…and how many children?"

"I have photos," she grinned, and showed him snapshots of two towheaded little boys and an angelic little girl, all blond curls and dimples. Her husband, Tom, was tall and athletic, with a pleasant smile. All five looked happy together, Travis thought. As though they fit.

"You're fortunate," he said. "A lovely family, Trish."

"And you? Have you married?"

He shifted in the seat. "Never have, no. I've spent most of my time overseas since you and I broke up. You name it, I've been there."

"It wouldn't be easy to meet women when you're on the move a lot, I suppose."

"You can always meet women if you want to."

"So you're still unattached," she said slowly. "Do you remember what I said to you the night I broke our engagement?"

"That you wanted a man who was head over heels in love with you," he said promptly. "Is Tom like that?"

Her face softened. "Yes. Even after three kids and the usual ups and downs of marriage. I lucked out."

"You knew enough to wait for the real thing." With an urgency that took him by surprise, Travis asked, "Did you know the minute you met Tom? Or was it more gradual?"

She took a sip of her martini. "After you left, and even though I was sure I'd done the right thing by breaking up with you, I was lonely. So I got a dog at the animal shelter, kind of an ugly dog actually, that no one else wanted to adopt. I was walking him in Deering Park one evening by the pond when he started to play with a very patrician collie. He fell in love with the collie and I fell in love with the collie's owner. And yes, I knew right away. I can tell you what Tom was wearing that evening and what we said, and how alive I felt. Utterly and wonderfully alive."

"And it's lasted..."

"As I say, we lucked out. It doesn't last for everyone,

Travis. But you have to be willing to take the risk. And in the rough times to work your heart out."

Moodily he stared into his Scotch. The moment Julie had stood up on the wharf and turned to face him, hadn't he in some primal sense recognized her?

"You've met someone," Trish ventured.

"Not really." He let a mouthful of the liquor slide down his throat, Julie's face in his mind's eye as clearly as if she were actually standing there.

"Come clean," Trish said pithily.

Exasperated with himself, Travis said, "I met this woman last Friday, you're right, and my hormones have been in an uproar ever since. But that's all it is. Lust."

"If it's lust, anyone will do."

He didn't want anyone. He wanted Julie. But it was still lust.

"One of the things I always admired about you was your honesty," Trish remarked. "You said it like it was. Surely you haven't lost that?"

"She's got me so riled up, I don't know what the truth is!"

"Maybe you've fallen in love with her."

He made an instinctive gesture of repudiation. "I don't know what love is, Trish…didn't you accuse me of that all those years ago?"

"I did, yes. You'd get just so close to me and then you'd back off. I was younger then and I had the world figured out, so I accused you of being afraid of intimacy. You'd lost your mother and you'd decided at the age of six that you weren't going to trust any female ever again." Her smile was rueful. "I wouldn't be quite so frank now. Or so sure that I was right."

"You probably were right, though. My mother disappeared between one day and the next. I don't remember the funeral, or any of the relatives visiting. I do know my dad would never allow her name to be mentioned. And then I was shipped off to boarding school as though nothing had happened. Two years later he married Corinne.''

''Little wonder you're afraid to trust. But if this woman is the right one, Travis, she's worth fighting for. Love's worth fighting for, that's what I'm saying. And now I'm going to shut up, and you're going to tell me about some of your adventures overseas.''

Travis dredged his memory for events both touching and funny; and half an hour later they left the pub. Trish reached up and kissed him on the cheek. ''It was lovely to see you again. Good luck, Travis. Keep in touch and make sure you bring her to dinner to meet the family.''

''Don't hold your breath,'' he said, and watched her leave. Not for the first time, he thought how wise a woman she was. He was glad she was happy.

He was even more glad she'd had the strength of character to break their engagement. He hadn't been in love with her, not really. He'd never fallen in love in his life. Now that he was alone, he could admit something else: while he'd had all the normal sexual urges for Trish of a man in his early twenties, he'd never been pulled to her the way he was to Julie.

But to suggest he'd fallen for Julie was ridiculous.

The condo seemed even more empty after seeing Trish's snapshots. Was this what he wanted for the rest of his life, Travis wondered, putting the bag of groceries down on the kitchen counter. A series of temporary lodgings; and no one to welcome him when he came home at the end of the day.

He'd always prided himself on his self-sufficiency. His independence.

Doggedly Travis cooked the steak and watched the late news. He worked several extra shifts that week, as well as volunteering at a local clinic. He also found out Julie's phone number, although he didn't call her. But he thought about her most of the time, far too much for his peace of mind. When the telephone rang on Friday evening, he raced to pick it up, absurdly certain that Julie would be on the other end of the line.

"Bryce here, Travis. How you doing, buddy?"

Normally Travis was glad to hear from Bryce; but tonight he had to swallow disappointment bitter as gall. "Fine…how are you and where are you?"

The last question was always relevant: apart from being a self-made millionaire and Travis's best friend, Bryce Laribee was an international consultant in computer programming who traveled the world over. "Bangkok. Hotter 'n hell. I'm heading for Hanoi tomorrow. You getting itchy feet yet?"

Bryce had been convinced Travis wouldn't last more than three weeks in Portland, Maine. "The practice is okay. I'm doing some freeby stuff in a downtown clinic as well."

"I knew it," Bryce chuckled. "Where are you headed come September?"

"I've got a couple of prospects. Mexico, near Cuernavaca. Or Honduras…any chance of us connecting this summer?"

"Give me a month. Then I should be back in the States." Bryce paused. "You mentioned you might try to get together with your father—did anything come of that?"

Briefly Travis described the party and the rather puzzling reconciliation with Charles. "It was all too slick, too easy. And for some reason he wants me out of Portland on the first flight. I can't think why."

"Sounds like your father has all the instincts of a Machiavelli without the brains," Bryce said caustically. "But you're not planning on leaving?"

"No. I guess not."

Bryce, who'd grown up in the slums of Boston, was

known for directness. "What's up? Did this really bother you? You don't sound like yourself."

Travis hesitated. "I met a woman."

"You meet lots of women. They trample each other to get to you first, you think I haven't noticed that?"

Travis grinned into the telephone. "You're not backward in that department yourself."

"So what's with this woman?"

"If I knew that, I wouldn't be sitting in this goddamned condo all by myself on a Friday night!"

There was a small silence. "Give, buddy."

There was no one Travis trusted as much as his old friend Bryce. At the age of twelve, Bryce had been admitted as a scholarship student to the boarding school Travis had been attending for six years. In Bryce's first week, Travis had saved him from certain explusion at least three times; then, together, they'd put the fear of God in the four bullies who'd been terrorizing the dorms after dark. Travis said, smiling, "Remember Jed Cathcart, the look on his face when you dumped that bucket of spaghetti all over him?"

"And then we wiped the floor with him and the spaghetti. Those were the days, Travis. Things were simpler, you knew who the bad guys were...now tell me about this woman. Name, age and vital statistics."

Stumbling at first, but gathering momentum as he went, Travis told the whole story, from the stormy meeting on the wharf to the equally stormy goodbye in her bedroom. "So that's that," he ended. "I've never chased a woman in my life and I'm not starting with her. Wouldn't do me any good, anyway."

"So why aren't you dating that nurse you told me about? The one with the big blue eyes. Sounded like she'd be willing."

Travis had had a coffee with the nurse on his Wednesday

shift; he could have asked her out then. "Too tall, too blond, wrong shape, you want me to go on?"

"You've got it bad, man."

"I'll get over it."

"You in love with this Julie?"

"No!"

"Not in the habit of falling in love myself, so I wouldn't know the symptoms. But it's not like you to pine like a lovesick teenager over a female who's given you nothing but grief. You know what you should do?" Bryce didn't wait for Travis to answer. "Call her up. Or better still, find out where she lives and knock on her door. See her again. Maybe you'll find out you've imagined the whole thing. So she's got green eyes. So what? Cats have got green eyes and you don't want to date a cat."

"She's as graceful as a cat. And just as self-contained."

"She's got claws, too." Bryce's voice roughened. "No broad's going to mess up your life, Travis, not if I have anything to say about it."

"You think if I saw her, I'd be over it?"

"Worth a try. Or maybe she'll have changed her mind and jump your bones."

"In my dreams."

"What have you got to lose? You're as cranky as a caged hyena."

"You got that part right." Travis grimaced. "Not that a second rejection'll make me feel any better."

"Don't be such a defeatist! Women drool all over you, I've watched 'em. Go for it, Travis. I'll call you next week and see what happened."

A few minutes later Travis rang off. He wasn't going to go and see Julie. If she didn't want him, that was her loss.

On which militant note, he went to bed.

CHAPTER NINE

ON SUNDAY afternoon it poured with rain. This suited Julie's mood. Her parents were coming for dinner and it would take her the rest of the afternoon to get ready. Her mother was a fanatic housekeeper. But why, thought Julie, as she wielded the dust cloth, did she think she had to clean her apartment from top to bottom before her mother could walk in the door? Was she still that much under Pearl Renshaw's thumb?

Julie loved her little apartment, which was owned by a wealthy and eccentric widow at the clinic whose arthritic pain she'd been able to relieve. She was paying through the nose for it, but it was only for a couple more months and her savings account was decidedly healthy at the moment.

She was living by the waterfront, on the top floor of an old brick building near the marina. She'd filled her tiny balcony with flowering plants, bought some attractive hand-painted furniture, and arranged some of her collection of artifacts from her travels on the walls. It felt like home.

Or it had, until she came back from Manatuck.

With a ferocious energy that had nothing to do with her mother, Julie scoured the tub until it gleamed. She wasn't going to think about Manatuck. Or Travis. Or the fact that her body, awakened by Travis, now refused to go back to sleep.

She'd read about desire in books. Even though she'd felt twinges of it now and then with one or the other of the men she'd dated, she'd concluded privately that the authors had overactive imaginations. She'd never been obsessed by a man, so that he haunted her sleep, her dreams and her daylight hours.

Never, until this last week.

Scrubbing the bathroom floor as sexual sublimation, she thought with an unhappy smile, and carried the bucket into the kitchen. Her knee still hurt. Another reminder of a time she desperately wanted to forget.

Her bedroom was immaculate, the bathroom pristine, and it only took a few minutes to tidy, dust and vacuum the living room and dining area. Which left the kitchen.

The rain was hammering on the skylight and streaming down the windows; she could scarcely see the harbor. A ginger ale. That's what she needed. And then she'd tackle the kitchen. She'd made a cheesecake this morning, so that much was done. As for the rest, she was planning a rather complicated Moroccan chicken dish that she'd organize once she'd finished cleaning.

At least work had gone well this week, that was one thing to be grateful for. She was finding the clinic a welcome respite from her normal work; she hadn't realized how stressful her overseas contracts had been until she'd come home to Portland for the summer. Besides, some of her clients were a delight. There was Abigail Masters, who'd found her this apartment, who smoked cigars and swore like a stevedore; Leonora Connolly, a retired dancer who was paying the physical price for her career with humor and grace; and Malcolm McAdams, a famous hybridizer of daylilies, who insisted on bringing his Manx cat to his sessions.

It was such a change from crushing heat, foreign tongues and equally crushing poverty…

Julie was just topping up the glass with pop when her buzzer sounded. She frowned. The little boy downstairs had a tendency to open the security door to whomever he pleased; she must speak to his parents about it. Again. She went to the door, peering through the peephole.

Travis was standing in the hallway. The glass jerked in her hand, spilling ginger ale on her shirt. She looked down at herself. Bare feet, a luridly bruised gash on her leg, cutoff shorts and her very oldest shirt which had a button missing in a rather strategic place.

Let him see her as she was. That should fix him.

She pulled the door open. His hair was plastered to his skull, his raincoat was dripping on the mat, and his eyes were even more blue than she remembered. He was carrying a rather bedraggled bouquet of sweetpeas. She went on the attack. "How did you find out where I live?"

"Asked one of my colleagues at Silversides."

"How did you get in the front door?"

"A kid with bright red hair let me in. You should complain about that."

"I have. His parents think he's a little angel who couldn't possibly be breaking the rules."

"Are you going to ask me in?"

Her heart was bouncing around in her chest, her knees were weak and her mouth dry. Too much adrenaline, she thought clinically. "Give me one good reason why I should."

"Because you want to," Travis said.

She wanted to kiss him senseless, Julie thought faintly. If only she'd taken yesterday's newspaper to the little coffee shop on the corner instead of opting for ginger ale in her messy kitchen. "You're wet," she said with blinding originality.

"It's raining. Or hadn't you noticed?"

So what was she going to say? You can come in if you promise to stay at least six feet away from me at all times? "I'm cleaning," she said. "I'm a mess."

Travis looked her up and down, taking his time about it,

laughter lurking in his eyes. As warm color crept up her cheeks, he said, "Are you last on the list?"

"After the kitchen."

He eyed the glass in her hand. "I like ginger ale."

As all her nerves screamed danger, she gave him what she hoped was a noncommittal smile. "You'd better come in. Here, give me your coat and I'll hang it in the closet."

Once she'd done so, he handed her the flowers. "These are for you. They were selling them at the market."

She frequently went to the market, which was only a few blocks from her apartment. "Where do you live?" she said, suddenly suspicious.

He crossed the living room, rubbing at the pane. "You should be able to see my place from here. The second group of condos."

On a clear day she'd be in full sight of his windows, she thought edgily. Just what she needed. "Do you really want pop? I could make you some coffee. Or there's beer."

"A ginger ale would be fine."

She fled to the tiny galley kitchen, where unwashed dishes were heaped on the counter. After rinsing the worst of the stain from her shirt, she filled a second glass and went back into the living room. Travis was standing on the sisal mat, looking around him with appreciation. He dwarfed the room; he also looked very much at home.

"Those carvings, aren't they from Bali?" She nodded. "And the pillows look like they came from a Calcutta bazaar."

"They did."

"You've traveled a lot."

She said rapidly, "I do overseas contracts all the time. I just came home this summer because my mother had a minor heart attack."

He picked up a delicately carved giraffe she'd bought in Tanzania. "Where have you worked?" After she'd rattled off the names of some of the countries, he added, "You didn't tell me any of this."

"I don't often talk about what I do. It makes people uncomfortable."

"So you've noticed that, too…you see, I do the same sort of thing." Travis named the international organization he'd worked for the last ten years, establishing that he'd left Tanzania the year before Julie had arrived.

She frowned at him. "I thought you were a rich doctor who looked after the rich."

"And I thought you catered to the privileged and pampered."

"You know the kind of things people think. Do-gooder with a savior complex."

"Guilt-dumpers. Disturbers of the status quo."

"Weirdos, wackos and neurotics."

He gave her a warm smile. "It's not easy work, is it, Julie?"

His smile made her tingle all the way from her head to her bare toes. "No," she muttered. "No, it's not. Would you like some more pop?"

"Sure." As she padded into the kitchen, he followed her. "I'll help you with the dishes."

If he'd dwarfed the living room, he filled the kitchen. Almost dizzy with longing, Julie picked up the sweet peas and buried her face in them. "They're my favorite flower," she mumbled.

He put down his glass on the counter. "It's interesting that we do the same kind of work…means we share a basic value system."

"So what?" she blurted.

"One more thing we have in common."

"You're playing games with me, Travis."

"Okay—I'll cut to the chase. Do you know why I'm here?"

She looked at him warily. "Not really."

"Then I'll tell you. I've thought about you all week, night and day. I'll be honest—I figured if I came here today and saw you again, I'd realize that you weren't anything special, that I'd been fooling myself."

She looked down at herself with a shaky grin. "You've got your proof. In spades."

"It wouldn't matter what you wore or how you looked," he said with suppressed violence. "The moment you answered the door, I knew nothing had changed."

She found she was gripping the edge of the counter with bruising strength, mostly to keep herself from pulling his head down and kissing him until neither one of them could breathe. She said carefully, "What exactly are you saying?"

"Hell, I don't know." He ran his fingers through his damp hair. "I want you as much now as I wanted you on Manatuck. I guess that's what I'm saying."

The intensity in his face made her tremble. She reached past him for the pop bottle, inadvertently brushing his bare forearm with her own. The pop was forgotten. Her hand stopped in midair. Then, very slowly, she lowered it to lie on his arm. She closed her eyes, oblivious to everything but his nearness and a tumult of longing. All those authors were right, she thought. Desire does exist. It's like fire, hot and urgent and leapingly alive.

In a strangled voice Travis said, "Julie…"

His arms went around her. She buried her face in his shoulder, inhaling the clean masculine scent of his skin, so very much a part of him, so uniquely his. Then, of her own accord, she looked up, took his face between her palms and kissed him full on the mouth. As she'd been wanting to do ever since he'd arrived.

She'd learned a thing or two about kissing on Manatuck. But just in case he doubted her intentions, she whispered in between fierce, heated kisses, "Make love to me, Travis. Now."

"There's nothing I want more in the world," he said, kissing her back with such blatant hunger that her body melted into his. Then, awkwardly because the kitchen was so small, he picked her up. "Don't kick the pop bottle," he added, his eyes giving her a very different message.

His eyes were undressing her. Against her cheek she felt the hard pounding of his heart, under her knees the sinewy strength of his arm. As he edged out of the kitchen, she said, "Down the hall on the right," and added with a tiny chuckle, "it's not usually so tidy."

Because the room was small, she'd bought a three-quarter spindle bed, covering it with an old-fashioned quilt. Not bothering to pull the quilt back, Travis laid her down on the bed and covered her with his big body, his weight on his elbows. She was trembling very lightly. Then his head swooped down like a falcon to the prey, his mouth plundering hers until she was nothing but an ache of passionate need.

Only then did Travis reach for the top button on her shirt. His fingers brushed her skin; his irises were a blazing blue. Straddling her, he eased her arms out of the shirt, then in the same intent silence undid her bra, tossing it to the floor. She said softly, "Take your shirt off, Travis."

His hands weren't quite steady as he fumbled with the buttons, and this, more than anything, touched Julie to the heart. Travis, she already knew, was a man both self-contained and very much in control of himself: that she should make him lose that control filled her with a confusing mixture of wonder and excitement. Very deliberately she reached for the zipper on her shorts, easing them down her hips, then kicking them to the floor. She said with a faint grin, "Because I always wear utilitarian cotton in the tropics, I go overboard on lace when I'm home."

"Black lace," he said huskily. Then with sudden impatience, he stripped off his slacks and briefs.

She wriggled out of the black lace. "Watch out for my knee, it's still sore," she said, and pulled his head down, her tongue darting to meet his in a kiss that seemed to last forever. A kiss in which the old Julie vanished.

The new Julie, not knowing quite what to expect yet utterly willing to find out, tugged at Travis's shoulders. "Lie on top of me," she begged, "I want to feel every inch of you."

He slid his mouth down her throat, finding her breast, his hips pressing her into the quilt. She wrapped her arms around him, glorying in his weight, crying out with pleasure as he laved her nipple with his tongue. Sensation lanced through her, fiery and imperative. With a sensuality she had never thought she possessed, she ran her fingers through his chest hair, tugging at it gently, following it all the way to his navel and then beyond.

Briefly he lifted his hips. And then she found his center, hot and silky, infinitely desirable. He groaned deep in his throat as she touched him, burying his face in her shoulder, his heart pounding against her ribs. As though he couldn't help himself, he eased her legs apart and plunged into her.

She gasped with delight, welcoming him and gathering him in. Inexpertly she moved her hips until he filled her, so that she scarcely knew where she ended and he began. Her own rhythms seized her, urgently and inexorably, mounting toward an unbearable peak. "Travis," she muttered, "oh Travis…"

"Sweetheart…" he said roughly, his fierce thrusts pushing her over the edge, the hard plane of his chest inflaming her nipples until she arched to meet him, crying out his name in an avalanche of release. He convulsed within her, his own cry echoing in her ears. Then he collapsed on top of her.

Julie lay very still, and for several minutes couldn't have said a word to save her soul. Gradually she came back to herself, to two hearts racing as one and a feeling of peace and fulfillment such as she'd never known. I've come home, she thought. It's taken me all these years and many thousands of miles, and now I've come home…

Abruptly Travis raised his head. "Julie, I'm sorry—that was over before it began."

A slow smile spread across Julie's face. "You're sorry?" she said. "I hope not. But maybe I'm the one who should be apologizing. I was so impatient, so demanding—in such a big hurry. I wanted you so much, I couldn't bear to wait."

Travis gave a sudden exultant laugh. "How about we both forget the word *sorry*? And how about we do it again? Say in five minutes. And this time maybe both of us can restrain ourselves so that it lasts longer than five minutes."

"You were timing us?" she said, batting her lashes at him.

"Not exactly. Too much else was going on. As you may have noticed."

"Who, me?" Julie chuckled. She'd never known laughter could be part of lovemaking. She was beginning to suspect that there was a lot she'd never known. Letting all her newfound wonderment show in her face, she said ingenuously, "So I'm supposed to kiss you with restraint? Is that the way it works?"

"No," he said, "you're supposed to kiss me like this."

He bent his head, finding her mouth, moving his lips over hers with tantalizing lightness. His tongue sought out hers, dancing with it, advancing and retreating. And at the same time, with exquisite pressure, he was stroking the warm slope of her breast, again and again.

Low in her belly, a deep, sweet ache was born. She had

time. That was what Travis was saying. Time to savor every sensation. Time to learn his body, to discover what he liked and what pleased him.

Was that what was meant by intimacy?

CHAPTER TEN

JULIE brought her hands to Travis's face, searching out the hard planes of his jaw and cheekbones, tracing his deepset eyes, her own smiling into his with a mixture of shyness and invitation. His hair, so thick and silky; the corded tendons in his neck; the dip of his collarbone and the swell of taut muscle that was his shoulder, she explored them all and found them all utterly entrancing. And the whole time she watched his face, losing herself in the brilliant blue depths of his eyes. He said unsteadily, "Have I told you yet today how beautiful you are?"

"If you did, I missed it."

"How your eyes are the green of a hummingbird's wings? How your skin is smooth as a river?" As he ran his hands down her body, she shivered in response, his voice casting a spell over her. "How you tremble when I touch you. Like this. Or like this."

His palms, curving to her hips, cupping her buttocks, then sliding to her inner thighs, did indeed fill her with a wild, sweet trembling. Tears suddenly blurred her vision. "No one's ever said such beautiful things to me."

He found the sleek petals of flesh between her legs, seeking out their heart, watching her face change as he stroked her very gently. "Does that give you pleasure?"

She thrust with her hips, briefly closing her eyes. "Yes, oh yes..."

She was drowning in desire, flooded by its tides. And she'd been ignorant enough to think it didn't exist. She knew better now. Desire existed. Desire for Travis, for his

95

big, muscular body and all the wonderful things he was doing to her.

Going on instinct, Julie moved her hands further down his body, roaming the corded muscles of his belly, the jut of hipbone and his taut flanks. "If I'm beautiful," she murmured, "so are you."

He suddenly rolled over, carrying her with him so that she was lying on top of him, pulling her face down to kiss her again. And all the time he was exploring her breasts and narrow waist, the flare of her hips, in slow, sensuous strokes. She kissed him back, moving his thighs apart so she could rub herself against him with a matching sensuality. "Do you like that?" she asked.

"Like it?" he gasped. "Julie, I love everything you do."

With sudden shyness she said, "You mean I don't disappoint you?"

His hands stilled. "You couldn't be further from the truth." He paused for a moment, as if searching for the right words. "You told me you'd made love a long time ago, that you weren't a virgin...but it's almost as though I am the first. There's an innocence about you that makes me feel very special."

She wasn't sure she liked the direction he was heading. "I'm doing my best to lose that innocence," she said lightly, "which will require your full cooperation."

"You've got it," Travis said, and lifted her to ride him.

She was more than ready for him; as he buried himself deep within her, she gasped with delight. Again Travis found the place where she was most achingly sensitive, teasing her flesh until she was shuddering with pent-up need, her head thrown back, her belly taut within the hollow of her rib cage. An inward throbbing seized her, wild as an ocean storm; she rode him as though he were the waves of the sea until the last barriers between them dissolved, and his own climax reared to meet hers.

The last fierce ripple ran through her; the sounds she was hearing were her own harsh indrawn breaths mingled with his. As though she were boneless, she sank down on top of him, holding him close, his body hair rough under her cheek. "It happened again," she said raggedly.

"I feel like I'm making up for a lifetime of hunger," Travis said hoarsely, wrapping his arms around her.

"I feel like I've been ambushed," she croaked. "I had no idea making love could be like that."

"Look at me, Julie."

She glanced up, the expression on his face catching at her heartstrings. Distantly she felt the stirrings of what was unquestionably panic. "Travis, I—"

"I want you to know something—I've never made love like that in my life," he said in the same hoarse voice. "I'd pictured seducing you slowly, taking my time, giving you the most pleasure I was capable of. But instead, both times, I was totally out of control. That's not like me...to lose myself like that."

Her one desire to defuse a level of emotion that terrified her, Julie said pertly, "It's not like me, either—you can take that to the bank."

To her relief he smiled. "We could try again. Although we may have to wait more than five minutes this time...I'm only human." His smile widened. "Tell you what. Why don't I take you out for dinner? Then we could come back here and make love all night. Or we could go to my place if you like."

"Dinner...did you say *dinner?*" In a flurry of bare limbs, Julie sat bolt upright, her face horror-stricken. "Moroccan chicken. Ohmigosh!"

"What's the matter?" Travis demanded. As she tried to scramble off him, he grabbed her by the wrist. "Surely the thought of a dinner date with me isn't that horrendous?"

She tugged futilely at his grasp. "My parents, they're

coming here for dinner. I'm making this fancy chicken casserole.'' Her gaze fell on the bedside clock, her voice rising. ''They're going to arrive in three-quarters of an hour.''

Travis said promptly, ''I'll do the dishes, and you cook.''

She looked at him as though he had two heads. ''Are you suggesting you stay for dinner with my parents?''

''Yeah...I guess I am.''

''No way! I'm not letting them within a mile of you. Let go, Travis, *please*.''

If anything, his grip tightened. ''What's the big deal with your parents, Julie?''

She struck at his hand. ''I am not going to tell you my life history when my mother and father will be ringing the doorbell in exactly forty-three minutes.'' She gave a moan of despair. ''They're always punctual. Precisely on time. They'll take one look at me and they'll know what I've been doing all afternoon. How could I have forgotten they were coming?''

''You forgot because we were doing something more important.''

How could she argue with him? She was the one who'd thrown herself at him. ''That's your interpretation,'' she said fractiously.

Travis released her wrist so suddenly that she almost fell sideways. ''You want me out of here? Right now?''

''Of course!''

His voice hardened. ''There's no *of course* about it. Not from my point of view. We just made love. Twice, in case you've forgotten. And now you want to hustle me out the door so your parents won't catch sight of me and think you've actually been with a man. How old are you, for heaven's sake?''

''Thirty,'' she muttered, scrabbling for her clothes, which seemed to be scattered all over the floor. ''What's that got to do with it? Do hurry, Travis.''

"Just you wait a minute," he said grimly. He stood up, towering over her, stark naked and angrier than she'd ever seen him. Taking her by the shoulders, he grated, "We made love. That means something to me, and I'm not going to walk out the door as though it never happened. We'll get together tomorrow evening after work. We can meet in the middle of the park, or in a coffee shop, or all the way out at the Spring Point lighthouse—I don't give a damn where we meet. But we're going to meet. And you're going to talk, Julie. You're going to tell me why you've never had a serious boyfriend in your life, and how that relates to your parents. Have you got that?"

It wasn't easy to be cool, calm and collected when wearing nothing but black lace briefs and confronted by a large, angry and entirely naked male; but Julie did her best. "That's your agenda," she said coldly. "You haven't asked me mine."

"I don't care if you've already got plans—cancel them," he grated, and with complete composure bent to pick up his scattered clothes. Julie averted her eyes from the long curve of his spine. She still wanted him, she thought, appalled. How could she? What was wrong with her?

Was she some kind of sex maniac?

An inner resolve, scarcely articulated, hardened into shape. "I—I don't think we should see each other again," she said.

Travis's hands stilled on his belt buckle. "Would you mind repeating that?"

"You heard."

"We've just been as intimate as a man and woman can be, and now you want me to vanish from your life?"

Chilled to the bone, Julie wrapped her arms around her waist. "Yes," she said, "I do."

His eyes never leaving her face, Travis reached for his

shirt. "You don't think two people should be involved in that decision?"

Flinching from his sarcasm, she said, "It's precisely because I don't want to be part of a couple that I'm making the decision."

"Do you have to sound so cold-blooded?"

He sounded anything but. Unbidden, an image of his face at the moment of climax flashed into her mind. Julie shoved it away, pain lancing her heart. "I'm trying to avoid disappointment in the future," she cried. "For both of us."

"You let me look after myself," Travis said grimly. "You're looking for guarantees, Julie, that's what you're doing. There aren't any, haven't you learned that yet?"

"I won't commit to any kind of long-term relationship with you...so what's the point of seeing you again? We'll both end up getting hurt."

"I don't understand—you've lived in India and Tanzania, yet you won't take the smallest of gambles in your personal life. What kind of parents have you got?"

"The kind that are a perfect advertisement for singlehood," she flared. "Travis, I have the right to say I don't want to see you again, and I'm exercising that right."

Doing up the buttons on his shirt, he said, "You're denying yourself the possibility of falling in love, of marriage and bearing children...is that the way you plan to live for the rest of your life?"

"The first time we met, you told me it was against your principles to belong to anyone!"

"Maybe I've changed," he said.

"Then that's your problem." She had to end this. "It would have been better if this afternoon had never happened, I was a fool to even let you in the door."

"You were the one who instigated our lovemaking."

"I made a mistake!"

"So an experience that damn near knocked me off my feet was nothing but a mistake?"

"Stop it! I can't take any more of this. Just go away and leave me alone, Travis—that's all I ask."

"You don't have a worry in the world," he said savagely, turned on his heel and left the bedroom.

Julie opened her closet door, grabbing a skirt and blouse off the hangers. She was trembling again, just as she'd trembled when Travis had undressed her. But now it was nothing to do with desire.

Dimly, as if the sounds came from another world, she heard Travis's shoes scrape on the front mat; then the apartment door slammed shut.

He'd gone.

She'd done the right thing. She knew she had. Yet all she wanted to do was throw herself across the bed and cry her eyes out. In the space of a few minutes, she'd plummeted from the bliss she'd found in his arms to this dead despair.

For it had been bliss. She'd felt whole, perhaps for the first time in her life. Travis had made her complete.

With a tiny moan of dismay, Julie ran for the bathroom and turned on the shower. Ten minutes later, dressed and more or less presentable, she hurried into the kitchen. She'd scrap making the Moroccan chicken. She had time to do the dishes, run a mop over the kitchen floor and thaw some pasta sauce that she had in the freezer. Thank heavens she'd made the cheesecake this morning.

Before all this had happened. Before her life had changed irreversibly.

Quickly Julie filled the sink with hot water. She mustn't think about Travis; she couldn't afford to. She squirted detergent into the sink and tossed in the dirty cutlery; when the buzzer sounded twenty minutes later, the clean dishes were stacked in the tray, the kitchen floor had dried, she'd added extra scallops and shrimp to the sauce and she'd just thrown the place mats on the table. The other thing she'd done was bury the sweet peas Travis had brought her in the depths of the garbage can.

Taking a long, deep breath, Julie walked to the door, opening it wide. "Hello Mum, Dad," she said, and lifted her cheek to be kissed. Her parents didn't do hugs.

"Hello, Julie," her mother said. "You look very flushed, are you feeling all right?"

"Of course she is," her father said heartily. "You're like me, never ill. Right, Julie?"

This was a not-so-subtle dig at his wife Pearl, who enjoyed a variety of ailments, many of them genuine. The minor heart attack she'd had in the spring had been lumped with everything else by her husband; Julie, more knowledgeable, had been encouraging her mother to eat a little less and exercise a little more.

Pearl ignored her husband's comment, passing Julie her wet raincoat. "What a terrible day...oh, you didn't get around to laying the table?"

How well Julie knew that air of faint reproach; all too often it had been directed her way. "A friend dropped in unexpectedly," she said, opting for a censored version of the truth. "So I'm not quite ready."

Her mother headed right for the kitchen. "Seafood pasta, how nice...you've heard they've been having trouble with the local scallops, have you? Some kind of algal growth."

"No, I hadn't heard," Julie said evenly. "Can I get you a glass of wine?"

"I'll stick to fruit juice, dear. Much better for you."

"Do you know why the French live longer?" Thomas Renshaw interposed. "Red wine, proven to cut down on heart attacks."

Julie said dryly, "I've only got white, Dad."

"If you'd had red, he'd have wanted white," Pearl said with a merry little laugh. "Wouldn't you, darling?"

Julie winced. "Speaking of heart attacks, how are you feeling, Mum?"

Pearl discussed her cholesterol level, her blood pressure monitor and the new cardiologist she'd seen last week. "Such a sweet man, I should introduce you to him, Julie."

Julie didn't want to meet another doctor. "You've had your hair done, it looks nice."

"It didn't turn out at all the color I wanted. I'll just have to change salons again."

"Are there any you haven't tried?" Thomas said, accepting a glass of wine. "I can't see what the big fuss is all about."

"When you had a full head of hair, you used to fret every time the barber cut it," Pearl remarked.

This was a double blow, for Thomas hated being almost bald; and was still fussy about how the remnant was cut. Julie turned away, taking knives and forks out of the drawer. "Would you mind putting these out, Dad? And the candlesticks are on the coffee table...it's almost dark enough to light them, isn't it?"

She was exhausted already, she thought unhappily, taking some rolls out of the bread box and turning on the oven to heat them. Then she bent to find the ingredients for a tossed salad from the bottom shelf of the refrigerator. Pearl took advantage of her husband's temporary absence to say, "Your father doesn't look well, but he refuses to go to the doctor...you just don't know what I have to put up with."

"You're not backward about telling me, Mum."

Pearl gave a theatrical sigh. "Well, you're my only child, who else can I tell?"

Do you love your husband? The question hovered on the tip of Julie's tongue. Exasperated with herself, she bit it back. What was the point of asking? For as long as she could remember, Thomas and Pearl had existed in an out-wardly polite state of constant warfare. No overt anger, no attempt to solve their differences; just an incessant sniping at each other that Julie loathed. There were lines of dis-content in her mother's carefully made-up face; her father's faded hazel eyes held neither hope nor laughter. She said with attempted cheer, "I made a fabulous cheesecake for dessert, you'll like it."

"Too many calories, I'm sure."

"You worry them off faster than you put them on," Julie teased. "Anyway, I used low-fat ingredients."

"When you've been married as long as I have, you have to keep up your appearance," Pearl said. "The pasta's boil-ing over, Julie."

Julie turned the heat down, set the timer and slung chopped tomatoes in the salad bowl. Luckily she had some homemade dressing left. Ten minutes later, they sat down to eat; her parents, as she'd learned long ago, didn't believe in dining after six-thirty.

The candles flickered light and shadow on the ceiling, and rain streaked the windowpanes. Pearl said, "I really must make you some curtains, Julie, anyone can look in."

"I'm three stories up...besides, I'll be gone in a couple of months, it's not worth it." She smiled at her mother. "But thanks for the offer."

"Oh, of course, you're leaving before winter...the older I get, the more I dread the winters. I miss you so much when you're overseas, dear."

I won't move back to Portland, I won't, Julie thought frantically, and felt guilt curdle her stomach. She should be a better daughter: closer to home, more involved. But she'd lived with her parents until she was nearly eighteen, and her presence hadn't made either of them any happier. In fact, the opposite had been true: their daughter had given them one more thing to argue about.

The cheesecake caused Thomas to complain that Pearl never made desserts, and Pearl to calculate how many calories he'd just devoured. Julie poured coffee, listening to the rain beat against the windows. What would Travis have thought of her parents? Had he met them, would he have understood why she'd sent him away?

"You're spilling the coffee," Pearl said sharply.

"Oh...sorry, I'll get a cloth."

"You don't seem yourself," Thomas said. "Is there anything you're not telling us?"

Oh, yes, Julie thought wildly. There's plenty. Starting with this afternoon, when I just about attacked a man I scarcely know and behaved like a wanton hussy in the bed just down the hall. *Wanton hussy* was a phrase she'd heard her father use about a woman in a television play. Which, as Pearl had pointed out, he'd watched right to the end. Julie said carefully, "I'm a little tired, that's all."

"I don't know why you had to take that job all summer," her mother said. "You could have spent more time with us."

"I can use the money," Julie said mildly. "More coffee, Dad?"

After dinner Pearl insisted on washing the dishes, they all watched a nature show, and then her parents left. Julie closed the door behind them and wandered back into the living room. Maybe she should have let Travis stay for dinner, she thought wretchedly. Wouldn't that have been the easiest way to show him why she was so dead-set against commitment? She'd once suggested to her mother that if Pearl was so unhappy, maybe she should get a divorce; affronted, Pearl had lectured her about the sanctity of marriage vows, the tribulations of a woman's lot and the lifelong duties of motherhood. Julie had never mentioned divorce again.

Restlessly she roamed the apartment. She couldn't go for

a walk, it was still pouring rain. She couldn't vacuum the apartment, it was already clean. And she couldn't sleep on the couch, the cushions were too thin. She forced herself to walk into her bedroom, get undressed and get into bed. But when she turned her head to the pillow, she caught, elusively, the clean male scent of Travis's body. Her fists clenched, Julie fought back tears that if they once started might never stop. She'd made the right choice, the only possible choice, by sending Travis away.

Hold that thought, Julie.

Closing her eyes, she started counting parakeets, which she'd long ago decided was a more colorful way of getting to sleep than counting sheep.

But it was a long time before her strategy worked.

CHAPTER ELEVEN

THE evenings home alone in her apartment were the worst. By Tuesday evening, Julie had it figured out: subconsciously, and despite the fact that she was the one who'd sent Travis packing, she was expecting him to get in touch with her.

Her mother phoned. So did Kathy, one of the nurses from the clinic, and her hairdresser. Travis didn't phone.

Why would he? She'd told him, unequivocally, to get lost. But to her horror, she realized she was furious with him for not phoning; for giving up so easily. Compounding her problems, Julie was sleeping very badly. While her mind might be saying she mustn't see Travis again, her body was giving her a very different message. Her body craved him, unrelentingly.

On Thursday evening, about nine-thirty, the telephone rang. Her mother, Julie thought glumly. No doubt Pearl was wondering why Julie hadn't dropped by all week. She picked up the receiver, trying to inject some energy into her voice. "Hello?"

"It's Travis."

His voice penetrated every pore, filling her with a tumult of helpless desire. She sank down on the nearest chair, clutching the receiver. "I told you to leave me alone," she said, surprised how forceful she sounded.

"I don't always do what I'm told—I thought you knew me well enough by now to realize that. What are your plans for the weekend?"

"I don't have any. With you or anyone else."

"Who else have you gone to bed with since last Sunday?"

"Five different men every night. Six on Tuesday."

"So you don't have time to go out for dinner with me Saturday evening?"

"No, I don't."

"Your loss," Travis said cheerfully, and cut the connection.

Puzzled and vastly disappointed, Julie listened to the hum on the line. He'd given up much too easily; nor had he sounded particularly upset. Nothing like Sunday.

He was getting over her. Already.

This thought should have made her happy. Instead, in a vile mood, she hauled on her Reeboks, went to the park and ran hard for over thirty minutes. Then she went to her fitness club, worked out and lifted weights. Her body was no doubt in better shape after all this activity. But it had done nothing to improve her mood.

She didn't want to be in the same room with Travis ever again. But she didn't want him getting over her too soon. How illogical was that?

Travis got in his car and headed for the clinic, glancing at his watch as he pulled out on the street. Perfect timing. He was being both deceitful and manipulative; but it was all in a good cause. At least, he hoped so.

Julie, as he well knew, had a mind of her own. Maybe she wouldn't even get in the car. Let alone agree to be driven anywhere by him.

It was up to him to persuade her. He'd never been one to back down from a challenge. And Julie was certainly a challenge. He shoved to the back of his mind the thought that he might just be banging his head against a brick wall, that Julie would once again give him the cold shoulder.

That she'd meant it when she'd said she didn't want to see him again.

It couldn't be true. How could he equate that with the woman he'd made love to in her apartment? Her innocence, that told him more clearly than words that her sexual experience had indeed been limited. The bemusement in her face when he'd touched her and she'd been seized by desire. Her generosity, her wholehearted abandonment, her heart-stopping beauty. His hands clenched on the wheel, Travis pulled up at a traffic light. He'd swear on a whole stack of Bibles that he was the first man to bring that woman into existence. So now was he supposed to sit back and allow her to be buried again? All because of her parents?

Or was he simply being an egotistical idiot who couldn't accept the word *no?* Who was acting out of wounded male pride?

He'd left the stately brick buildings of Old Port for the suburbs. The one word he was trying very hard to keep out of his calculations was that awkward word *love*. Bryce had asked him if he was in love with Julie, and he'd denied it instantly. This maelstrom of lust, frustration and longing that had him in its coils had nothing to do with love.

Although how would he know? He wasn't exactly an expert on the subject. And Julie, he suspected, was even less so.

He'd handled finding out she had no plans for the weekend rather well. He only hoped that hadn't changed since last night.

The grounds of the clinic boasted close-clipped lawns and flowerbeds filled with frilly petunias. Travis drove around to the side entrance, the one nearest the physiotherapy department. By some judicious questioning, he'd found out when Julie's shift ended; he'd already known, from conversations he'd had with her, that she took the bus to work, renting a car only when she had an expedition in mind.

He was fifteen minutes early.

It was a very long fifteen minutes, during which he had time to relive every detail of the time he'd spent with Julie, ending with their cataclysmic lovemaking and her obdurate refusal to see him again. For the tenth time, he looked at his watch. She was now five minutes late.

The side door swung open. A dark-haired woman in a crisp white uniform was running down the steps.

Travis got out of the car. Julie saw him instantly and stopped dead on the bottom step. Her face was a study of conflicting emotions; but surely there'd been, elusively, a flash of joy? "Hi, Julie," Travis said. "I was out this way and wondered if you wanted a drive home?"

It wasn't a complete lie. Neither was it the complete truth. "Do you have patients here?" she said suspiciously.

"I come out here sometimes, yes." That at least was the truth, he thought. "Hop in, it'll save you waiting for the bus."

She was chewing on her lower lip; if she had felt joy, it wasn't showing now. "I am tired," she admitted, slowly walking toward his car.

She was standing in the sunlight now; the faint shadows under her eyes filled him with a helpless yearning. "All the more reason to get a lift," Travis said casually as he leaned over and opened the passenger door.

She got in, closed the door and did up her seat belt. His heart thudding against his ribs, Travis said inanely, "Friday afternoons…what would we do without weekends?"

"You said it." She gave him a faint smile. "I thought this job would be a sinecure after some of the overseas stuff I've done. But it's really hard work…although more rewarding than I'd expected."

As he drove out of the grounds, he asked her a few

technical questions, pleased for more than one reason when she launched into a discussion of some controversial new treatments. By the park, instead of turning right, he turned left; only five minutes later did she say, puzzled, "This isn't the way downtown. You're not heading for Old Port... you're going toward the Veterans' Bridge."

His mouth dry, Travis said calmly, "That's right. I'm abducting you."

"What?"

"It's summer, you have no plans and neither do I, and there's a wonderful resort on a beach a few miles south of here."

"You're taking me away for the *weekend?*"

"Yep."

"Are you out of your mind?"

"Not that I'm aware of."

"I won't go!"

"Relax, Julie. Live a little."

"Don't you tell me what to do. The next traffic light, I'm out of here."

Travis hadn't rehearsed what he'd do if she reacted this way. "You can do that if you want," he said. "Although if you really don't want to go, I'll drive you home—"

"Oh sure," she interrupted, "you think I believe one word you say?"

"If you're dead set against changing the smallest thing about yourself, I'll drive you straight home," he said in a hard voice. "And that's a promise."

"I did change something! Last Sunday afternoon. I never behave like that, leading a man on, just about hauling him into my bed and then behaving like some kind of sex maniac...I never behave like that. Never!"

He glanced over. Her voice had had a telltale quiver, and tears were filming her eyes. "I know you don't," he said. "You believe me?"

"Of course I do. For Pete's sake, I was the man you were in bed with. You think I didn't learn a whole lot about you while we were making love?"

"You did?"

"Innocent, trusting, generous, wild...you were all those things. And then you showed me the door faster than you can say *bed*."

She reached into her purse, pulled out a tissue and blew her nose. "That's because you scare the heck out of me."

"You think I'm not scared?" he asked; and with an uncomfortable lurch realized it was true.

She looked full at him. "Come off it, Travis. You, scared?"

"I've never abducted a woman in my life. Never wanted to until you came along. Listen to me for a minute. When I was six, my mother vanished...when I went to bed she was there, and when I woke up in the morning she was gone. I was told she was in New York. But then a few days later, my father told me she'd died. I can't remember a single detail of the funeral, or if any of the relatives came to stay over. When I tried to ask where she was, my father ordered me never to mention her name again. Then he took me to a boarding school outside Boston and left me there. So I lost the island, too, which was a place as near to heaven as I could imagine."

Travis paused. His blue eyes had been very far away; slowly he brought them back to rest on Julie's face. "Something shut down in me after that, and I suppose you could call it love. I don't know what I feel for you, Julie. I only know it's stronger than anything I've ever felt before, and that if I turn my back on it, I'm shortchanging myself and possibly you as well."

He seemed to have run out of words. But he'd just spent two minutes stopped at a red light and she hadn't jumped out of the car.

Julie said blankly, "Well, that was certainly honest."

"Don't ask me why we're pulled to each other the way we are because I don't have the answer," Travis said roughly. "But it's got to mean something. This might sound as conceited as all get-out but I'm going to say it anyway—I think it means something for you, too. Don't run away, Julie. Life's too short for that."

She was gazing down at her clasped hands. "You really were okay with the way I behaved on Sunday?"

"Okay? I loved it...couldn't you tell?"

"I—I guess so."

She didn't sound convinced. He said with all the force of his personality, "You took huge risks, you followed your heart and allowed yourself to be who you really are. That made me feel about ten feet tall—why wouldn't it?"

"Passion," she whispered. "It's such an overused word and I never knew I was capable of it."

"If you spend the weekend with me, neither one of us knows where that'll lead us. But the alternative is to close down. Bury something that's both rare and precious. I don't think we should do that."

She swallowed hard. "Working in Tanzania was a piece of cake compared to this."

"So was Angola," he said wryly.

"I don't have anything to wear except my uniform."

"I bought some stuff for you." He smiled at her. "In the hopes that you were abductable."

"Clothes? For me? How did you know my size?"

"Photographic memory," he said solemnly, and watched her blush. "A couple of dresses, a swimsuit, sandals, underwear and a nightgown."

Her blush deepened. "A nightgown, hmm?"

"There's not much to it."

"I'm frightened, Travis," she muttered.

"I'll do everything in my power to make you happy this

weekend,'' Travis said forcefully. As for what happened after the weekend, he was as ignorant of that as she was. And maybe just as frightened. One day at a time, he told himself and accelerated to the maximum speed.

Half an hour later he'd checked in at the main lodge, and was driving along a narrow dirt road overhung with silver birches toward their chalet. It was the end one, sheltered by thick spruce, with a wide deck facing the beach, where waves danced in the evening sun and rocks gleamed in the wet sand. Julie got out of the car, stretching her legs. ''It's a lovely place,'' she said.

She'd been very quiet for the last part of the journey. He could have asked her about her parents, but something had held him back. Now he said casually, ''Why don't we go for dinner, you must be hungry.''

The inside of the chalet was luxuriously furnished, the bed king-size, the bathroom fitted with a whirlpool tub. Travis dumped the bag of clothes on the chesterfield that overlooked the ocean. ''I hope you like them.''

She took out the dresses, her face lighting up with spontaneous pleasure. ''They're great—but you must have spent a wad of money.''

''We can talk about that later…I'll wait for you on the deck.''

He stood by the railing, gazing out to sea, aching to hold her in his arms and reassure himself that she really did want to be here. Don't rush her, Travis, you've got all weekend. And you know perfectly well what'll happen if you touch her.

He went back inside in a few minutes. Julie was just emerging from the bathroom, wearing the sundress he'd picked out because it was as green as her eyes. It also showed rather a lot of bare skin. He said lightly, ''Ready to eat?''

She nodded, hurrying for the door. Side by side they

walked back to the lodge. The dining room was on an inlet, overlooking the bay and the sunset's orange and saffron glow. They discussed the menu, the wine list, the weather, his job and hers, meanwhile eating fish chowder and game hens with wild rice. The waiter cleared away their plates, passing them dessert menus. Julie read through hers, chattering away about her addiction for dark chocolate. He'd never thought of her as a woman who had to fill the silence with idle talk.

The waiter left. Travis said with no finesse whatsoever, "I don't want chocolate. I want you."

She dropped the menu and said in a rush, "You haven't as much as touched me since we got here. I thought you'd changed your mind. That you regretted bringing me here."

Nothing could be further from the truth. He reached over and covered her fingers with his, feeling them curl into his palm. "I didn't want to grab you the minute we walked in the door."

"I noticed that."

"I figured I should show a little subtlety this time."

"So is it chocolate mousse or me?" she asked, her dark lashes falling to hide her eyes.

He pushed back his chair, still holding her by the hand. "I'll tell the waiter to put this on our room account...let's go."

"We shouldn't run. It wouldn't look good."

In a voice pitched for her ears alone, he said, "I want you, Julie, don't ever doubt that."

"It's mutual," she said with a dazzling smile that took his breath away.

They didn't actually run to the chalet; but they held hands the whole way, and once they were indoors Travis took Julie in his arms and kissed her with a passionate and protracted intensity that she more than matched. Hastily he detached himself to draw the blinds, watching her kick off her sandals and pull her dress over her head. He'd bought her lace underwear; wondering if his heart could force its way out of his chest, he saw how the sweet curves of her breasts were cupped in the delicate fabric. "Every time I see you," he said huskily, "I can't get over how beautiful you are."

She walked toward him, holding herself proudly under his gaze, the slim lines of her thighs pale in the dusk. "Make love to me, Travis," she said.

He took her by the waist, pulling her toward his hips, where it was more than obvious that he was ready for her. Had he ever known with such certainty that he was exactly where he wanted to be? More than that, he was with the one woman who could fill an inner loneliness he'd scarcely known was his. He pushed this thought aside to examine later, and with all the skill he possessed set out to make Julie as happy to be here as he was.

Later, when Travis looked back on a weekend he knew he'd never forget, there were images that rose in his mind. Julie seducing him in the nightgown he'd bought her, which clung to all her curves and almost bared her breasts. Julie wearing nothing at all, holding out her arms to him in the big bed. The play of expression on her face. The soft, intimate sound of her breathing in the middle of the night, as she slept curled into his body. Her laughter. Her grace. Her sudden tears after a lovemaking as elemental as a cyclone…

They made it to the dining room for Saturday lunch and Sunday breakfast. Once, they walked on the beach for fifteen minutes. The rest of the time they spent in the chalet, ordering room service when they realized they were hungry for something other than each other. They talked very little, letting their bodies speak for them. If Travis thought about it at all, he must have decided subliminally to leave the subject of Julie's parents for another time. He and Julie were building a foundation for the future; any discussions would be better based on that foundation.

He had no idea what he meant by that vague word *future*.

On Sunday morning after they'd made love in the tub, splashing rather a lot of water on the floor in the process, he said, "I wish we could stay all week...I'm not ready to go home."

She gave a lazy chuckle. "I'm going back to work to rest up."

"Can't take the pace, huh?"

"You're too much for me."

"Haven't heard you complaining."

She swiped at his chest with the towel, her smile fading. "This has been a perfect weekend, Travis. But we do have to go back to normal."

He captured her hand in his. "I've got meetings tomorrow night that I can't get out of. But why don't you come to my place on Tuesday after work?"

She brought their linked hands to her cheek, closing her eyes. "I can't get enough of you," she said faintly.

"I'm not going to vanish the minute we leave here, Julie."

So he'd understood, she thought slowly. "This has been so magical, how can we possibly transpose it to our ordinary lives?" she said with a touch of desperation.

"We can. And we will."

The dark hair on his chest was sleek as a seal's pelt. She laid her other palm over his heart, feeling its steady pounding against her skin. "Tuesday night," she said with attempted levity. "It's a date. And now I guess I'd better get some clothes on. I'll wear the other dress, the one I haven't tried yet."

"It's the color of the ocean where I first saw you," Travis said.

Her lashes flickered. Once again, in a few words, he'd

pierced her to the heart. She walked back into the bedroom, pulled on her underwear and slipped the dress over her head. Then she stood still, trying to memorize her surroundings. A sun-drenched room with the sound of waves and the soft whisper of pine boughs coming through the open windows. And a bed in which she'd found a happiness she hadn't known existed.

How was she going to bear leaving here?

She wanted to stay forever.

CHAPTER TWELVE

By Monday evening, Julie wasn't sure about anything. In the middle of the night, she'd woken up in her three-quarter bed reaching for Travis; he hadn't, of course, been there. But rather than waking to memories of the bliss she'd experienced in his arms, she'd instantly been suffused by a cold anxiety that she couldn't dispel, no matter how many parakeets she counted.

Yes, it had been a fabulous weekend. The ultimate getaway with a handsome, sexy man. But one weekend didn't make a relationship; had nothing to do with permanence. While she was almost sure Travis wanted to keep on seeing her, what did she want?

She didn't want commitment. She certainly didn't want marriage. So why was she even contemplating seeing him again? Wasn't she getting deeper into trouble every time they got together?

Or did she just want a series of wild weekends that were utterly divorced from her normal life? Even she could see that wouldn't work, not with a man like Travis.

Eventually Julie went back to sleep, the alarm waking her from dreams that left her feeling frazzled and exhausted. She worked all day, caught the bus home and had leftovers for supper. The apartment seemed very empty without Travis and tomorrow evening an age away.

But she didn't want intimacy. She didn't.

Even if she scarcely knew what it was.

With an impatient sigh Julie changed her clothes and went out for a walk. She crossed the cobblestone street, her brow furrowed in thought. Travis had suggested she sleep at his place last night; but she'd demurred. He was moving too quickly for her, she needed time alone, one by one she'd trotted out all the clichés. She believed every one of them. So why did she miss him so unceasingly?

Then her steps slowed. Consciously or unconsciously, she'd been walking in the direction of her parents' street. She might as well drop in. Considering everything that had happened to her since last Friday, she might even see them with new eyes.

It was worth a try. But when she climbed the front steps of the freshly painted bungalow and rang the doorbell, there was no answer; her father's car was gone from the driveway. They'd probably be back soon. She'd been wanting to go through some of her old books in the attic in order to reread a couple of them; now was as good a time as any. She let herself in with the key her mother had given her, and went straight upstairs. The attic was very warm, and rather less tidy than the rest of Pearl's domain.

Which box had the books been stored in? And why hadn't she labeled it? Julie started opening boxes at random, finding sets of old dishes, all her father's account books for the last twenty years, and then a box of old photo albums. She picked up the first album, suddenly curious. Below it, facedown, was a gold-framed photograph. Carefully Julie lifted it out and turned it over.

It was a wedding photo of a young couple, the bride in a slim-fitting white dress with a trailing bouquet of roses, the groom lean and handsome in a tuxedo. The bride's arm was tucked confidingly into her new husband's, his hand lying protectively over hers; they were both smiling radiantly into the camera.

It took Julie a full ten seconds to realize that the two people in the photograph were her parents. The groom was Thomas, the bride Pearl.

She sat back on her heels, staring at the two faces with

strained intensity. They looked so carefree, so joyful. More than that, she realized, as all her new knowledge came to the fore, they looked physically close, their body language speaking of the bed they would share that night.

They were total strangers to her. Had she ever seen them look like that in real life?

No. Never.

Happiness doesn't last, she thought numbly. Neither does desire. Thomas and Pearl had once been as delighted with each other's company as she and Travis had been all weekend. While it might be true that not all relationships head the same way, it could equally be true that she and Travis could be as doomed as her parents, and the thought made Julie go cold.

She grabbed for the next picture frame, her hands shaking so badly she almost dropped it. Her mother and father in a formal pose, Pearl holding a three-year-old in a pretty pink dress. The child was herself. Thomas was standing stiffly behind his seated wife, his hand placed on her shoulder with a rigid correctness; while both he and Pearl were smiling, the radiance was gone. These were smiles for the camera, not smiles of spontaneous happiness.

Something had gone wrong by the time she was three. Had it been her fault? Hadn't they wanted her?

With a whimper of distress Julie put the photos back in the box, jammed the album on top of them and closed the cardboard flaps. Her books were forgotten. She scrambled to her feet, wiping the dust from her shorts, and ran downstairs. The driveway was still empty. In such a confused state of mind that she was frantic to be gone before her parents returned, she quickly locked the door behind her and hurried down the street.

There was no sign of her father's car. Nor, when she got back to her apartment building, was it parked near there; how ironic if they'd been trying to visit her while she was at their place. She scurried upstairs. Never had her apartment seemed such a haven. Throwing herself down on the chesterfield, Julie realized that she was crying. They were slow tears of despair, loss and deep sadness, all the anxieties she'd locked away since childhood pouring out.

She was crying for her parents, for the happiness and intimacy that they'd lost. She was also crying for herself. For, of course, this confirmed all her fears. Any long-term relationship with Travis was out of the question. She couldn't bear to experience the slow erosion of passion, or the destruction of the intimacy she'd so tentatively explored in his embrace.

It was all too easily lost, leaving nothing but emptiness and bitter memories.

Nothing was to be trusted, happiness least of all.

She mustn't see Travis again.

Julie took this resolve to bed with her, cried herself to sleep, and woke heavy-eyed in the morning. She was busy all day at the clinic, and glad to be so; when she got home, there was a message on her machine from Travis. "Call me as soon as you get in. I'll take you out for dinner—the contents of my refrigerator look like a bacteriology experiment gone wrong. But I did change the sheets on the bed. See you soon."

She mustn't cry. Not again.

She'd better phone him. Get it over with.

All her movements leaden, she picked up the receiver and punched in his number. He picked it up on the first ring. "Julie?"

He sounded so eager. So happy, she thought with a pang of pure agony. Her voice seemed to have disappeared. "Julie," he repeated sharply, "are you there?"

"Yes," she croaked.

"What's the matter? You sound terrible."

What was worse, his happiness or his concern, so immediate she could almost feel it? "I—Travis, I'm not coming over tonight. Or any night. We mustn't see each other again."

"*What* did you say?"

"I don't want to see you again," she said more strongly.

"Stay where you are. I'm coming over."

"No, you can't!" But he was gone. Slowly she put the receiver back in its cradle.

She was still in her uniform. But what did it matter? She'd repeat what she'd already told him and then he'd really be gone. Forever, this time. The way it had to be.

She went to the bathroom and washed her face in cold water, carefully applying blusher and lipstick in an effort to make herself presentable. All too soon, the buzzer rang, loudly and imperatively. A cold lump of dread lodged somewhere below her heart, Julie went to the door.

Travis walked in, closed the door and took her in his arms. For a moment she sagged against him, oblivious to everything but the comfort and security of his embrace, the familiar warmth of his body. Then she stiffened, pushing him away. He stared down at her, missing, she was sure, not one detail of her ravaged appearance. "What's up?"

She said rapidly, "I can't go on with this. I don't want to see you again."

"You already told me that. Why, Julie? What's happened between Sunday afternoon and now?"

"Passion, happiness, love—none of them last."

"They last if you want them to. If you work at it."

"You might believe that. I don't."

His eyes narrowed. "You weren't talking this way on Sunday. Have you seen your parents since then?"

"Why can't you just accept what I'm saying?"

"Because it's not good enough. We're lovers, we spent the weekend together—and now you think you can fob me off with a bunch of generalizations about happiness?"

"All right, then. Let me tell you what happened." Speaking very fast, she described what she'd found in the attic and how it had affected her. "My parents were happy once. Just like us on the weekend. You've never met them...but believe me, they're not happy now." Her voice broke. "They hate each other. But they're too damn polite to say so. So they snipe at each other continually, until I can't bear to be around them. It was like that the whole time I was growing up, a thin layer of civility that hid any honest emotions, so that I never knew what was really going on. What I could trust."

She was crying again. She swiped at her cheeks, furious with herself. "There were all kinds of petty rules that I was supposed to obey. All for my own good, of course. Especially once I reached puberty, because heaven forbid there should be any straight talk about sex. I don't know if they even had any sex. They never touched each other and I can't remember my father ever giving my mother a hug."

She jammed her hands in the pockets of her uniform. "I rebelled against almost all the rules and left home the summer I graduated from high school." Scowling at him, she went on, "The one area where I didn't rebel was sex. I was afraid to, I guess. I think even then I sensed I'd be in real trouble if I did. And I was right. This weekend proves my point. I'm not going to end up like my parents, I'd rather be single my whole life. So I want you to go now. And I don't want to see you again."

He took her by the shoulders. "We wouldn't end up like your parents—I know we wouldn't."

She could feel the force of his willpower, unbending as steel, and called on all her reserves to withstand it. "I disagree."

"This is the second time you've pulled this stunt—made love with me, then shown me the door."

"I can't help it! Don't you see, Travis? Now is the time to end this, while it's still just sex between us, while we—"

"Just sex?" he interrupted incredulously. "Is that all I mean to you?"

"We spent the whole weekend in bed. What's that if it's not sex?"

"We made love, Julie."

"That's just an expression. A cover-up—like my parents' politeness. We had sex, Travis. Great sex. Amazing sex. But don't let's pretend it was anything else."

"If that's what you think," he said in a hard voice, "then I'm out of here. I won't be treated as a prize stud. Not by you or anyone else."

Inadvertently she'd found the weapon she needed. "I don't see what the big deal is," she said coldly. "Sex like we had is probably pretty rare. But it's still just sex."

"I wasn't even a person to you, was I?" he said with icy control. "And I thought it was supposed to be men who were guilty of that particular fault."

She wanted to cry out that he was wrong, that it had been something about him, specific and impelling, that had broken through her self-imposed celibacy. But she couldn't tell him. She had to end this quickly, before she broke down and wept like a baby. "Don't try to tell me you're in love with me," she said, "because I won't believe it."

"Whether I am or not is none of your business," he grated. "It's been a long time since I misread someone so badly...you'd think I'd know better by now. Goodbye, Julie. Have a nice life."

Very quietly he shut the door behind him. Moving like an old woman, Julie snapped the latch and put the chain in its slot. Then she walked into her bedroom, threw herself across the quilt and began to weep.

Three weeks went by, during which Julie went through the motions at home and at work. The days at work were the least difficult, because she enjoyed her patients and was enough of a professional to shut out her personal life. The nights alone in her spindle bed were the worst. There, Travis haunted her waking thoughts and her dreams; after ten days she had blue shadows under her eyes and had lost four pounds.

On the weekends she went camping in the Adirondacks, had dinner with Kathy and Michael, and attended a three-day music festival; any activity was preferable to sitting in her apartment staring at the four walls and remembering with aching clarity the passion-filled hours she'd spent with Travis at the resort. As the days—and nights—slowly passed, he made no attempt to get in touch with her. And how could she blame him?

It was always a relief to go back to work on Monday mornings. The Monday after the festival was particularly busy. At two-thirty, Julie grabbed a coffee and a muffin and went to the empty staff room with them. The muffin was stuffed with fruit and bran; she chewed it valiantly, wishing her appetite would come back. To top it off, she felt bone-tired from morning to night. It really had been just sex between her and Travis, she thought fiercely, washing down the muffin with a gulp of coffee. Sex, plain and simple.

"You look very militant, Julie," an amused voice said from the doorway.

With a nervous start, Julie looked up. Then she put down the last of the muffin and smiled with genuine pleasure. "Leonora," she said, "how nice to see you. But have I missed something? Do you have an appointment today?"

Leonora Connolly had had a series of appointments with Julie earlier in the summer. She was a tall, statuesque woman with very blue eyes, and a wealth of dark hair faintly streaked with grey. Julie had liked her from the start, and had done her best to alleviate some of the damage that a lifetime as a professional dancer had inflicted on Leonora's tendons and ligaments.

Leonora smiled. "May I come in? No, I don't have an appointment. I was visiting a friend who's been admitted here for a few days, and thought I'd drop by and tell you how much better I've been feeling since our sessions. I'm so grateful to you."

"Don't forget that you worked hard, too," Julie laughed. "I can't claim all the credit. Can I get you a coffee? As hospital coffee goes, it's not bad."

"No, thanks, I can't stay."

Julie's brow furrowed in puzzlement. "You know, it's funny but you remind me of someone. Someone I've seen recently..."

"Oh?" Leonora said, her jaw tensing slightly.

Her fingers unconsciously tightening around her cup, Julie said flatly, "Oh. I remember now. It doesn't matter."

"Tell me who, Julie. Please."

There was an insistence in Leonora's voice that took Julie by surprise. With huge reluctance she said, "I met a Dr. Travis Strathern a few weeks ago. His eyes are very like yours, such a deep blue...Leonora, what's wrong?"

For the other woman had paled, briefly looking every year of her age. Leaning against the doorframe, she blurted, "Did you like him?"

"He's apparently a very fine doctor," Julie said evasively.

"I didn't mean professionally. As a man. What did you think of him?"

Gossip and indiscretion were characteristics Julie would never have applied to Leonora Connolly. Puzzlement overcoming her reluctance, Julie said, "Travis? Forceful, charismatic, articulate. He says it like it is. No games." She grimaced. "Tall, dark and handsome. A male counterpart to you, in that respect."

Leonora said faintly, "I see."

"Do you know him? Leonora, you don't look well, can I get you something?"

"He's my son," Leonora said.

Her head whirling, Julie put her cup down on the table. Whatever she might have expected Leonora to say, it wouldn't have been this.

For Travis's mother was dead.

CHAPTER THIRTEEN

THE silence stretched out. Realizing she had to say something, Julie faltered, "Leonora, Travis can't be your son. He told me his mother died when he was six."

"It's a long story," Leonora said. Awkwardly she straightened, looking every year of her age. "Is there somewhere we could go to talk in private?"

The grace and elegance of Leonora's movements had been the first thing Julie had noticed about her; although this soon had been followed by admiration for her innate dignity of spirit. For Leonora to abandon both must mean that she was deeply upset. "We could go to my office," Julie said. "It's small, but I can close the door."

Quickly she led the way down the corridor, ushering Leonora into a cubicle that contained little more than a desk, two chairs and some shelves. She closed the door and sat down. "I shouldn't have mentioned the likeness between you and Travis," she said remorsefully. "I didn't mean to upset you."

"How well do you know him?"

And how was she supposed to answer that? "I met him at a party. I've only seen him a couple of times since then," Julie said, more or less truthfully.

"I have to tell someone what this is all about," Leonora said helplessly. "It's driving me mad."

"Take your time," Julie said gently.

"Yes." Leonora took a deep breath and launched herself. "I always wanted to be a dancer. I started lessons when I was just a child, and it was obvious from the beginning that I had more than ordinary talent. And then when

I was eighteen, I met a man called Charles Strathern. Handsome, forceful, dynamic…well, you get the picture. I fell madly in love and into his bed without once considering the consequences. It's an old story, Julie. I ended up at the altar pregnant. Travis was born five months later.''

Julie sat very still, her heart racing under her uniform. Instinctively she knew Leonora was telling the truth; nor was it difficult to picture this imperious, talented woman as Travis's mother. ''Go on,'' she said softly.

''I tried my best to be a good mother. But in essence I don't have a maternal bone in my body. I soon went back to dancing lessons, and then began teaching dance in Boston, getting away from all my responsibilities as often as I could. It wasn't enough, because the whole artistic scene on the East Coast was too conservative for my taste; but I had to make do with what was available. I'd realized a year after I was married that Charles wasn't the man for me, but I made the best of that, too. Then, when Travis was five, I got pregnant again, this time with twins.''

''Twins?'' Julie echoed.

''A boy and a girl, born just after Travis turned six. Brent and Jenessa.'' Leonora looked down at her fingers, clenched in her lap. ''I felt so trapped, so confined. At first I was angry with the whole world. But I couldn't take that anger out on my children, it wasn't their fault. So it turned inward, and I grew more and more depressed. Finally, I went to New York, to see a world-renowned psychiatrist whom Charles knew…there was a recital while I was there by an avant garde dancer from Paris, Madeleine Mercier. I went to see her dance, and two days later I, too, was in Paris. I simply ran away. Abandoned my marriage and my children.''

Her head buzzing with questions, Julie sat very still. There was more to come, she knew.

''I'd never been known for forethought,'' Leonora said

wryly. "The day I arrived in Paris, I phoned Charles, to tell him I'd fly home every two months to see the children. He said I was to change my name, and that if I ever showed my face in Boston or on Manatuck again, he'd ruin me. His lawyers, he said, would be sending me divorce papers, and he would get sole custody of the children." She gave a reminiscent shudder. "I thought of flying home that very day. But Madeleine had already taken me on as a pupil, and I was sure if I waited a few weeks he'd calm down. However, by the time I got in touch with him again, he'd already told Travis that I had died. I found out later he'd invented a fictitious funeral in Philadelphia, where I was born. The twins, of course, were too young to know about any of this."

"How could Charles have done that to his own son?" Julie said, aghast.

"I'd wounded his pride. I'd made a fool of him."

"He's never told Travis the truth about you."

"That's why I'm here. To make peace with Travis, if that's possible. But I've been too afraid to contact him." She gave Julie a shaky smile. "It's ludicrous, isn't it? I'm living in the same town, and I haven't made a move to see him. Or the twins. Brent, I gather, works in Boston, while Jenessa's an artist, living in a little village west of Boston."

Travis had never once mentioned that he had a sister. Nor, for that matter, had Brent. Julie said reluctantly, "After you left, Travis was sent away to boarding school, and for two years wasn't even allowed back to Manatuck."

"One more betrayal...he loved that place." Leonora raised her head, with its crown of dark hair. "Julie, I'm going to ask a favor of you. A huge favor. You've met Travis. He trusts you enough that he's told you what happened when he was six. I want you to tell him that I didn't die, that I'm here in Portland, and I want to see him. You could prepare him, so that it won't be such a terrible shock for him.''

"I couldn't!''

"Please...I don't often beg for anything, I have more than my share of pride, too. But I'm begging you now. The truth is, I'm afraid. Afraid that he won't consent to see me at all.'' Her smile was twisted. "I've danced in front of the toughest critics in Europe, and I'm afraid of my own son. But why should Travis want to see me? I left him, abandoned him, ran away as though he didn't matter at all.''

Leonora's eyes were bleak with remembered sorrow. Briefly Julie rested her head in her hands. "I don't really know Travis that well,'' she said in a muffled voice.

"Let me tell you something—I liked you from the first moment I met you. You're honest and courageous. You, more than anyone I know, can do this.''

For a wild moment Julie considered telling Leonora about the weekend she'd spent in Travis's arms; and how she'd then sent him away, because she, too, was afraid of him. She looked up. "I'll do it,'' she said, her voice sounding as though it came from a long way away. "But you've got to give me a couple of days to think about it, and rehearse what I'm going to say.''

"Of course.'' Leonora slowly unclenched her hands. "Thank you, Julie. More than I can say.''

"Maybe we should wait to see how this all turns out before you thank me.''

"You'll do the best you can. The rest is up to Travis.''

Julie pushed herself to her feet. Her cold hands pressing against the desk, she said, "I've got to go back to work, Leonora. I have an appointment in five minutes.''

The older woman hesitated. "You'll let me know as soon as you see Travis?''

"Yes, of course,'' Julie replied. Briefly Leonora rested

one hand on Julie's shoulder; then she walked away down the empty corridor.

Julie watched her go. Three weeks ago she'd told Travis their relationship was over. Now she was committed to seeking him out, as the bearer of shattering news.

To say that she was afraid was a massive understatement. And yet, beneath the terror, wasn't there a grain of pure joy that she would be seeing him again?

Travis was late home from work on Wednesday evening. It had been an exhausting day. Far too much paperwork, two patients who seemed to think he had nothing to do but immerse himself in their imaginary symptoms, and a tragic prognosis he'd had to deliver to another of his patients, a young woman with three small children.

His exhaustion stemmed from more than a bad day at work. Try as he might, he couldn't get Julie out of his system. More times than he'd care to admit he'd pulled back with his hand actually on the receiver to phone her; twice he'd driven past her apartment, just to see the lights glowing from her narrow windows. He was obsessed with her, he thought savagely. Worse, nothing he did loosened her grip one iota.

He hated being so helpless. So entrapped.

He tossed a package of frozen pasta in the microwave and hit the buttons. He didn't even like pasta. But he lacked the energy to barbecue anything, and he didn't want to eat by himself in a restaurant.

He was a mess.

He went into the bedroom, hauling his shirt over his head and searching for a clean T-shirt in the drawer. He should do a wash. Maybe he'd get around to it on the weekend. Although Bryce, on their last conversation, had suggested that Travis make use of Bryce's cottage north of Portland next weekend. Get the hell out of that condo, is what Bryce

had actually said. Along with a fair number of uncompli-
mentary remarks about Julie.

What was he going to do at the cottage? Think about
Julie from Friday night to Sunday evening, that's what.

The T-shirt slung over one shoulder, Travis went back
into the kitchen and opened the microwave. He'd forgotten
to pry open the corner of the pasta box. Steam had ruptured
the cardboard seal, splattering rigatoni all over one wall of
the microwave. Then the doorbell rang, a melodious chim-
ing that made Travis swear out loud. If it was the blond
bombshell down the hallway who was pursuing him with
all the subtlety of a bulldozer, she was right out of luck.

Not bothering to look through the peephole, he yanked
the door open, a blistering refusal already on his tongue.
His jaw dropped. *"Julie!"* he gasped.

In one quick glance he took in every detail of her appearance: slim white jeans, a coral silk shirt with the
sleeves rolled up, coral lipstick and blusher and eyes a
wide, terrified green. She'd come back, he thought in a
great flood of gratitude and joy. She'd changed her mind.

He put his arms around her waist, lifted her over the
threshold, slammed the door shut with one foot and began
kissing her. He could feel the shock run through her, the
sudden rigidity of her spine, and ignored both. She'd come
back. She was in his arms, where she belonged. His Julie,
his beautiful Julie…

With another of those surges of passionate gratitude, he
realized she was kissing him back, her hips pressed to his,
her palms clasping his bare ribcage. Her lips were soft and
warm, she smelled delicious, her body fitted his embrace
as though made for it. He forgot what a desert the last three
weeks had been, forgot that he was furious with her for
leaving him. Swinging her off her feet, he headed for the
bedroom.

The bed wasn't made and there was dirty laundry scattered all over the rug. But what did that matter?

Wholly intent on where he was going, it took Travis several seconds to realize Julie was beating on his chest with her fists. "Travis, let me down!"

He smiled at her, a smile of unquenchable happiness. "Hey, stop that. You came here to make love with me and I'd rather do that in bed than on the hall floor."

"I didn't!"

"Sure you did. You don't kiss a platonic friend the way you were just kissing me."

"Travis, I didn't come here to go to bed with you," she said frantically. "I have something to tell you, something very important."

He looked at her blankly for the space of five full seconds. "You're pregnant."

"I'm not! Don't be silly."

"There's nothing silly about it. That rainy Sunday afternoon at your place we made love twice, and neither time did we use protection. That, dear Julie, is how babies get made."

"This is something else altogether," she said impatiently. "I don't even know where to begin but I sure know it isn't in your bedroom." Still pushing at his chest, she looked around her. "Which is a mess."

He put her down, his hands tight on her shoulders. She meant it. She hadn't come here to revive their affair. "So what if my bedroom's like a pigsty?" he snarled. "I miss you day and night and doing the laundry hasn't been a priority."

"I didn't mean to kiss you back," she quavered, "I'm sorry about that. It just…happened."

"Oh sure. You had nothing to do with it."

She wriggled her shoulders free. "I'm going into the

living room, you're going to pour me a glass of wine and then you're going to shut up and listen to me!"

"It had better be good, that's all I can say."

He followed her down the hall, trying to ignore the swing of her hips in her white pants. "Find a chair," he said. "White wine or red?"

"Red. The more robust the better."

He opened a very expensive bottle of Merlot and poured two glasses. Julie was standing by the window, looking out over the harbor. When he passed her the glass, she took a gulp and said raggedly, "Earlier this week, I found out something about your past. Now I've come to tell you about it. It's big stuff, Travis, so please listen carefully...I'll do my best to give it to you straight."

For the first time since she'd arrived, Travis really heard her. His nerves tightened. What did she mean? What could she have found out about him to make her look so serious? He, too, took a substantial mouthful of wine.

She began with Leonora, whose eyes so strikingly resembled Travis's, and slowly unfolded that long-ago story of abandonment and deceit. Travis had been sitting on one arm of a leather-covered chair; when she got to the fake funeral in Philadelphia, he stood up. Taking her by the arm, he said harshly, "You're not making this up?"

"You know I wouldn't do that."

He raked his fingers through his hair. "So this is true, what you're telling me."

"Yes."

His ears were ringing, while his head felt as though it were floating somewhere above his body. His mother was alive. That was what Julie was telling him. She was now describing Leonora's long career in Europe, and her recent return to the States, each word inscribing itself indelibly on his brain. Was he going to wake up, and find out he'd been dreaming?

"Because I'd told her I'd met you, Leonora asked me to come and see you," Julie finished. "To break the news to you. She's an exceptional woman, Travis, I've liked her from the first moment we met. So I agreed."

She couldn't think of anything else to say. Travis looked stunned, as though she'd hit him on the head with a two-by-four. And why wouldn't he? His father had told him his mother had died; and that lie had stood unchallenged since Travis had been a little boy. She waited to see what he would do, her one longing to put her arms around him and offer him comfort.

She couldn't do that. Because she'd end up in his bed.

Quickly she pulled a folded piece of paper from her pocket and passed it to him. "This is Leonora's phone number and address. She's hoping you'll get in touch with her. I said I'd ask your permission to give her your phone number."

Travis looked at her as if she were a creature from an alien planet. "I'm supposed to get in touch with her?"

"Or else she'll phone you," Julie said patiently.

"She's expecting me to pick up where we left off twenty-eight years ago?"

"Of course not. But she very much wants to see you."

He said in a hard voice, "I'll think about it."

"I can see it's been a terrible shock—"

"She didn't die. She walked out on me and the twins. You think that makes me want to see her?"

"Don't shoot the messenger, Travis," Julie said softly.

He let out his breath in a long sigh. "Yeah...if I go and see her, you're coming with me."

"Me? This has nothing to do with me!"

"You know her. She thought enough of you to make you the go-between."

Julie swallowed. She was being drawn in deeper and deeper. Yet wouldn't Leonora also welcome her presence?

Leonora, she knew, was terrified of seeing Travis again. And maybe she herself could help in some way to smooth the path of a meeting fraught with pitfalls. She took a deep breath. "All right," she said steadily, "I'll go. When?"

"I didn't think you'd agree quite so easily," he said, an ugly edge to his voice. "This Leonora must be quite the woman."

"Worthy to be your mother," Julie said evenly.

"Friday evening. Seven-thirty. I'll pick you up at your apartment."

"Travis, I'm sure she regrets—"

"Will you go to bed with me?"

Julie flinched. "No."

"Then finish your wine and get out of here. I'm not in the mood for chitchat."

It would be all too easy to make a scathing retort. Julie put her glass down. "This must have been a terrible shock."

"Keep your sympathy—I don't need it."

She raised her chin. "I'll see you on Friday."

"I'll look forward to it," he said with heavy sarcasm.

Julie stalked to the door of the condo and let herself out. It shut behind her with a decisive snap. She went home, phoned Leonora to let her know about Friday, evaded any discussion of Travis's reaction, then went for a run at the park. It was only when a mallard waddled in front of her, followed by two fluffy brown and yellow ducklings, that she remembered something.

Travis had thought she was pregnant.

She wasn't. Of course. Although he was right: When the two of them had fallen into her bed, they'd used no protection.

In the heat of the moment, it had never occurred to her; which showed how out of practice she was, she thought ruefully. And she was willing to bet it wasn't Travis's usual style. Her brow furrowed. Her period was notoriously irregular; for years she'd blamed this on a combination of tropical heat and antimalarial pills. But as she counted backward in her mind, her steps slowed. She'd never been this late before.

Coincidence, she thought brusquely. And hadn't she read somewhere that stress could foul up your cycle? She'd had enough emotional ups and downs since she'd met Travis to skew any woman's cycle. She wasn't pregnant. Just the same, she wasn't going to tempt fate by going to bed with Travis again.

Then another, equally unpleasant thought occurred to her. Leonora had fallen head over heels in love with Charles; but seven years later had run away from him, from their children and their marriage. One more example of a love that had died, and one more reason she was right to keep her distance from a man with eyes so blue that they saw right through her.

CHAPTER FOURTEEN

FRIDAY evening found Julie sorting through her wardrobe. Jeans wouldn't cut it for this crucial meeting of mother and son. Nor was she going to wear either of the dresses Travis had given her. Frowning, she chose a softly swirling skirt and sleeveless top in malachite-green, with matching sandals she'd bought from a vendor in Athens. She was waiting downstairs in the lobby when Travis drew up in his black car. She ran outdoors and climbed in the passenger seat. Busying herself with the seat belt, she said, "How was your day?"

He said tightly, "Every time I see you, it's as though I've never seen you before…there's this jolt in my chest just like I'd stuck my finger in an electric socket."

"The whole reason I didn't look at you when I got in was to avoid just that reaction," she said irritably. "So what, Travis? We aren't going to act on it, that's the point."

"The gospel according to St. Julie."

"That's unworthy of you!"

"I'm not in the mood to fight fair."

"At least give Leonora a fair hearing," she flashed.

He pulled away from the curb without answering. She sneaked a glance at his profile, which was unyielding, hard-jawed and tight-lipped. He was impeccably dressed in tailored trousers, blue shirt and a silk tie. Just like we were going on a date, she thought painfully.

Nothing could be further from the truth.

Ten minutes later Travis was following Julie up the steps of an attractive apartment complex only five minutes from the clinic. Give Leonora a fair hearing, Julie had said to him. As though that was a simple choice. They rode up in the elevator, then he was striding down a gold-carpeted hallway behind her. Julie tapped on one of the varnished doors, walked in and gestured for him to enter. Feeling like a robot whose circuits had shorted, Travis stepped inside.

The woman who had been waiting for them said with poignant restraint, "Hello, Travis."

She was tall, elegant and instantly remembered. Older, obviously, but in an essential way unchanged. He felt as though he were a little boy again; he also felt an upsurge of purely adult rage that he did his best to tamp down. Shaking hands with her would be absurd; yet he wasn't ready to hug her. He said stiffly, "I asked Julie to be here, I hope you don't mind."

"Not at all." Leonora produced the semblance of a smile. "Julie's been a good friend to me...can I get you a drink?"

A few minutes later Travis found himself seated by a bay window across from his mother. His mother. He said ironically, raising his glass, "Cheers...Julie told me you had a very successful career in Europe. It's funny I never read about you."

"One of your father's conditions was that I change my name...Connolly was my grandmother's maiden name. Added to that, such success as I had was in a fairly narrow field. Avant garde dance isn't to everyone's taste."

The evening light struck her high cheekbones, so like his own. Although she looked poised, her speech had been stilted, and a little muscle was jumping in her jaw. "You've taken a long time to get in touch," he said.

"Your father made me promise never to get in touch with you...I've kept that promise for nearly thirty years. But there's nothing he can do to harm me now. So I came back." She suddenly leaned forward. "You have every right to be angry with me, Travis, don't think I don't understand that.''

"The twins never even knew you.''

"Nor I them.''

"That was your choice.''

"I was never a maternal woman. The mistake I made was in marrying Charles.''

"So you admit you made mistakes.''

"Have you never done something you've bitterly regretted?''

He leaned forward, feeling his shirt pull tight against his shoulder blades. "I've never married or had children—that way I can't abandon my wife or my child. That's one mistake I won't make.''

"I had no idea Charles would react so cruelly! I was young, on my own in Paris, threatened with ruin if I as much as wrote you a letter. Charles wielded a lot of influence—even from Boston he could have made my life untenable.''

"Just the same, I'm sure you understand my difficulty,'' Travis said. "You couldn't be faulted for dying. Very few of us want to do that. But for abandoning me to my father's less than tender mercies—yes, I fault you for that. If you were young, I was much younger. Just a boy. And very much alone.''

Tears were glittering in Leonora's blue eyes. Julie saw them and forced herself to keep quiet. This scene was between mother and son; now that she'd brought the players together, she had no lines to speak. She only wished she could rid herself of that recurrent image of a motherless, dark-haired boy exiled from his beloved island, set down among strangers in a distant school. No wonder he'd never trusted enough to marry or have children.

"When I left for Paris, I had every intention of returning to Boston five or six times a year,'' Leonora said. "What happened to you was terrible, far beyond anything I could have contemplated. But now I'm asking you as an adult to try to forgive me for my part in that. What your father did is between you and him.''

''Unfortunately Charles was no more a paternal figure than you were maternal. Jenessa never goes near him. Nor, since I was sixteen, have I. Brent is the heir apparent.''

''I plan to get in touch with both of them,'' Leonora said flatly. ''But it was essential that I approach you first.''

''If you're expecting gratitude, you're out of luck.''

''Just give me a chance, Travis, that's all I ask.''

Travis tossed back his drink. ''If you want to tell me about your career, I'll listen.''

As a concession, it was a small one, Julie thought, trying to see it as better than nothing. The conversation limped along. Julie sipped her white wine and when Travis stood up twenty minutes later, was heartily glad to get to her feet.

Goodbyes were said. Briefly, a further meeting was discussed, without any decision being reached as to time or place. Travis made no move to touch his mother, nor did Leonora reach out for him. Then Julie and Travis were retracing their steps to his vehicle. Her jaws aching with tension, Julie sat in silence as he drove back to Old Port. He pulled up outside her apartment. ''Thank you for coming with me,'' he said.

He sounded cold and distant rather than grateful. She said evenly, ''I can't very well start a fight with you when we're parked on the sidewalk outside my apartment. Too bad.''

''You want a fight, Julie?''

''Yes, as a matter of fact, I do.''

''I'd be delighted to oblige.''

''Then let's go in.''

She wasn't inviting him in for any reason other than to blow off steam, thought Julie. Sex was the last thing on her mind. They climbed the steps in a taut silence. As soon as she'd closed the door of her apartment, she went on the offensive. "You've had since Wednesday to absorb the facts, Travis—your mother's alive and well and living in Portland. What are you going to do about her?"

"My mother died a long time ago."

"You've been given what a lot of people would give a fortune for—a second chance."

"Then I'm not most people."

"You can't just ignore her!"

"Try me."

"That's horribly cruel."

"I grieved her loss for years and now all of sudden she reappears and asks for my forgiveness," he said with brutal clarity. "Yet you think I should instantly forget the past and start acting like a son again? Give me a break. Life doesn't work like that."

"There's something else—why did you never mention to me that you had a sister? That Brent had a twin? Are there any other little surprises you've been keeping from me? Stray wives I'm likely to meet on the street? Children scattered around the globe?"

"No—I don't operate that way! Jenessa never comes within ten miles of Dad, and there was enough going on that weekend on Manatuck that I just plain didn't get around to mentioning her."

Rather grudgingly, Julie found she could accept this. But she wasn't finished. "You know how I see it? You're so lucky to have a mother like Leonora. She's artistic and talented and passionate. She takes risks. She's out of the ordinary."

"That's the problem—don't you see?" he retorted. "A six-year-old wants an ordinary mother. One who's there at bedtime and in the morning when he gets up. One he can take his problems to as well as his accomplishments. Sure,

Leonora's had an amazing career. But from my perspective, the cost was too high.''

Her eyes blazing, Julie demanded, ''Would you have preferred a mother like mine, who was always there and never stopped trying to control me? Who was so scared of her emotions she buried them all, and denied me my own along with it? My mother's no more maternal than Leonora—Leonora's just more honest about it. And I'm like you, I've never married, either. Too scared to. Too afraid that I might turn out like my mother.''

To her horror Julie suddenly collapsed on the chesterfield, buried her face in her hands and started to cry. Travis sat down beside her, clumsily putting his arms around her. She struck him away. ''Go home! Leave me alone. Neither one of us has got the guts of a-a flea.''

''Let's prove you wrong,'' Travis said urgently. ''Let's take a risk. Both of us.''

''We're not going n-near my bedroom.''

''I'm not suggesting we do. I've got to get out of town, Julie. Breathe some clean salt air, try to get my sense of proportion back. My friend Bryce offered me his cottage for the weekend. Come with me, you can have your own room if that's what it takes. I just want to be with you by the ocean. That's all.''

''That's a lot,'' said Julie.

''If I spend one more day cooped up in that bloody condo, I'll go out of my mind.''

''I understand the feeling,'' she said with a small smile.

''I dare you to come with me.''

If she didn't want to end up like her mother, she didn't want to be alone like Leonora, either. Wasn't sitting in her apartment all weekend on a par with Pearl's behavior? Besides, she was still feeling deathly tired, a symptom she was doing her best to ignore. A weekend by the sea was just what she needed; it would also take her mind off the fact that her period was now two days later than it had been on Wednesday.

She wasn't pregnant. She couldn't be. She didn't even want to consider the possibility with Travis sitting so treacherously close to her. "I never could refuse a dare," she said.

"Go pack," Travis ordered.

His smile made him look ten years younger, Julie thought humbly. She got up, washed her face in the bathroom, threw some clothes in a case and came back into the living room. "We'd better go. Before I change my mind."

Twenty minutes later, after Travis had also packed a bag for the weekend, they were on the road, driving north. Julie sat back, closing her eyes, and fell asleep with the suddenness of a child.

Travis drove on, stealing sideways looks at his companion. She'd lost weight, he thought. And the shadows under her eyes were new. He was almost sure he was the reason.

He had a weekend to persuade her that separate rooms was a very bad idea; and that after the weekend, he wanted to keep on seeing her. If he suggested they share a room, would that be another dare she couldn't refuse? The way her dark lashes lay on her cheeks and the soft curve of her mouth in sleep filled him with an emotion he could only call tenderness.

A brand-new emotion.

He couldn't be in love. He'd never fallen in love, not once. After his broken engagement, he'd had women through the years, of course he had. But he'd always been careful to caution them that romance, commitment and marriage weren't part of his vocabulary.

There'd been those who'd tried to change his mind. But they hadn't succeeded.

So what was different about Julie?

She hadn't liked the way he'd spoken to Leonora. To his

mother, Travis corrected himself inwardly. The two words felt strange, almost as though they had no connection to him. Why was he so angry with his mother, when his father had behaved even more reprehensibly? Leonora hadn't left home meaning never to return. It was Charles who'd ensured her absence would be permanent. Logically, it was Charles he should be angry with. However, logic didn't seem to have much to do with that constrained meeting in Leonora's apartment. He'd felt like a chunk of granite on the beach. And as cold as the waves of the sea.

He owed Leonora an apology, he supposed. He might even be able to have a civilized conversation with her at some point in the future. But how could he ever revive the instinctual love a child has for his mother? Hadn't that died, all those years ago? He and his mother were strangers to each other.

One thing he would do. He'd visit Charles very soon, and have it out with him. That would give him considerable satisfaction. As for Jenessa, once Leonora had contacted her, he'd phone and find out how she felt about this revelation.

Another thing he needed to do was visit Julie's parents. With or without her consent. Although he still didn't know if he was in love with Julie, less and less could he contemplate being without her. Whatever that meant.

The last three weeks had felt like three years.

The miles rolled by, the shadows lengthening across the road as it wound along the coastline. He started watching for the signpost that indicated Bryce's driveway. Yesterday, when he'd been almost sure he'd act on the invitation, he'd phoned the couple who kept an eye on the cottage for Bryce; by now, they'd have cleaned the place for him and stocked it with groceries. He was glad he'd done that. He didn't want to have to leave the cottage for something as mundane as groceries. He wanted to spend every minute of its peaceful seclusion with Julie.

When he turned off the highway a few minutes later, Julie woke up. "Are we there?" she mumbled.

"Just about."

He pulled up beside the cottage, letting the view speak for itself: a private beach, the curl of waves on the sand, a scattering of islands skirted with foam and then the open ocean. Nearer to hand, he and Julie were enclosed by tall pines and stands of young maple. A couple of times since Bryce had bought the property seven years ago, Travis had come here on vacation. It was, he supposed, as near to Manatuck as he could get.

Julie said softly, "How beautiful..."

"You are, yes," he said.

She flushed, ducking her head. Then she looked straight at him. "I don't want separate rooms. Do you?"

His heart leaped in his chest. "Nope."

"Well," she said with a grin, "that was easy. And even though I lust after you, Travis, I'm also very hungry. Is there anything to eat in this utterly marvelous place?"

"Besides you, there's a refrigerator full of groceries."

"Refrigerator first," she said. "Me afterward."

He captured her hands in his, smiling into her brilliant green eyes. "Promise?"

"You bet."

"If you're afraid of ending up like your mother," he said dryly, "I don't think you have a worry in the world."

"I don't want to talk about mothers. Yours or mine."

"What, no fights?"

"One of the things I like about you—apart from your body—is that you catch on fast."

"You know what?" Travis said huskily. "Right now I wouldn't change places with anyone in the world."

"Neither would I," she said, almost inaudibly.

Julie wouldn't say what she didn't mean. Feeling light-headed with happiness, Travis said, "Let's grab our stuff, raid the refrigerator and light the barbecue. Or else, dearest Julie, you're going to find yourself in the bedroom."

"Steak—or even a hamburger—takes precedence," she said primly, and scrambled out of the vehicle.

Travis got out, too. "Come here," he said.

She walked around the hood of his car, flung her arms around him and burrowed her cheek into his chest. "Okay. Now what?"

"Now this," said Travis, and kissed her with all the passion and skill he was capable of. When he finally raised his head, his heart was thumping as though he'd run the Boston Marathon. He said unevenly, "I won't need a match to light the barbecue."

"I don't care if it's hot dogs," she whispered.

"One of these days I'll have to thank Brent for inviting you to Manatuck."

Julie laughed. "I'm sure he'll be impressed."

"You and I wouldn't have met, otherwise."

"I'm glad we did," Julie said with sudden intensity.

"So am I," said Travis, and kissed her again.

Somehow this interchange set the tone for the next two days. He and Julie spent a good deal of that time in bed, although they also made love up against the pantry door and, rather uncomfortably, underneath a pine tree. They swam, cavorting in the chill waves. They washed dishes together, discussing the politics of dictatorship and the perils of guerilla warfare. They barbecued shrimp, smothered pancakes in fresh strawberries and cream, and hiked in the woods. Travis sang in the shower; Julie taught him a Tanzanian tribal dance. They laughed a lot.

When they were loading their bags into the car on Sunday evening, Travis put a hand on Julie's arm and said forcibly, "This weekend wasn't just about sex, Julie."

She glanced over at him. "No," she said uncertainly, "it wasn't."

"When will I see you again?"

"Thursday?"

"Not until then?"

"Monday I'm taking my mother to a movie that she wants to see and my father thinks isn't worth the price of admission. On Tuesday I'm meeting my friend Kathy after work—remember her, Andrea's mother? And every Wednesday I work late."

He quelled a flicker of unease. "I'll meet you at the clinic on Thursday around five-thirty?"

"That'd be fine." She took one last look around, adding with a touch of desperation, "I hate to leave here, Travis. I'm not ready for the real world."

"This is the real world. You and I together, there's nothing more real than that. Anyway, we can come back. Bryce won't be needing the cottage for a while."

She made an indeterminate sound and climbed into the car. Travis accelerated up the driveway. He'd purposely not suggested she stay at his place tonight. He'd rushed her last time; he wasn't planning on repeating that mistake. But he wanted her to stay. He wanted her to move in with him, he thought with a tiny lurch of surprise; even though he'd never lived with a woman in his life. More than that, he wanted some kind of commitment from her.

He was only here another three weeks, while her contract expired in the middle of September. Then what? She'd mentioned the possibility of going to a clinic in Thailand, while it looked more and more likely that he'd be heading off to Mexico.

Was that what she meant by the real world?

CHAPTER FIFTEEN

BY TEN o'clock the next morning, Julie had lost her breakfast twice over. Leaning on the basin in the washroom nearest to her office, she stared at her paper-white face in the mirror. The flu. It had to be the flu. It couldn't be morning sickness.

She splashed cold water on her face and went back to work. Apart from the tiredness that had been dogging her for a couple of weeks, she felt fine the rest of the day. The movie was about the mishaps of a family wedding and made both her and her mother laugh, a brief intimacy that felt very precious to Julie. That night she slept as soundly as a baby, cautiously ate a bowl of cereal the next morning and didn't even make it to the apartment door before she had to rush to the bathroom. Afterward, not giving herself time to think, she picked up the phone and was lucky enough to get an appointment with her doctor during her lunch hour the following day.

When she saw him, he only confirmed what Julie already, in her heart, knew to be true. She was pregnant.

She walked out of his office like a woman in a daze. If she had to be pregnant, why couldn't the father have been some shadowy, insubstantial character who'd fade into the wallpaper now that she'd conceived? But Travis wasn't like that. Travis was flesh and blood, all too real, with an incisive intelligence and a temper to go with it. It was difficult to imagine him fading into anything.

What was she going to do? She had a date with him tomorrow night. She had less than thirty hours to come up with an answer.

The baby wasn't the issue. It was quite clear to her, and had been ever since the doctor had pronounced the word *pregnant,* that she would have the baby and rearrange her life to take care of it. If she had to trade off her wandering work habits with a real, live baby, the baby won hands down. It was interesting, Julie thought slowly, what a visit to a doctor's office could teach you about yourself.

The problem wasn't the baby. The problem was Travis.

She had to tell him. Didn't she?

Eventually, she thought. With a bit of luck, she wouldn't start to show until late September, by which time he'd be in Mexico. That gave her a few weeks' grace. She'd have to be utterly discreet about the morning sickness; she knew from experience how gossip flourished in clinics and hospitals, whether they were in Maine or Calcutta.

She'd start getting up earlier; get it over with before she even left her apartment.

Feeling slightly better for these decisions, Julie caught the bus back to work. On Thursday, despite her best intentions, she still felt very queasy when she arrived at the clinic. Her first appointment wasn't until nine-thirty. She'd catch up on some paperwork in the meantime.

She was compiling her monthly statistics when a tap came at her door. "Come in," she called, scowling down at her desk because two columns that were supposed to add up refused to do so.

"Good morning, Julie," Travis said jauntily.

Her jaw dropped. Travis. Right in front of her. Standing on the other side of her desk, dwarfing her tiny office. Sickness rose in her throat, her face suddenly cold and clammy. With all the willpower she possessed she tried to force the nausea down. "I'm not—" she began, then gasped, "Excuse me," and ran for the door, pushing past him as though he were a piece of furniture.

She made it to the bathroom just in time. Ten minutes

later, knowing she had no other choice, she went back to her office. "What's wrong?" Travis said tersely, his eyes fastened on her pale cheeks.

"I must have eaten something that disagreed with me," she said rapidly. "I feel better already, it's nothing. What are you doing here?"

He kicked the door shut behind him. "You're pregnant, aren't you?"

"I wish you'd stop saying that," she said peevishly. "Do we still have a date for tonight?"

"Julie, answer me. Are you or are you not pregnant?"

"Yes," she said, "I am."

"Then we'll get married as soon as we can."

"I—*what* did you say?"

"And we'll stay married. No child of mine is going to be abandoned the way I was."

"It's customary to ask a woman if she wants to get married. Not tell her."

"These are exceptional circumstances."

Her temper rose one more notch. "I don't want to get married. Don't take it personally, Travis, it wouldn't matter who you were. The answer's no."

"You don't get it, do you? You're not being given a choice. I'll get a special licence, probably for next week."

"You don't love me," Julie said in a stony voice.

"This isn't about love. Or romance. It's about a child who's going to have two parents. Not one."

"I had two parents who don't love each other. That's the worst thing you can do to a child!"

"I've never met your parents, but I'd be willing to bet that you're as different from your mother as you can be. And if I'm like your father, I'd be surprised."

"We're not in love—we can't get married," she said desperately.

"We mean something to each other, you know that as well as I do. We'll build on that, Julie."

"You're not listening to me!"

"I've been offered a plum position in a new hospital in Mexico, near Cuernavaca. They have a physio clinic, you could get a part-time position there."

"You've got to stop this—I won't marry you."

He said flatly, "There's something I haven't asked you, something very obvious. Do you hate the idea of being pregnant?"

"No, as a matter of fact, I don't," she said truthfully. "But as a single mother, Travis."

"That's out of the question."

"According to you."

"It's my child, too," he said with menacing softness.

"Why didn't we stop and *think* before we made love?"

"Because there's something elemental between us," he said ruthlessly, raising one hand and running it down the side of her face to the hollow at the base of her throat, where her pulse quickened in spite of herself. "Don't bother denying it."

"You can't base a marriage on passion!"

"There are a lot worse things to base it on." He frowned down at her. "I'll look into the licence this morning. Then I want to meet your parents. In the meantime, I'll call Bryce and see if he'll be best man. Who do you want to stand with you?"

"You're like an avalanche, carrying everything in its path," Julie said furiously. "What about your mother, will you invite her?"

His smile didn't reach his eyes. "That'd throw Charles into a tailspin. Although, the more I think about it, the more convinced I am that he already knows Leonora's in Portland, and he staged that fake reconciliation with me to get me away from her."

"Have you been in touch with her?" Julie persisted.

For the first time, Travis wouldn't meet her gaze. "Not yet, no."

"If you're to marry me," she taunted, "you'll have to, won't you?"

"There's no *if* about it, Julie."

He was standing altogether too close. She squeezed past him, putting her desk between them, and found the courage to ask the only meaningful question. "Why do you want to marry me, Travis?"

"I told you. Because of the child."

"Nothing to do with me, then."

"Come off it—you spent last weekend with me, you know how well we're matched."

She said with true despair, "But that won't last!"

"I disagree. But even if I didn't, do we lock ourselves in separate cages, stay alone for our entire lives? I don't think so."

Was that why she wanted the baby, Julie wondered with uncomfortable honesty. So she wouldn't be alone? She wanted the baby, but not the baby's father.

As though he'd read her mind, Travis said abruptly, "Were you going to tell me you were pregnant?"

"I only found out yesterday."

In a voice like a knife blade, he repeated, "Were you going to tell me?"

"Yes," she said dully, "eventually."

"When it suited you. After I'd left Portland."

She lowered her eyes, ashamed. Put like that, her plan sounded shoddy and underhanded. "I haven't had much time to think," she said defensively.

"Nor are you going to," he said grimly. "I'll let you know the date of the wedding as soon as I've looked after the legalities. Tonight we'll go and see your parents."

"Oh, no, we won't," she flared. "If this travesty of a

marriage is to take place, I'm going to see them first. By myself. To break the news.''

"Then we'll go together tomorrow night.''

The force of his willpower beat against her, as pitiless as the surf on the ocean. A cliff might seem impregnable, she thought, but the water's ceaseless pounding would eventually topple it. "You're taking for granted that I'll marry you.''

He smiled crookedly. "I dare you to marry me.''

She didn't smile back. "I don't like being taken for granted.''

He suddenly pounded his fist on her desk, making her jump. "This is all wrong, the way we're going about this! Remember the weekend, Julie. I don't know if I love you. I always figured I didn't know how to love a woman, I'd lost that capacity when my mother disappeared. But I'm sure not indifferent to you, nor you to me. Give us a chance, that's all I ask. Look how we laughed and made love and talked all weekend…I'm more real with you than I've ever been in my life.''

She stared up at him, shaken. She couldn't fault him for honesty, she thought, and sought for an answering honesty in herself. "To marry you…it frightens me more than I can say.''

He closed the distance between them, reaching out for her. But Julie shrank from him, knowing if he so much as laid a finger on her she'd weep as though her heart was broken. Travis stopped dead in his tracks, a flash of pure agony lacerating the deep blue of his eyes. But then it was gone, leaving her to wonder if she'd imagined it. He said coldly, "I'll call you later in the day.''

As he wheeled and left her office, she made a tiny, instinctive gesture toward him. But he was striding away from her and didn't see it. Reaching for her chair like a blind woman, Julie sat down. Travis disappeared around a corner.

The man who wanted to marry her. Because she was pregnant.

In her lunch hour Julie phoned Leonora, asking if she could come and see her right after work. So at five forty-five, Julie was walking into Leonora's cool, austere living room. It was interesting, she thought numbly, that it was to Travis's mother, not her own, that she'd come for help. She said, "I have to talk to you."

Leonora sat down in a graceful flow of movement. "Is it about Travis?"

"Yes." Absently Julie tugged at a loose thread in her uniform. "I wasn't wholly truthful with you about Travis and me."

"I'd wondered," Leonora said mildly.

"Until I met him, I'd only slept with one other man, back in my college days. My parents' marriage is a disaster, and I'd long ago decided marriage and commitment weren't for me." Warm color crept up her cheeks. "And then I met Travis, and I just about dragged him into my bed. Not that he was unwilling," she added hastily.

"I'm sure he wasn't."

"We have these huge fights all the time. We spent last weekend together and it was wonderful and then on Wednesday I found out I was pregnant."

For the first time, Leonora was taken aback. "Julie..."

"Travis dropped in to see me at my office this morning. I have this awful morning sickness and he guessed right away. He insists we're to get married immediately. Leonora, I can't marry him! We don't love each other."

"If you don't marry him, what will you do?"

"Have the baby. Find a job somewhere in the States and settle down."

"On your own."

Julie raised her chin. "What's wrong with that?"

"And where does the baby's father fit into this picture?"

"I don't know! I guess he'd visit sometimes."

"Julie, I've only seen Travis as an adult that one evening here in my apartment, but I can't imagine he'd be satisfied with so peripheral a role. He would at least demand joint custody."

"But—"

"You'd be tied to him for the next seventeen or eighteen years. Why not marry him? There's obviously something very powerful between you."

"Sex," Julie said in an unfriendly voice.

"I'd call it passion."

"I thought you'd be on my side!"

"This is my grandchild, Julie—or had you forgotten that?"

She had. Julie buried her head in her hands. "Ever since I met Travis, I haven't been able to think straight," she wailed. "I had my life under control. Lots of adventure and travel, work I love, and no ties. I wish I'd never met him!"

"But you have," Leonora said reasonably. "Travis was abandoned as a child. Do you seriously think he'll abandon his own child?"

"Then what am I to do?"

"Marry him. I'm not saying you'll have a peaceful, uneventful life, you're both too strong-minded for that. Too independent. However, if you're willing, I think you might find love with Travis. But only if you're willing, Julie."

Julie bit her lip. She'd come running to Leonora for sympathy and for comfort. But Leonora's standards were far too stringent to offer anything easy or sentimental. So she, Julie, was once again being forced back on herself.

"Travis is behaving abominably toward you," she said.

"He isn't ready yet," Leonora said with painful truth.

"And no, my suggestion that you marry him isn't to further my own cause. I wouldn't do that to you."

Julie pushed herself to her feet. "You're an amazing woman, Leonora. In all this mess, one thing's clear—I'd be delighted to have you as a mother-in-law."

Leonora smiled, giving Julie a brief hug. "That's very sweet of you. In my heart of hearts, I'm convinced you're made for each other, you and Travis. That's easy for me to say but not as easy for you to hear."

"You'd be invited to the wedding. If there is one."

"I'll attend. When it happens."

"You're very like Travis," Julie said darkly. "I'll talk to you soon. 'Bye."

She hurried home to her apartment. When she got in the door, the phone was ringing. Picking it up as if it were something loathsome she'd found under a rock, she said, "Hello?"

"Travis here. We're on for Sunday afternoon, three o'clock at St. Margaret's. I'll let Charles and Leonora know, as well as Brent and Jenessa. I talked to Bryce and he'll fly in on Saturday."

Her heart jouncing in her chest, Julie said, "You're taking my consent for granted."

"You'll see your parents tonight. Don't forget I want to meet them tomorrow night. You and I can go for dinner first, I'll pick you up at six-thirty."

He sounded as impersonal as if he were a booking agent, she thought with a spurt of fury. "Yes, sir."

"I've gotten a substitute for my medical practice from Monday until Thursday. I called the clinic and they're willing to give you three days off. So we'll go back to the resort. I was able to get the same cottage."

"You're treating me like a cipher!"

There was a taut silence. "What kind of flowers do you like?"

"Anything but roses. I've always hated clichés."

"This wedding will be as far from a cliché as it can get," he said. "Let me tell you something, Julie, and then I'm going to hang up. When I thought of settling in Mexico while you took off to Thailand, I didn't know how I was going to stand it."

And just what did he mean by that? Abruptly Julie realized she was holding a receiver that was humming in her ear. Damn him anyway, she thought, and banged it back in its holder. Flowers, church, a best man and a honeymoon: they were nothing but window-dressing.

Yet somehow, tacitly, she seemed to have agreed to this travesty of a wedding.

She threw together a salad, then went to see her parents to tell them she was getting married. Predictably, her mother turned misty-eyed and sentimental, while her father asked some very pointed questions about Travis's financial state. Neither thought to ask if she was happy. But as she got up to leave, her father said suspiciously, "It's all very sudden, Julie. Is this a shotgun wedding?"

"Really, Thomas, how crude of you, of course Julie wouldn't do anything like that," Pearl said, and smiled at her daughter. "We haven't asked you what you'd like for a wedding present, darling."

Like a tidal wave and just as unstoppable, Julie was suddenly overwhelmed with rage. She closed her eyes and counted to ten. It didn't help. White-faced, she said in a clipped voice, "You know what I'd like? I'd like you two to go to a marriage counsellor or else get a divorce. One or the other."

"*Julie!*"

For once they'd spoken in unison. But not even this minor miracle could deflect Julie. "Why do you think I've scarcely had a boyfriend, let alone contemplated marriage? Because my parents put me off love and marriage by the time I was five. You won't have an honest fight, will you? You'd rather make digs at each other all day long, never resolve anything, live like enemies under the same roof. Yes, I'm pregnant. Pregnant and terrified that I'll end up like you.''

"I won't tolerate you speaking to us like this," Thomas snapped.

"It's too late, Dad—I already have. And you know what?" Julie added with an incredulous laugh. "It feels great. Let me tell you something else. As a little girl, I always thought it must be my fault—that I was the reason you didn't get along. But I'm not going to think that way anymore. You were adults. You were responsible.''

"That's not—" Pearl sputtered.

Julie swept on. "One more thing before I leave. I want both of you to go upstairs to the attic, look in the box with all the albums in it, and take out your wedding photo. Take ten minutes to sit there and look at it. See if you recognize yourselves...I sure didn't." She grabbed her purse. "I'll see you tomorrow evening. Good night.''

She ran down the steps and marched along the sidewalk. But once she was out of sight of the prim little bungalow where she'd grown up, Julie took a detour into a small park near the elementary school. Sinking down on an empty bench, she realized her hands were trembling like leaves in the wind. She rested them on her knees, watching them impersonally, as if they didn't belong to her. Would her parents go up to the attic? Or would they, as usual, bury her request in a barrage of mutual recrimination?

She didn't know. Oh, Travis, she thought, staring blindly at the gravel path, what are we doing?

CHAPTER SIXTEEN

PROMPTLY at six-thirty on Friday evening, Travis drew up outside Julie's apartment. Inside, the little red-headed boy he remembered from his first visit was bicycling up and down the hallway, banging into the walls with indiscriminate enthusiasm. Travis pushed the buzzer, restlessly moving his shoulders while he waited. He'd been behaving atrociously, giving Julie orders, refusing to consult her in any of the decisions about the wedding; he couldn't seem to help himself. He must try to apologize tonight. If she'd let him.

Once they were safely married, the ring on her finger, he'd relax. They'd have three days together beside the ocean, in the cottage with the big bed. They'd be fine.

Impatiently he pushed the buzzer again. Perhaps she'd been late from work and was still in the shower. He'd like to surprise her wet and naked, he thought, desire like an ache in his belly.

A couple had entered the building behind him; the man held the security door open for him. "Thanks," Travis said briefly, and took the stairs two at a time. But when he knocked on Julie's door, there was no answer. He stood still, straining to hear any sounds through the wood.

Only silence. He knocked again, louder, visited by the unpleasant certainty that she wasn't there. The apartment was empty.

The ache in his gut was no longer desire, but fear. He waited another few minutes before knocking again, again without a response. Then he ran downstairs. He hadn't gone to his condo after work; maybe there was a message there for him.

Fear transformed itself into terror. She was in the early stages of pregnancy. Surely she was all right?

As he lunged for the door, the little boy said, "She went away."

Travis turned. "Who?"

"The lady with the green eyes."

"What do you mean, she went away?"

"After lunch she came downstairs with a suitcase and got in a red car and drove away."

"Do you know where she went?" Travis croaked.

"I didn't ask. My mother says it's rude to ask people too many questions," he said virtuously.

Wishing the boy's mother a thousand miles away, Travis said, "Thanks for telling me."

"She didn't even smile at me. Perhaps she's mad at me."

"I don't think she's very happy right now," Travis heard himself say. "She's not mad at you."

The boy gave him a gap-toothed grin, hauled his bicycle around in a circle and pedaled fast toward the end wall. Travis let himself out, wincing at the thunk of rubber against plaster. When he got to his condo, there was no note from Julie among his mail; but his answering machine was blinking. Steeling himself, he entered his password.

"Travis, this is Julie. I—I'm really sorry, but I can't go through with this. The wedding, I mean. I've rented a car and I'm going away for a few days, please don't try to follow me. I need to be alone to think. I just don't know what to *do,* ever since I met you my life's been out of control...I'll be in touch sometime next week. I—good-bye."

His first reaction was relief that she hadn't had a miscarriage; his second, fury that she could run away. But how could he blame her for not being able to think? He hadn't been behaving very rationally the last couple of days.

How about the last couple of months?

He poured himself a beer and stood by the window, watching one of the island ferries pull away from the dock. He had no idea where she'd gone. Even if he did, she didn't want him following her. So was he going to placidly sit home and wait for her to phone?

It was too late to reach Bryce and tell him not to come. How was he going to face his best friend? And what was the point in having a best man if there wasn't to be a wedding?

He knew what his third reaction was. He just didn't want to admit it. Pain, pure and simple. Julie had turned him down. Worse, she'd run away from him.

What other choice had he given her? What room to negotiate? None. No, he'd been too busy playing the macho, masterful male.

He slathered peanut butter on a thick wedge of bread and munched it standing by the window. Comfort food, he thought. Sticks to your ribs and the roof of your mouth. He washed the sandwich down with the last of his beer, cleaned his teeth, looked up an address in the phone book and left the condo.

The woman who answered the door of an obsessively neat bungalow bore almost no resemblance to Julie. He said politely, "Mrs. Renshaw? I'm Travis Strathern, Julie's fiancé. Is she here by any chance?"

"She's supposed to be with you."

"May I come in?"

The living room was tidy, bland and excruciatingly clean, as different from Julie's warm, eclectically decorated space as it could be. Then a man walked into the room. Dessicated, thought Travis, and introduced himself. He said, sitting down without an invitation, "Julie's run away.

It's largely my fault, I haven't handled things well the last few days. Do you have any idea where she might have gone?''

"Run away?" Pearl squeaked.

"She's pregnant," Thomas said accusingly.

"Yes. Does she have a favorite haunt she might have gone to?"

"If she did, we wouldn't know about it," Pearl said, twisting her fingers in her lap. "Julie was always a very private child."

"Nonsense, Pearl."

"It's not, Thomas. We were too busy arguing to pay her much attention."

Thomas puffed up like a bantam rooster. "Must you discuss our private lives in front of a stranger?"

"He's not a stranger. He's the man who wants to marry Julie and he's the father of our grandchild," Pearl announced, then sat down hard on a puce wing chair, looking astounded at her own effrontery.

Despite the confusion of emotion in his chest, Travis was intrigued. He said intuitively, "Did Julie come to see you last night?"

Pearl looked at Thomas, who looked at Pearl. Neither seemed prepared to answer him, so Travis added carefully, "Julie's very afraid of marriage. She seems to think that love doesn't last. That it can't."

"Ridiculous," Thomas snorted.

"We've ruined her life," Pearl wailed.

Travis said forcefully, "Your daughter is the only woman I've ever met with whom I want to spend the rest of my life. Yes, she's pregnant, but that isn't why I want to marry her. She stands up for herself, she loves adventure, she's intelligent and capable." He broke off with an impatient gesture. "Hell, I sound like I'm writing a resumé. She's also so beautiful she cuts me to the heart."

Pearl quavered, "Thomas, you used to tell me how beautiful I was. A long time ago."

Thomas looked at her across the room. His voice creaking like a hinge that needed oiling, he said, "You still are, Pearl."

As Pearl blushed like a young bride, Travis saw the first fleeting resemblance to her daughter. He had no idea what was going on, although he sensed it was cataclysmic. Before he could think what to say next, Pearl blurted, "Julie was very angry with us last night. So this afternoon, Thomas and I phoned a marriage counsellor. Our first appointment is next week."

Julie must have been angry, Travis thought, smothering a smile. "That's a big step," he said in his best bedside manner.

"All this therapy stuff, don't know what good it does," Thomas huffed.

"We're going to find out," Pearl said. "Julie gave us an ultimatum, Mr. Strathern. She was really extremely angry." And she gave a small, secret smile.

Thomas had better watch out, thought Travis with another inner quiver of amusement, and got up to leave. "So neither of you has any idea where Julie might have gone?"

"Give us your phone number, and if we hear from her we'll contact you," Thomas suggested.

This was a huge endorsement. Travis did so, and took his leave. His next stop, he'd already decided, was Leonora's. He'd arrive without warning and take the risk that she wasn't home. But when he pressed her intercom, she answered, the connection so poor he couldn't tell if she was pleased to hear from him or not. Again, he took the stairs two at a time. He'd be in shape for his wedding, he thought wryly. If there ever was one.

"Hello, Travis," Leonora said.

She was wearing a slim-fitting denim skirt and a white

sweater, her hair pulled back with a vivid scarlet scarf. She looked both wary and pleased to see him. He walked into the living room and stood by the window, his back to the light. "Julie and I were to have been married on Sunday," he said. "But she's run away. Do you know where she is?"

"No. She was here yesterday afternoon. She's very afraid of commitment. And of her own feelings."

"She went to see her parents yesterday and read the riot act to them." He smiled at the tall, elegant woman who was his mother. "I'd like to have been there."

"Step one, anger. Step two, forgiveness," Leonora said.

"Are you applying that to me as well?"

"I know you're angry with me. And rightly so."

He said in frustration, "My mother died. I'm having trouble bringing her—you—back to life."

"I do understand." For a moment Leonora's voice faltered. "I only hope it's something you want to do."

"You're very direct."

"As are you. Julie, I'm sure, would agree with me."

"I've handled this fiasco of a wedding like a bull in a china shop."

"More like a herd of elephants in a glass factory," she said. "Did you give her an engagement ring?"

"No! It isn't that kind of wedding."

"What kind is it? You're engaged to be married, aren't you?"

"You're making me feel like a four-year-old caught with his hand in the cookie jar."

"You're in love with her, you know that."

"I lust after her and I like her," Travis said vigorously. "I don't call that love."

"In your way, you're as afraid of love as Julie is, that's why you've hounded her into this wedding. But riding roughshod over her isn't the way to win her." Leonora hesitated. "I'm always nervous about handing out advice. But as a young woman I turned my back on the love of my children to pursue my career as a dancer. That decision came at an extraordinarily high cost, Travis. In the long run, love is all we have."

"Do you regret being a dancer?"

"No. But if I'd been wiser, I might have been able to have dancing and my children."

"Charles might never have allowed that."

"Maybe." She gave a restless shrug. "Enough of the past. If I knew where Julie was, I'd tell you."

"You would, wouldn't you?" Impulsively he added, "Do you have any videos or film clips of your dancing?" As she nodded, he went on, "I'd like to borrow them. Soon."

"I'd be delighted to lend them to you."

He said slowly, "You'll never beg for my attention, will you?"

"Proud. Stiff-necked. I've been called both," she admitted. "No doubt you've inherited some of my less admirable characteristics as well as my best."

"Just ask Julie," he responded with a wry grin. Then he sobered. "I'm going to be in Portland for at least three more weeks. Will you stay here that long?"

"I'll stay as long as you want me to," Leonora said.

"I'm glad," Travis replied, and watched tears tremble on her lashes. Rare tears, he'd be willing to bet, and without even thinking about it crossed the carpet and hugged her.

She felt slight in his arms. Very briefly she rested her forehead on his shoulder. Then she moved back. "I never stopped loving you, Travis. You're always welcome to come and see me. You and Julie."

"I don't even know where to look for her!"

"She won't vanish off the face of the earth. She'll come back, you'll see."

It was these words Travis was holding in his mind as he drove back to the condo, where he had one more phone call to make. Julie would come back, Leonora was right. Julie was that kind of woman. But she might well come back intent on being a single mother for the rest of her days.

On Saturday afternoon, Travis was standing on the wharf where he'd first seen Julie. As he'd turned the last corner in the road and seen the tall wood pylons, he realized he'd been cherishing the hope that by some miracle he'd find her here again.

The wharf was empty. The launch was about thirty feet out, Oliver at the wheel, Charles standing on the deck. As *Manatuck* bumped against the dock, Travis looped the hawsers around one of the metal rungs. "Oliver," he said, "do you mind sitting in my car for a few minutes? This won't take long."

"No sweat," said Oliver, winked at him, and ambled up the hill.

Travis jumped aboard. Charles said curtly, "This had better be important, Travis. We have guests at Castlereigh."

Automatically bracing himself on the slight swell, Travis said, "I've seen Leonora. Twice."

A gull screamed into the wind. Waves slapped at the wharf. Very much on his dignity, Charles said, "She signed a legal document swearing she'd never come back."

"You told me she'd died. Then you exiled me from Manatuck."

"It was for your own good. She abandoned you. And the twins. Heartlessly."

"She acted without thought. She was young and probably foolish. But I don't think she was ever heartless. It was you who was heartless, Dad, lying to your own son about his mother's death."

"I acted for the best."

In a flash of insight, Travis said, "Leonora abandoned you. That was the issue, wasn't it?"

"Nonsense!"

"That's why you pretended there'd been a funeral in Philadelphia. To save face. Don't bother arguing, I know I'm right. I just never figured it out until now."

Charles's face was a study in conflicting emotions. Then he burst out, "I adored her from the first moment I saw her. She was everything I wasn't— creative, passionate and free. And so beautiful, black hair to her waist, her eyes like the shoals off Manatuck. I knew I had to have her. Possess her. She was mine, and only mine."

Unconsciously he was standing taller against the rail, his pale blue eyes very far away. Travis said shrewdly, "But she wouldn't allow you to own her. Because you're right, something about her will always be free."

And wasn't Julie the same? he realized with another of those jolts of insight. Pushing this thought aside, he waited for his father's reply. "Dancing, it was always her dancing," Charles rasped. "Once you were born, she was fanatic about getting back into shape, and insisted on taking lessons in Boston. I let her, I thought it was best. But I should have refused."

"If you had, she'd have run away sooner."

"We had terrible arguments, and somewhere in the middle of all that, she fell out of love with me." Charles's laugh was bitter. "But I still loved her. I couldn't help myself. We'd stopped sleeping together months before the twins were conceived…that happened one moonlit night on the island, when I came across her dancing on the grass, her bare feet wet with dew."

Remembering, his father's face was lit with wonder;

Travis stayed silent, feeling an unexpected tug of sympathy. The words dragged from him, Charles said, "I thought that having the twins would keep her home. But it did the opposite, made her desperate to escape. So she flew to Paris one night when I was away on business, and I found her letter when I got back."

As the sun disappeared behind a cloud, Charles went on, "I was out of my mind. Literally. Yes, my pride was in ruins. All my friends would laugh at me, my business associates, my enemies. But worse than that, I still adored her. I couldn't let her go because I'd never really possessed her. So I buried her. Pretended she'd died. Threatened her with financial and artistic ruin if she ever reappeared. Then I divorced her secretly, and two years later met Corinne. Who's Leonora's opposite in every respect."

"Do you still love Leonora?" Travis asked gently.

Charles finally met his son's gaze. "I don't know. I suppose not, it's all a very long time ago." With difficulty, he added, "I shouldn't have done what I did, Travis. I knew it was wrong even while I was doing it. But I couldn't stop—I was the one possessed. And you paid the price...if it's any help, I've felt guilty for years."

Travis hadn't quite finished. "You always pushed me away. Me and Jenessa."

"Isn't it obvious why? Look at yourself in the mirror! You're the male counterpart of your mother, hair color, blue eyes, cheekbones...every time I looked at you, I saw her. As for Jenessa, she's an artist, creative and driven, just as her mother was. So I did my best to crush that in her."

It made perfect sense. Travis ran his fingers through his wind-disordered hair. "I didn't steal the ring."

"Brent confessed to that just last week, when I told him under no circumstances was I cutting you out of my will. He'd buried it under the apple tree by the gazebo. It's at the goldsmith's being cleaned. I should have known you wouldn't have done that, Travis, I'm sorry.''

"Apology accepted," Travis said, feeling something longheld loosen in his chest. "I'm glad Brent came clean."

"I spoiled him for years. I shouldn't have."

A chastened Charles was something new, and again Travis felt a flash of fellow feeling. He said flatly, "I was to have married Julie on Sunday. She's pregnant with my child. But she's run away and I don't know where she's gone."

He had his father's full attention. Charles said wryly, "History repeating itself. Don't make the same mistakes I did, Travis. Swallow your pride, tell her you love her and let her be who she is."

Charles, unlike Leonora, wasn't chary of handing out advice. With a faint smile Travis said, "If I find her, I will."

Charles clapped him on the shoulder. "Good luck, son."

"Thanks, Dad," Travis said, investing the words with more than their ordinary meaning. "I'll need all the luck I can get."

"Come and visit us. Anytime," Charles said gruffly.

"I'll do that."

As Charles signaled to Oliver, Travis tramped up the slope. He needed more than luck. He needed Julie. He said goodbye to Oliver, got in his car, pulled a U-turn and drove away. This time he was heading for the airport to meet Bryce, who was flying in from Australia.

Charles, like Leonora, seemed to take it for granted that he loved Julie. But if this was love, Travis didn't recommend it. It hurt too much.

CHAPTER SEVENTEEN

TWENTY-FOUR hours later, Travis was aimlessly throwing flat pieces of slate into the waves at Bryce's cottage, trying to see how many times he could make them skip into the air. While it was a warm day, the sun glinting on the water, he felt as blue and unsettled as the swell. He should never have given in to Bryce's insistence that they spend the day at the cottage; it was too full of memories of Julie. He'd said something to that effect, but Bryce hadn't listened.

Footsteps padded down the sand toward him. "Brought you a beer," Bryce said. "By the look of you, you need it."

Travis wiped his sandy palms down his shorts. "Thanks."

"When are you going to tell me what this is all about?"

At the airport, Travis had given Bryce only the barest of outlines: Julie had run away, and the wedding was off. Since then, he'd talked about everything under the sun but Julie. "Did you bring me here in the hopes I'd spill the beans?"

"You got it."

"You never did fight fair."

"No fun in that," Bryce grinned. The wind tugged at his thick, sun-streaked blond hair. He was Travis's height, toughly built, his gray eyes as restless as a winter sky.

"Let's go sit on the porch," Travis said abruptly.

"I've got some nachos and salsa, I'll bring them out. If all else fails, we can always get drunk."

"It wouldn't be the first time."

As Bryce put the bowl of chips on the porch table, he

said reflectively, "I've been thinking. You know what? You're well rid of this Julie. She's led you around by the nose ever since you met her. You don't need that."

"She's pregnant," Travis exploded.

"You didn't tell me that." Bryce's gray eyes skewered Travis to the chair. "You sure the kid's yours?"

"Dammit, of course I am!"

"No *of course* about it. Could be anyone's."

"You don't know Julie."

"Not sure I want to," Bryce said. "So do you want this kid?"

"It's mine," Travis said, and heard an uncanny echo of his father's words.

"It's yours and hers," Bryce replied with unarguable logic. "You figure she's after your money? You're not exactly a pauper."

"She'd hardly be running away if that were true."

"Women can be devious," Bryce said, shooting a sideways glance at his friend.

"There's not a devious bone in Julie's body."

"Good body?"

"Back off, Bryce."

Bryce took a handful of nachos. "You're head over heels in love with this broad."

"You're the third person to tell me that in the last two days and don't call her a broad," Travis said tightly. "I wish everyone'd stop analyzing my feelings."

"If you don't love her, why do you look like a whipped dog? Although if you do love her, I don't know why you're sitting on my front porch. You should be out searching for her."

"She doesn't want me coming after her," Travis said in exasperation.

Bryce drained his beer. "Let's stop kidding around. If I've been pushing you, it's because I wanted to find out what was going on. Fact one, you love Julie. Fact two, it's driving you nuts sitting around waiting for her to come back to Portland. Fact three, a good private investigator with connections could find out where she's gone in no time, and maybe that'd put your mind to rest. Fact four, I came several thousand miles to be best man at your wedding, and I still plan to do that. But to have a wedding, we need a bride.''

"Let's stick with fact three," Travis said in an ugly voice. "You think I haven't thought fifty times of hiring someone to find out where she is and then of turning up on her doorstep? But don't you see? If she doesn't come back to me of her own free will, what's the use? The days when I could hogtie her and drag her to the altar are gone, Bryce. Julie wouldn't stand there and say *I do, I will.* She'd say *I don't* and *I won't.* It's one of the reasons I love her.''

His last three words hung in the air. He buried his head in his hands, his voice muffled. "Why was I the last one to see it? Of course I love her. I fell in love with her weeks ago when she stood up to meet me on the Manatuck dock and I told her she was trespassing."

Briefly Bryce rested a hand on his arm. "She'll come back, buddy. She's got to."

"Or you'll be the one doing the hog-tying?" Travis said sardonically. "Tomorrow morning I'll drive down the coast—you're right, I can't sit around doing nothing for one more day. The irony is, we've got the next three days off, both of us, for a honeymoon."

"If you find her tomorrow, you can still use 'em. And now I'm going to get a couple more beers and throw some pork chops on the barbecue."

Left alone, Travis stared out at the horizon, that knife-sharp edge where water met air. He was in love with Julie. He wanted her to be his wife, to live with him and bear his child. But most of all, he wanted her to love him back.

He wished he shared Bryce's confidence that one day this week there'd be a wedding.

Julie wasn't staring at the horizon that Sunday evening. She was staring at the television screen. She had been for the last four hours. Sitcoms, documentaries, and a cooking show. The news and weather were next.

Her bedroom was very comfortable. So it should be, she thought morosely. She was paying top dollar for the privilege of sprawling on a canopied bed with embroidered linens. If she had to be unhappy, she might as well do it in style.

She was no nearer knowing what she was going to do than she had been Friday afternoon, when she'd driven all the way to New Hampshire and found this uppercrust inn. Yesterday, once she'd gotten over morning sickness, she'd shopped all day, buying herself a couple of maternity outfits and falling for two tiny outfits that would be fine for a boy or a girl. Today she'd hiked in the hills, eating a picnic lunch on an outlook over the village and sighting several deer.

Was unhappiness a measure of love? If so, she was in bad trouble.

Today was to have been her wedding day. Right now, she'd be in Travis's arms.

She got up and paced up and down, her arms folded across her chest in a futile effort to banish the pangs of desire that had been attacking her at all hours of the night or day. Then she took out the miniature pale yellow pyjamas with their teddy bear motif on the collar, gazing at them as though they could give her some answers. By running away, she was saying to her unborn child that one parent was enough.

Was that true? Or was she robbing the baby of what

every child should expect as its birthright? Two loving parents and a stable, happy home.

Had her parents taken her advice? Was Leonora right when she said Travis and Julie were meant for each other?

The news had started, beginning with international stories. Julie clambered up on the bed, fluffing up the pillows, watching an item on Tanzania with interest. After a recap of the stock markets, the local news followed. The first segment described a horrific pile-up on the turnpike just north of here. Julie winced away from some of the images; a considerable portion of her work at the clinic dealt with the traumatic aftereffects of car accidents. Then her heart suddenly skipped a beat. The camera had zoomed in on one particular car. A black sportscar, she realized, panic-stricken. To her untutored eye, it looked like a Porsche the same as Travis's. It was crushed between the guardrail and the wreckage of a camper.

There was no sign of the driver. Even as she watched, two ambulances left the scene, lights flashing and sirens wailing. It couldn't be Travis. It couldn't. Or had he been on his way to find her?

What if he were dead?

With a whimper of terror Julie grabbed the phone book from the bedside table. Her hands were shaking so badly she could barely turn the pages. She found the number she was looking for, and contacted the hospital. But after a frustrating five minutes of delays, she was informed that the hospital couldn't give out any names until the next of kin had been notified.

The police, she thought desperately. Maybe they'd tell her. The receptionist passed her on to someone called Ellison. She said, trying to speak clearly through the icy lump in her throat, "There was a black sports car in the pile-up on the turnpike. All I want to know is if the driver's name was Strathern. Travis Strathern. I—I'm his fiancée."

"Just a moment, please." The silence stretched out, each second an agony of time. Then the police officer's deep baritone said, "I'm not at liberty to reveal the name of the driver. But I can assure you it wasn't Strathern...are you still there, ma'am?"

"Yes," Julie gasped. "Yes, I'm here. Thank you so much." Then, hurriedly, she replaced the receiver, tears blinding her vision. That horrible tangle of black metal hadn't been Travis's car. With a quick prayer for the unknown driver, she flicked off the television and climbed off the bed.

Her knees were trembling; she felt light-headed and dizzy. She couldn't have borne it if Travis had died. Not before she'd told him she loved him.

Because, of course, she did. She loved him with all her heart. Why else had he broken through her defences, bringing her such singing happiness in his bed? Why else had she laughed and played with him, talked and fought with such passion and depth of feeling?

She loved him. And she was bearing his child, a felicity that brought a blissful smile to her face. She wrapped her arms around her body, hugging her newfound knowledge. She could go back home and marry him. She'd leave first thing in the morning; it was too late to set out now. Quickly she reached for the phone again.

But when she punched in his number, she got his voice mail, just as she had when she'd left the message that she was running away. She put down the receiver. Later, she thought. I'll talk to him later.

But at midnight, by which time her eyes were bleary from watching so much television, Travis still wasn't home.

He'd had made no claims to loving her. They'd never discussed any of the basics of marriage, issues like fidelity. Could he be with someone else?

Every nerve in her body repudiated such a conclusion.

Travis wasn't like that. He might be angry and arrogant; but he wasn't facile or shallow. He wouldn't go from her bed to someone else's, she was certain of this. So where was he? On Manatuck with Charles and Corinne?

She'd once found herself face to face with a lion; but she lacked the courage to phone Castlereigh at ten minutes past midnight. Julie showered, pulled on her nightgown and got into bed. If she loved Travis with all her heart, perhaps, just perhaps, he'd fall in love with her.

At quarter past two, on what should have been the first afternoon of his honeymoon, Travis pulled into a fast-food place for lunch. He'd driven south to the New Hampshire border, stopped at a beach on the way back and stared for a long time at the sea, and now he was hungry. A hamburger would do as well as anything.

The restaurant was crowded. He found a table next to a family with children, placed his order and took out the newspaper, with its front page photo of the pile-up in New Hampshire. In a cold funk last night, he'd checked to make sure Julie's name wasn't among those dead or hospitalized. He tried to concentrate on a story about lumber tariffs. The baby at the next table was exercising its lungs in competition with the rock music blaring from the overhead speakers. Travis glanced over as the baby's father lifted the child out of its carrying bed. The screaming stopped. Its lower lip still quivering, the baby gave its father a watery, toothless and utterly charming grin.

That's all he wanted, Travis thought painfully, watching the mother rummage through a diaper bag and produce a bottle, which she passed over with a quick smile at her husband. He wanted to be a husband and a father. Julie's husband. Julie, whom he loved more deeply than he'd thought it possible to love anyone.

Sure, he jeered inwardly. That's all you want. Just heaven and all the stars.

Somehow he'd win her back. His survival depended on it.

The hamburger was excellent, as was his coffee. When he'd finished, Travis stood up, fumbling for his wallet in his back pocket, and weaved his way through the crowded tables to the cash register. The restaurant door was pushed open. A woman walked in and started down the short flight of stairs toward him. He made a choked sound in his throat.

She was wearing the flowered sundress she'd had on the first time he'd seen her. Her hair was a gleaming helmet under the lights. "Julie," Travis said in a cracked voice.

She looked up and saw him. For a moment she was frozen in place. Then her foot slipped on the step. As she lurched forward, grabbing for the rail, he lunged toward her. She fell into his arms. Bracing himself against her weight, he hugged her to him, joy rising in him like an unstoppable tide. "Julie, darling Julie, are you all right?"

"Yes." Her arms tightened around his neck, almost choking him. "Oh, Travis, I'm so glad to see you, I love you so much. What are you doing here? Were you looking for me? I'm on my way home, I would have left last night but it was too late. Are you happy to see me?"

He began to laugh helplessly, burying his face in her neck and inhaling the sweet scent of her skin, so familiar and so badly missed. "You're squashing my larynx and did you say what I thought you said?"

She looked up, her green eyes smiling into his blue ones, her hands sliding down his chest. "I said rather a lot."

"The important part. That you love me."

"Yes, I said that. Would you like me to say it again?"

"I would. Just in case I'm dreaming."

"You're not dreaming," she said with a beatific smile. "You don't know how I've longed to be in your arms, I'm so sorry I ran away. I realized afterward that Leonora ran away and left you, too—I shouldn't have, Travis, but I was so confused and unhappy.''

"Julie," he said imperiously, "do you love me?"

"Yes, Travis," she said, "I do."

"Thank God for that." Bending his head, he kissed her at some length and with a great deal of pleasure.

A teenage boy at one of the tables gave a shrill whistle; a ripple of laughter ran through the restaurant. "We've got an audience," Julie said.

"Will you marry me?"

Her smile deepened. "This isn't the most romantic of settings."

He looked around; a number of the patrons were watching the two of them with interest. He reached down to the nearest table, grabbed the bouquet of pink and yellow artificial flowers and presented it to her with a flourish. Then he brought her free hand to his lips, and with lingering sensuality kissed her fingers one by one. "Dearest Julie, I love you more than I can say. I was a total jerk to push you the way I did and you had every right to run away. If you'll marry me, you'll make me happier than I deserve, and I swear I'll do everything in my power to make you happy.''

"Yes," she said, "I'll marry you," and kissed him very explicitly on the mouth.

There was a burst of applause. Julie dropped a curtsy, her cheeks pink. Travis said, "By Thursday at the latest? Bryce has to go to Hong Kong on Friday."

"I'll marry you tomorrow, if you like."

"Five minutes from now wouldn't be too soon." Looking deep into her eyes, he said huskily, "You're my heart's desire. Since you left, Leonora, Charles and Bryce have all insisted I was in love with you. But I was the last one to see it. I'm sorry about that."

"You're forgiven. I wasn't too swift in that department myself." Quickly she told him about her phone calls to the hospital and the police station. "That brought me to my senses. But you weren't home last night, so I couldn't tell you."

"I was at Bryce's cottage. Missing you every moment of the day and remembering everything we did there."

"Everything?" Her blush deepened. "Oh Travis, I can't believe how happy I am."

"Let's go home." He let his gaze wander to her cleavage. "Your place or mine, I don't care."

"Actually, I stopped here because I was hungry. I'm eating for two, remember?"

"You could order takeout," he said. "It's faster."

"So you're in a hurry to get home?" she said innocently.

"In a hurry to take you to bed," he said. "It feels like forever since we made love."

"I hope I'm worth waiting for."

"You are," Travis said. And she was.

The following afternoon, on the lawn of St. Margaret's Church, a group of people stood talking among some rather puny rose bushes that could have done with Corinne's touch. The bride, in a simple white sheath, was carrying a spray of orchids, and looked as radiant as a bride could be. Her husband, tall and debonair in a morning suit, stood close by her side, the sun glancing off his dark hair. The ceremony had been simple, the words both poetic and profound; Travis and Julie were still in their grip.

Charles, also in a morning suit, had already introduced Corinne to Leonora; all three were valiantly making conversation. Julie beckoned her own parents over. "You look lovely, Mum," she said sincerely.

Pearl's dress was made of leaf-green linen; her hat was massed with flowers, and her cheeks flushed with excitement. Thomas, unexpectedly handsome in his morning suit, tucked Pearl's arm into his and said gallantly, "You're a beautiful bride, Julie. Your wedding photo will be on the bookshelves in the living room beside our own. We bought a new frame for ours, by the way."

"I can tell that you did, Dad," Julie said obliquely, hugging her father and kissing her mother.

Pearl said in a rush, "We both want to thank you, Julie. What you said to us was such a shock that it brought us to our senses." She hesitated, then plunged on. "The way we behaved was never your fault. You see, I always wanted four or five children, but Thomas only wanted one...so I was angry with him all the time. It was years before I found out that I couldn't have had another child anyway."

"I shouldn't have been so stubborn," Thomas said stiffly.

"Oh, Thomas, neither should I." Pearl smiled at her daughter with endearing shyness. "It's as though we've cleaned house the last few days, and thrown out all the garbage. It feels wonderful."

Julie blinked back tears. "You're both very brave...I'm so proud of you. Now why don't you come and meet Travis's parents?"

Bryce was talking about sailing to Brent, who was on his best behavior, just as though he'd never forced his way into Julie's bedroom or marooned her on an island. They, too, joined the others. As the conversation became more general, and a move was made toward the church gate, where limousines were waiting to take them to a reception at the city's finest restaurant, Bryce said to Julie, "I'm glad I was able to be here and meet you, Julie. I know you'll make Travis very happy."

She smiled. "You've been a good friend to Travis over the years."

"No more than he to me." For a moment Bryce's jaw

hardened. "I owe him a lot—I'd have ended up on the streets, if it weren't for him."

"Someday you must tell me about that."

"I will." He added abruptly, "Any idea why Travis's sister didn't show up for the wedding?"

"Jenessa? Not really." Julie bit her lip. "I know she and Charles don't get along. But I was hoping to meet her...she doesn't live very far away."

"Mean-spirited of her," Bryce said lightly. "At least Kathy, your matron of honor, is married. So no one's trying to hook me up with her."

"Remember that Travis was a confirmed bachelor," Julie teased.

"The woman's not born who can get me to the altar," Bryce said confidently.

"That's what I thought about myself," Travis interjected, smiling at his new wife with such love in his eyes that Julie wanted to melt into his arms. "Are you feeling all right, darling?"

"Both of us are fine."

"Then I think we should head for the reception. Champagne is called for. Our respective families are doing wonders—let's reward them with Dom Perignon."

Bryce had gone ahead. Julie said impulsively, "Travis, when your contract's up in Mexico, would you think of settling in Maine for a while? We'd be nearer to all the grandparents that way."

He brushed her cheek with his lips. "The thought had crossed my mind—but I'd wondered if you'd be reluctant to give up your travels."

"Home is where you are," Julie said simply.

Travis gave her the smile he reserved for her alone. "Leonora's going to live either in Boston or New York and teach dance...she told me that just before the ceremony."

"So we could be close to all of them."

"We could build a summer home on Bear Island, as well. I want our children to run free every summer, just as I did."

"Children?" Julie repeated, her head to one side. "Aren't you rushing things a bit?"

"I doubt we'll be satisfied with one."

"I suspect you're right. Travis, it all sounds perfect and I'm so unbelievably happy. I do love you."

Travis grinned at her. "A few minutes ago, I thanked Brent for bringing you and me together. He took it like a man."

"That wasn't very nice of you," Julie laughed. "We'd better catch up with the others. After all, the sooner we get to the reception, the sooner it'll be over and we'll be alone together."

"So you're thinking that way, too."

"I am."

"Good," said Travis.

AT THE
MILLIONAIRE'S
BIDDING

by

Lee Wilkinson

Lee Wilkinson lives with her husband in a three-hundred-year-old stone cottage in a Derbyshire village, which most winters gets cut off by snow. They both enjoy travelling and recently, joining forces with their daughter and son-in-law, spent a year going round the world 'on a shoestring' while their son looked after Kelly, their much loved German shepherd dog. Her hobbies are reading and gardening and holding impromptu barbecues for her long-suffering family and friends.

CHAPTER ONE

THE latch clicked, and Dave Benson came into the dark, cramped cloakroom that adjoined the office, closing the door behind him with care.

After that lunchtime's unexpected phone call, it had been agreed that he, with his technical know-how, should tackle their possibly important visitor.

Eleanor glanced up from making the tea he'd requested, her clear grey eyes hopeful.

Dave answered her unspoken question. 'Yes, it *is* Robert Carrington the financier, and the job on offer is just the kind of thing we were hoping for...'

Though his words were encouraging, it struck her that he was looking far from pleased.

'Apparently Carrington's fed up with living and working in London, and he'd like to start running his business from home. He owns some manor house or other near Little Meldon, and he wants to set up an office and a communications network with state-of-the-art equipment.'

'That sounds wonderful!' she exclaimed.

'It would be if I could clinch the deal, but he's an awkward man...' There was irritation in Dave's voice and a scowl on his darkly handsome face.

'Though he must have *known* we were a small firm, he keeps quibbling about our capabilities, and about the travelling time involved. 'I've assured him we can cope, but so far I've been unable to convince him.'

While she watched him, trying to hide her anxiety, Dave poured himself a mug of tea and, sitting in the single rickety chair, reached for a ginger biscuit and dunked it moodily.

Through the small, grimy window Eleanor could hear the roar of passing traffic on the Edgware Road, and closer at hand the rattle and bang of a tailgate being dropped, as goods were delivered to one of the ground-floor shops in their building.

As Dave continued to sit there, she asked, 'Shouldn't you be getting back?'

'He's talking on his mobile. When it rang, the arrogant swine lifted an eyebrow and asked, "Would you mind?" as though I was the office boy.'

'When you do go back, for goodness' sake be careful,' she begged. 'Don't let him see how you feel about him.'

'I think he already knows,' Dave admitted. 'We've rubbed each other up the wrong way from the word go. You'd better see if *you* can handle him.

'According to the media, he's tight-lipped about his private life, but in public, at least, he seems to like the ladies, so maybe a woman will stand more chance.'

Knowing it shouldn't have to hinge on sex, and wishing, perversely, that he'd said a *beautiful* woman—but knowing full well that the adjective wasn't justified—Eleanor agreed, 'I'll do my best. Though I remember reading an article about him in *Finance International* that suggested he has a reputation for being a tough nut.'

'Well, if we don't manage to crack him, we're in big trouble.' Dave ran a hand through his black wavy hair. 'It's a miracle a man like Carrington came to us in the first place, and we just can't afford to lose this chance, so promise him anything he wants.'

'I can't see the sense of promising something we may not be able to deliver,' she objected uneasily.

'Damn it, Ella, don't go all ethical on me. By the time

he finds out whether or not we can deliver, we'll be well into the job. He'll be forced to settle for what he can get.

'Our best card, maybe our only card, is that he wants the work put in hand straight away, and the job done as quickly as possible. The big firms will already have full order books, which means a wait. Tell him the next job we had scheduled has been put on hold for the present...'

There *was* no next job. Despite all their hard work the order book had remained depressingly empty.

'And emphasise that we can make a start as soon as he says the word go. Monday, if that suits him. Though we'll need a substantial cash advance before we can order any equipment.'

'But surely Greenlees will—'

'Greenlees have clamped down. They won't let us have as much as a mouse mat until we've paid what we owe them.'

'They've *been* paid. Our account was settled as soon as the money came in from the last job.'

When the grim look on Dave's thin face failed to lighten, she insisted, 'I sent the cheque off myself at the beginning of the week.'

'It bounced,' he said flatly. 'I had a nasty email from them this morning, and an even nastier phone call from the bank.'

'There must be some mistake,' she protested.

'There's no mistake.'

She shook her head unbelievingly. 'I'm sure there was enough money in our bank account to cover it.'

'As it happens there wasn't.' His brown eyes were hard. 'When I went to pick up that software package, Burtons insisted on being paid there and then. By the time I'd written them a cheque we were flat broke.'

'I hadn't realised things were that bad,' she said shakily. 'Why didn't you tell me?'

'There didn't seem any point in worrying you.'

'You *should* have told me. It was supposed to be my job to pay the bills. If I'd known, rather then send Greenlees a worthless cheque, I would have gone in to see them and asked for more time. It would have saved us the embarrassment of—'

An ugly look on his handsome face, Dave snarled, 'Rather than standing here arguing, suppose you get out there and do your stuff? And don't forget that Carrington's our last hope, so offer him anything he wants, the moon if necessary. We *have* to get this job if we're to stay in business.'

The cold certainty in his voice scared her half to death. She knew instinctively that if they lost the business, she might well lose Dave.

Without the promise of a brighter tomorrow, she had nothing to offer him. Or at least nothing exciting enough to hold him. Her future would be as bleak and grey, as empty, as her past.

Somehow she *had* to persuade Robert Carrington to give them the job.

Taking a deep breath, she glanced in the spotted mirror to check her appearance. What she saw there failed to boost her morale. Dressed in a plain charcoal suit, she looked thin to the point of gauntness, and her heart-shaped face appeared pale and strained in the gloom.

A stray tendril of sable hair had escaped from her otherwise neat chignon. Tucking it into place, she squared her shoulders and, picking up the tray, which she'd set with care, made her way into the office.

A man was standing by the window, his back to the room, looking out on to the street four floors below, where car tyres left a series of snails' tracks on the dark, wet tarmac.

Tall and well-built, with broad shoulders, his hands hung

loosely by his sides, relaxed but alert, and his short, thick, corn-coloured hair curled a little into the nape of his neck.

He turned, without haste, and the first thing she noticed was that his brows and lashes were several shades darker than his hair.

From Dave's rather derogatory, 'He seems to like the ladies', she had imagined him to be in his fifties and handsome in a heavy, florid way; a flashily dressed stereotype, with a practiced charm.

He was nothing of the kind, and somehow his appearance threw her totally. Robert Carrington was quite young, in his early thirties, she guessed, lean and powerful-looking, dressed in a grey business suit with a plain blue tie.

His hard-boned face was tanned and tough, and far from handsome, and if he had any charm he was keeping it well hidden.

As she continued to stand and stare at him, he raised a single brow.

Colour flared in her cheeks and, feeling a complete fool, she put the tray down on the desk with a rattle, and moved to greet him.

At close quarters he seemed to tower over her five feet seven inches, and she guessed he must be well above six foot.

'Mr Carrington... I'm Eleanor Smith.'

He took her hand in a light, firm grip, and she found herself looking straight into thickly lashed eyes that were green and bronze and speckled with gold. Just like a wolf's eyes.

Caught and held, she was unable to look away.

'As in Smith and Benson?' His voice was deep and attractive, and his question broke the spell.

'Y-yes,' she stammered.

Glancing at the tea-tray, he asked with a fine irony, 'So you're just standing in for the office girl?'

With an effort, Eleanor pulled herself together and said as coolly as possible, 'Unfortunately we're short-staffed at the moment.'

Withdrawing her hand she retreated with what dignity she could muster, while he watched her a shade satirically.

Needing to bolster her confidence, she went to take a seat in the big leather chair behind the desk asking politely, 'Won't you sit down, Mr Carrington?'

He strolled across the room and took a seat in the small swivel chair opposite.

Chairs made no difference to who was boss, and they both knew it.

Reaching for the teapot, she enquired, 'Milk and sugar?'

His hard face slightly amused, as though he was playing some game, he answered, 'A little milk, no sugar.' Adding unexpectedly, 'I'm sweet enough.'

You could have fooled me.

Oh Lord, had she said that aloud?

Whether she had or not, he *knew*, she could read it in his tawny eyes.

Her hands not quite steady, she poured tea into one of the porcelain cups and passed it to him.

As he made to take it, she let go too quickly, and the cup tilted, splashing tea into the saucer and onto his trousers.

While she stared at him, frozen with horror, he calmly put down the cup and, producing a spotless handkerchief, proceeded to mop up the mess.

When Dave had spilled tea into his lap he had jumped to his feet cursing volubly.

This man's reaction was so unnervingly restrained that she would almost have preferred the cursing.

'I-I'm terribly sorry,' she apologised. 'I hope you're not scalded?'

'Nowhere vital,' he said drily and, balling the handker-chief, tossed it into the waste-paper basket.

Desperate to retrieve the situation, she offered, 'Let me get you a fresh cup.'

He shook his head. 'Call me a coward, but I don't think I'll risk it.'

Watching the colour rise in her cheeks, he added quiz-zically, 'In any case, there's still almost a full cup. A little tea goes a long way.'

There was no doubt in her mind that he was enjoying her confusion. Dave was right, Robert Carrington was an utter swine.

But she mustn't let her dislike show. Through sheer stu-pidity she had already done more than enough damage. 'I'm sorry,' she said again.

He waved an expressive hand. 'Think nothing of it.' Then, looking at the empty cup on the tray, he suggested smoothly, 'I do hope you're planning to join me?'

'Well I—'

'Otherwise I might start wondering if you're really the office girl standing in for the boss.'

Only too aware that she had made more of a hash of things than any self-respecting office girl, she managed a smile and poured out a second cup of tea.

'Cheers.' He raised his cup and drank.

Knowing he was making fun of her, she gritted her teeth and took a sip of the tea she didn't want, shuddering at the memory of all those other cups of grey, lukewarm liquid that had passed as tea.

She had hated tea ever since.

'Just as a matter of interest,' he pursued levelly, 'how many personnel *do* you have? I couldn't get a straight an-swer from Benson.'

'Well, I'm sure he must have explained that we're a very small firm and—'

'How many?'

'Two.'

'I see.'

Firmly, she said, 'That's all it normally takes. Though of course it depends on the size of the job in hand and how quickly it has to be done. If we do need extra staff—carpenters, electricians, fitters—we employ them on a temporary basis.'

That had been their plan, though it hadn't yet become necessary.

'Your job for instance… I understand you want it completed without delay, so—'

'What's happened to Benson? Do I take it he's chickened out?'

Angry at the interruption, she answered as evenly as possible, 'He had an afternoon appointment.'

'Cold feet, more likely,' Robert Carrington opined. 'So he decided he'd send a beautiful woman to soften me up?'

Caught out by the jibe, she quickly responded, 'I may not be beautiful, but I *am* the senior partner. No one *sends* me to do anything.'

'Good for you!' he applauded.

Rising to his feet, he came round the desk and, putting a hand beneath her chin, turned her face up to his own.

She sat as though metamorphosed into stone, while he studied the widely spaced grey eyes beneath dark winged brows, the high cheekbones and straight nose, the generous mouth and pointed chin.

Then, running a fingertip along the jagged silver thread of scar tissue that ran down her left temple and cheek, he asked, 'What makes you think you're not beautiful?'

Inside her head she could still hear the voice saying, ''It's a pity she's got that ugly scar''…and sure he was just baiting her, she answered recklessly, 'I *do* own a mirror.'

'So how would you describe yourself?'

'Colourless. Nondescript. *Scarred.*'

'It's no use looking into a mirror if you're prejudiced. Try looking into other people's eyes to see what their opinion is.' His glance fell on her modest ring. 'Your fiancé's for instance.'

She had looked into Dave's eyes and seen only her own opinion reflected there.

Almost before the depressing thought had crossed her mind, Robert Carrington had returned to his chair and was regarding her steadily across the desk.

As though it had branded her, she could still feel his touch, and she was forced to repress a shiver while she struggled to regain some semblance of composure.

Though her every instinct urged her to run and hide, she knew she must make her peace with this tough, complex man sitting opposite.

It was *necessary.*

Desperate to get back on course, she said, 'I'm sorry. I'm afraid we've strayed from the point, and I'm sure you're much too busy to waste your time.'

'Oh, I wouldn't describe it as *wasted,*' he objected lazily. 'Sometimes it's useful to digress a little. It helps to really focus the mind.'

She counted to ten. 'Well, now we've *digressed a little*, perhaps we can get back to business?' Her tone, though pleasant, implied that *she* hadn't got all afternoon to waste, if *he* had.

His tawny eyes narrowed and, without further ado, he called her bluff. 'Well, I'll quite understand if you're too busy to give me any more of your time—'

'No! No, that's not what I meant. Of course I'm not too busy.' The hasty interruption betrayed her desperation all too clearly.

Wanting only to put her head down on her arms and

weep tears of anger and frustration, she sat up straighter and lifted her chin.

'Mr Carrington, you must know we want this job, and I can only assure you that if you give us the chance we'll do our very best.'

And it would have to be their best. She was already convinced that he wasn't the kind of man who would be prepared to settle for anything less than the moon, if that's what he'd been promised.

Running long fingers over his smoothly shaven jaw, he asked thoughtfully, 'How long have you been in business?'

Knowing it was useless to prevaricate, she answered reluctantly, 'Not quite a year.'

Glancing around, as though weighing up his surroundings, he asked, 'And you've had this office for the same length of time?'

He sounded far from impressed.

'Yes,' she answered, and thought wryly that it was just as well he hadn't seen it when they'd first taken it over.

The walls had been painted a stomach-turning green, an abandoned rusty-grey filing cabinet had leaned drunkenly against the wall, and worn linoleum in squares of ginger and black had adorned the floor.

While Dave had gone out searching for orders, she had set about refurbishing the place.

The cabinet and linoleum disposed of, a good second-hand carpet, a desk and two chairs, a couple of coats of white paint, and a few cheerful pot plants had made a lot of difference.

By the time they had installed the reconditioned computer equipment it was starting to look good, and she had been pleased with the result until she saw it through Robert Carrington's eyes.

'Hmm,' he said. Then, 'Perhaps you'd like to tell me how Smith and Benson came into being?'

Though politely phrased, she recognised it as an order rather than a request.

She wanted to look forward rather than back. But unless she was prepared to go along with this difficult and arrogant man, there might be nothing to look forward to.

Taking a deep, steadying breath, she told him the bare bones of it. 'It was Dave's idea. The technical side of computers and communications has always been his forte. He's brilliant at it.'

'What about you?'

'I knew nothing whatsoever about business, but so we could go into partnership, and I could pull my weight, he encouraged me to take a course in practical business studies.'

'What did that cover?'

'Office equipment and layouts, how to instal and use the latest technology, and computer programming. Rather to my surprise, I found it both interesting and enjoyable.'

'Which college did you go to?'

'I didn't go to college. I went to special evening classes.'

'For how long?'

'Almost a year.'

'Why evening classes?'

When she didn't immediately answer, he added, 'It just struck me that was the hard way to do it.'

'I needed to keep working to support myself.'

'What kind of job were you doing?'

'I was working in a hotel.'

'As a receptionist?'

'What makes you think that?'

'You have an attractive voice, and you speak well.'

Dave had said much the same thing.

Seeing Robert Carrington was waiting for her affirmative, a kind of stubborn pride made her inform him flatly, 'As a matter of fact I worked in the kitchens.'

'All the time you were doing the course?'

'Yes.'

'No parental help?'

'No.'

'Couldn't Benson help to support you?'

'He wasn't in a position to.' In fact *she* had supported Dave during his final year at college.

'So what made you decide to go into business, rather than just have a job?'

'It was something we both wanted to do. I suppose we liked the idea of being free to work for ourselves...'

In truth she had, at first, only wanted something that was *hers*. A small business of some kind, a second-hand book-shop, or a tearoom perhaps, ideally with some living-accommodation over it.

Security and independence.

Only later had her dream widened to include Dave.

She had been a quiet, introvert child who, as Matron put it, "lived inside her own head". Though rated as highly intelligent and bright, her grades at school had been only a little above average. She had shone at nothing.

When she finally left the classroom to start work in the kitchens at the children's home, her sights already set on the future, it had been without too many regrets.

As soon as she was old enough, she had thanked the staff for their years of care and escaped from the grey drab-ness of Sunnyside, taking with her nothing but a few clothes, an abiding love of books and music, and a knowl-edge of plain cooking.

She had found herself a job as a kitchen assistant in a busy hotel less than a mile away from Sunnyside. The hours were long and the work hard, but with the job went a small room.

It was dark and draughty and overlooked the yard and

the dustbins, but it was *hers*. Her refuge. Her private domain. She felt a heady sense of freedom. For the first time in her life she was in control of her own destiny.

Though the wages were far from good, because she had bed and board and no travelling expenses, she could save. She *did* save. Every penny.

The rest of the hotel staff, mostly young and out for a good time, invited her to join them at the local pubs and clubs, and no doubt thought her odd when she refused. But though she was always polite and friendly, she made no attempt to mix, and after a bit they stopped asking, and let her go her own way.

As soon as her working hours had been established, she took a job at the nearby supermarket stacking shelves in the evenings and on her day off. Adding to her bank balance.

After a while she moved to the checkouts where late-opening shopping meant she was working even longer hours, and by the time she crept into bed each night she was too tired even to dream.

But perhaps she didn't need to. After more than three unrelenting years of hard work and dedicated saving, she was really getting somewhere. Another year, and she could start looking for a suitable shop to rent, and begin to turn her dreams into reality.

One Friday night, just before closing time, she had glanced up to see a young man in jeans and a thin, shabby jacket unloading a few meagre items from a shopping basket.

Dave.

Though she hadn't seen him for more than five years, she would have known him anywhere. That handsome face, with its thin nose and dark brown eyes, the curved brows and lock of black wavy hair that fell over his narrow forehead like a question mark, was unforgettable.

Her heart gave a strange lurch.

He too had been at Sunnyside, and for a long time she had worshipped him from afar, dreaming of the day he would finally notice her.

But two or three years older than her, he hadn't seemed to know she existed. When he had eventually left, without even a goodbye, she had felt desolate and bereft.

'Well, hello there. It's Ella, isn't it?' All at once he was smiling down at her, his slightly crooked teeth very white in his dark face. 'This is a real blast from the past.'

'I'm surprised you remember me,' she admitted a shade awkwardly.

'Apart from getting a bit older, you haven't changed much.'

'Neither have you.'

As she began to put his goods through, he asked, 'How long is it since you left Sunnyside?'

'Over three years.'

'You must have been glad to get away. God, how I hated that place! So what have you been doing with yourself since?'

'Working.'

'Are you shacked up with anyone?'

'No, I—'

'I do wish these checkout girls wouldn't stop to gossip,' the woman in the queue behind him remarked in a loud voice.

'And I wish these old biddies wouldn't be so cantankerous,' he retorted, equally loudly.

'I really shouldn't be talking,' Eleanor said guiltily.

'Why not?' Fishing in his pocket, he added, 'Surely they don't own you body and soul?'

'No, but—'

'Oh, hell!' he exclaimed. 'With coming out in a rush I

forgot to pick up my wallet. I'm afraid I can't take the stuff.'

'Do you have a credit card?'

'That's in my wallet, too.' He made to hand her the carrier back.

'Take it. It doesn't amount to much. I'll put it in out of my own money.'

'Sure?'

'Sure.'

'Look, what time do you finish?'

'In about ten minutes.'

'See you outside.'

He was waiting in the street for her, looking cold and pinched in the chill September wind.

'The Capuchin is still open if you want a hot—' He broke off abruptly. 'Damn! no money.'

'It's all right, I'll pay.'

As they walked the short distance to the coffee-bar, she realised that though she was wearing flat heels, they were almost exactly the same height. At one time he had been taller than her, but now he was rather on the short side for a man.

Waiting by the steamy counter, she noticed him eyeing the clingfilmed ham sandwiches and asked, 'Are you hungry by any chance?'

'Starving. I was intending to get something when I'd shopped. Didn't have time to eat earlier.'

When they were seated opposite each other, two packs of sandwiches and two mugs of coffee on the ringed and stained, piglet-pink, plastic-topped table, he asked, 'So how's the world been treating you? Tell me everything you've been doing since you escaped from *Colditz*.'

As she told him what little there was to tell, he wolfed his pack of sandwiches, and swallowed his mug of coffee. Though he was as handsome as ever, he looked thinner than she remembered him, as if he hadn't been taking care of himself.

All her childhood feeling for him returning in a rush, she pushed her own sandwiches and mug across, and asked, 'Can you manage these?'

'Don't you want them?'

'To tell you the truth I'm not hungry,' she lied, 'and it isn't that long since I had a coffee.'

'Why do you work in a hotel as well as the supermarket?' he asked curiously, as he started into the second pack of sandwiches.

'I'm saving hard. I'd like to be able to set up a little business of my own.'

'Wouldn't we all!'

Something about his reaction made her feel uncomfortable.

As though sensing it, he asked more mildly, 'How close are you?'

'Another year at the most and I should be able to start looking for somewhere suitable. I was thinking of a second-hand bookshop, or a maybe a tearoom,' she explained.

Contempt in his voice, he said, 'Surely that kind of thing is only for old maids?'

Hiding her hurt, she asked, 'What about you?'

'The same kind of dream, only keeping up with tomorrow's world. When I've graduated—and I'd like to get a really good degree—I want to start my own business.'

'Doing what?'

His dark eyes glowed. 'Setting up and programming computer systems, with the emphasis on communications.'

'So you're at college?'

'Yes. After two or three years of drifting from job to job, I decided to go for it.'

'You got a grant?'

He shook his head. 'I didn't want to mortgage my future,

so I've been working evenings and weekends to pay my fees and keep body and soul together.'

'It can't be easy.'

'No, it isn't,' he admitted bleakly. 'Though I'm good at the technical side, and getting excellent class marks, I'm finding it a struggle. There's never enough time.

'This coming year's workload looks like being even heavier, but unless I can win the lottery, I have to find another job as soon as possible. A long bout of flu last month lost me my last one.'

She felt moved to protest. 'But if the workload's that heavy...'

'I'll have to manage somehow. No option. When I leave college and start my own business it will all have been worth it.

'Pity you're not into this modern technology lark,' he added thoughtfully. 'I could do with a partner. Someone to run the office. You've got a nice voice, the sort that sounds educated, though I don't know how the hell you've managed it...'

Eleanor remembered, from when she was quite young, the Matron of Sunnyside remarking, 'The child speaks well. She's obviously from a good background... Which ought to make things easier...'

'So you'd be ideal...' Dave was going on. 'Weekends and suchlike, when we had no one coming into the office, you could help with the actual installations. It's not difficult once you know how.'

All at once her dream of a solitary future was replaced by a warmer, much more exciting prospect. But she knew rather less than nothing about computers and technology.

As though reading her mind, he said, 'If you were remotely interested, there's a school nearby that runs the kind of special business courses that would cover pretty well everything you'd need to know.'

'I am interested,' she assured him. 'But I couldn't afford to leave work.'

'You wouldn't have to. The classes are held on weekday evenings, so you could keep your job at the hotel, and still work weekends at the supermarket if you wanted to.'

'How long are the courses?'

'They run until next summer. By then I'll have graduated, so the timing will be spot on. Hopefully you'll have a good background knowledge of business, and I'll have all the technical know-how we need. If I'm lucky I might even have made some contacts that could put work our way.'

He was contributing so much... What if she was a drag on him?

Seeing her anxious frown, he said, 'Don't worry, I'm sure that by then you'll be in a position to pull your weight.

'To start with money's bound to be a problem, unless we can manage to get a bank loan. Once we're underway, of course, we'll be able to get short-term credit facilities from the suppliers, as well as asking the clients to put some money up front.

'The trouble is, if we approach a bank they'll expect us to be in a position to finance at least part of it ourselves.'

'Well, we should be able to.' Excitement made her sound breathless. 'I told you, I've been saving.'

He looked unimpressed. 'I don't suppose what you've managed to save amounts to much. I reckon we'd need a minimum of seven or eight thousand.'

'I've got a bit more than that,' she told him with quiet triumph.

His jaw dropped. Then, fired with enthusiasm, he cried, 'In that case we're as good as in business! If you're game?'

'I'm game.'

'Now all I need is a job to see me through till next

summer... Of course I'd have a better chance of doing really well if I didn't *have* to work, but—'

'You don't have to work. If I can boost my earnings with a weekend job at the supermarket, there should be just about enough money coming in for us both to scrape by on.'

'You're a jewel, partner.'

'I won't be able to save, and there won't be anything left for luxuries but—'

'Luxuries? What are luxuries? And with over eight thousand sitting in the bank you don't need to save.'

He leaned across the small table and, taking her face between his hands, kissed her full on the lips.

Her heart began to pound and her colour rose. She could never remember anyone kissing her before, and certainly not in that way.

'I can see us really going places, kiddo,' he told her, jubilantly. 'And maybe one day, when we're successful and raking in the cash, we can extend the partnership.'

'What do you mean...?'

'Marriage... Why not?'

To be loved. To belong to someone. It was more happiness than she had ever dared dream of, and she wanted to cry.

CHAPTER TWO

OVER the next few months, with both of them working all hours, they hardly saw each other. Once a week they snatched a late-evening coffee together, and on very odd occasions a takeaway pizza.

Instead of living in student accommodation, Dave shared a small self-contained flat with a college friend. Though Eleanor paid his share of the rent for it, she had never been there, and wasn't even sure where it was.

'Off Station Road,' Dave had answered casually, when she'd asked.

More than a dozen streets ran off Station Road, but knowing by now that he hated to be what he called "crowded" she let the matter drop.

As the festive season approached, learning that she had Christmas Day off, they began to make plans to spend it together. At the last minute, however, Dave rang up, sounding hoarse and snuffly, to say he had developed a stinking cold and all he wanted to do was stay in bed.

He rejected her offer of nursing and, when she looked like persisting, pointed out irritably, 'At the moment you're the breadwinner, so what's the point of *you* catching it and having to stay off work?'

Though bitterly disappointed, she couldn't deny it made sense, and when one of the kitchen staff failed to turn up, she worked in their place.

Unfortunately, Dave's cold lasted over New Year, and it was well into January before they arranged to meet again.

That night she left the light and warmth of the supermarket to find a biting wind was driving flurries of snow down the dark street.

They had been planning to have a spot of supper together and, thinking he still looked far from well, she suggested that if they got fish and chips they could take them back to his flat. 'It's much too cold to stand eating them in the shop doorway.'

Dave looked horrified. 'Do you want to get me slung out? My dragon of a landlady has very strict rules. No smoking. No loud music. No wet washing hanging about. No showers after eight. And *definitely* no visitors. In any case, Tony will be home.

'Tell you what, if you give me a bit extra spending money, just for once we'll eat in the cafe.'

'Of course.' She fished in her bag and gave him her last ten-pound note.

Completely besotted, she would have given him anything he'd asked for. Herself included. But though he kissed her from time to time, he never tried to take things any further.

When she rather hesitantly made it clear that she would sleep with him if he wanted her to, he said, 'Don't think I'm not tempted, kiddo. But for one thing I'm working so hard I've no energy left, and for another, I can't afford to be distracted. There'll be enough time to have fun when our business is up and running.'

She could only admire his dedication.

In the end it paid off handsomely. He graduated with top marks and, to celebrate, they went out looking for an office to rent.

'One with a reasonable address, if possible,' Dave decreed. 'Where you *are* can make a big difference.'

Finding something that fitted the bill was easier said than done. The rents were astronomical. Then, when they'd almost given up hope, in a rather rundown building just off the Edgware Road, they found what they wanted.

Or at least the best they could afford.

That first hurdle over, it meant changes all round. Dave would no doubt want to move, and when she had worked her notice at the hotel, she would need to find somewhere else to live.

Full of barely suppressed excitement, she waited for Dave to suggest they find a small flat and move in together. When he said nothing, she plucked up courage and broached the subject herself.

He shook his head. 'I was planning to stay where I am. Apart from the fact that Tony needs my help with the rent, it's cheap and reasonably comfortable, and handy for the tube.'

'But I thought we could be together...'

'Too much of a temptation, kiddo.'

'Oh, but surely—'

'Look, we have to be sensible about this. We need time to build up the business before we can afford to take any chances. If you got pregnant where would we be? Right up the creek without a paddle. Say we give ourselves a year...'

A year...

'For that length of time we'll need to work all hours, seven days a week. Then if everything's going well we'll start to relax a bit, get married, tie the knot in the good old-fashioned way. Tell you what, as soon as we've been paid for our first job, I'll buy you an engagement ring.'

She couldn't help but think it sounded like a sop.

Seeing she still looked far from happy, he added, 'Oh, and as it's your money that's getting us started, I think you should rate as senior partner, and your name come first on our business cards.

'After all,' he added magnanimously, as she began to shake her head, 'You've more than pulled your weight.'

She really didn't care whose name came first. Just his praise would have been enough.

After a fortnight of fruitless searching, her luck changed and she found a one-roomed flat complete with a kitchenette and a tiny bathroom at a rent she could just about afford. It was within walking distance of the office, which meant she would save on tube fares.

Having bought a small second-hand van, Dave had promised to help her move in her few possessions, but when the time came he was busy, so she managed on the tube with a couple of battered suitcases.

Her new flat was cramped and shabby and three flights up, but the bed-settee was reasonably comfortable, and compared to the room she had lived in for the past four years, it was the height of luxury.

She felt like a queen.

As soon as she was settled, she set about furnishing and repainting the office. That done, inside a week they were in business. Their printed cards read:

Smith and Benson
Computer and Communication Systems Installed

Within a few days they had established contact with the necessary suppliers, and secured their first job.

It was heady stuff.

Her only disappointment was that she still saw very little of Dave. When they weren't actually working, he was always out and about trying to drum up business.

Once or twice he took her to the cinema, or to eat in some cheap restaurant. He never came to her flat.

'Avoiding temptation...' he told her, when she suggested he came round occasionally. 'If you're lonely, buy a second-hand telly.'

Used to being on her own, she wasn't exactly lonely, she just missed him, and a television was the last thing she wanted. Books and music had always been her pleasure and her solace.

Some three months later, after they had been paid for their first job, true to his word, Dave bought her an engagement ring.

Slipping it onto her finger he asked, 'There what do you think of that?'

A twist, with a couple of small zircons, it was clearly inexpensive, and at least one size too large, but she was thrilled with it.

'As soon as the money starts rolling in, we'll change it for diamonds,' he promised.

She didn't need diamonds. The ring he had put on her finger meant everything to her. Commitment. A future together. Love.

Perhaps afraid of the answer, she had never asked the question before, but now as he kissed her, she said, 'Dave, do you love me?'

'Course I do.'

'It's just that you've never told me.'

'I'm not very good with words, but you must know I love you. We're a pair. A partnership. I don't know what I'd do without you…'

For the next few weeks that assurance had kept her floating on cloud nine.

As they neared the end of December, finding they had finished their current job and had nothing else on their books until early January, Eleanor started to plan for their best Christmas and New Year ever. Dave's birthday was on the thirty-first of December, so it would be a double celebration.

When, wanting his input, she mentioned her plans, he said, 'I'm sorry but I won't be here. I've more than earned a break, so I'm joining Tony and the boys on a cheap trip to Belgium. We go on the twenty-fourth and come back January the second.'

'Oh, but I thought we'd be spending Christmas and New Year together—'

'I can't afford to miss this chance. It'll be the first holiday I've had for years. Pity it's a men only, boozy thing, but that's the way it goes. I'll bring you back a present to make up for it.

'I don't suppose there'll be much doing as regards business. Between Christmas and New Year is a bit of a dead period, so why don't *you* have a break?

'All you really need to do is pop into the office each day to check for mail and emails…'

So once again she had found herself facing the prospect of a solitary Christmas and New Year. But refusing to give way to gloom, she had decorated her tiny flat with holly and mistletoe, made mince pies, and stocked up with library books and CDs.

Christmas Eve she had gone to hear a carol concert, and Christmas morning she had walked in the frosty park and fed the ducks.

New Year's Eve loomed, empty and lonely. She bought a cheap bottle of wine to see the new year in and, unused to drinking, got a little tipsy. Only then, thinking how lovely it would have been if Dave had been there, had she shed a tear.

He had returned on January the second, as promised, bringing her back a few tacky souvenirs. 'Just to prove I've been thinking about you.'

Somehow the assurance had rung hollow…

Becoming suddenly aware that Robert Carrington was waiting for an answer to a question she hadn't even heard, Eleanor pulled herself back from the past and stammered, 'I-I'm sorry?'

'I asked if you had any regrets about going into business?'

'No. None at all.'

Though if they didn't get this job, it looked as if they
wouldn't be in business much longer.

Apparently reading her thoughts, he asked, 'What are
your future prospects?'

Knowing instinctively that it was make or break, she said
carefully, 'They should be good. Dave's brilliant at what
he does, and we're both prepared to put our hearts and souls
into it, but to succeed we'll need to get the work.'

'How secure are you financially?'

Her lips tightening, she said, 'I don't believe you have
any right to ask that.'

His green-gold eyes pinned her. 'Before I entrust any
work to you I've a right to know what your chances are of
going bust on me. A lot of small firms are disappearing
down the drain at the moment.'

'I hope we won't be one of them.' It was the best she
could do, and she held her breath and waited.

Apparently it was good enough. He let that go and
smoothly changed tack. 'When are you due to begin your
next job?'

She started to tell him it had been put on hold, as instructed, then, knowing full well he wouldn't believe a
word of it, she admitted bleakly, 'At the moment we have
no next job.'

'I see,' he said slowly. 'So it rather depends on me?' His
voice held satisfaction, and as he spoke he smiled a little.

Eleanor knew then, without the slightest doubt, that he
had no intention of giving them his work. Like a wolf picking up the scent of prey, he had picked up just how desperate she was, and had been stringing her along.

She jumped to her feet abruptly. 'Well now you've had
your fun perhaps you won't mind if—'

'Sit down,' he ordered. Adding, 'Please,' almost as an afterthought.

There was so much quiet authority in his voice, that she found herself obeying.

'Tell me, what makes you think I've just been amusing myself?'

She refused to back down. 'Well, you have, haven't you? It's obvious.'

Tawny eyes gleaming, he asked, 'Would it alter your opinion if I offered you the job?'

'It wouldn't alter my opinion, but it would make the last half-hour or so worth it.'

He laughed, and she noticed that his mouth and teeth were just perfect.

'I'm glad to see you have spirit. I thought you might have had it all knocked out of you.'

Startled, she asked, 'What made you think that?'

'Instinct mainly. I have a feeling that life hasn't been too kind.'

The last thing she wanted was Robert Carrington's pity. 'It's been kinder to me than it has to a lot of people,' she informed him briskly. 'I've never been ill-treated or gone hungry. I'm healthy and able to work. I've a place of my own and someone who—' Unable to say the words, she stopped speaking abruptly.

'Someone who loves you?' he hazarded. 'In that case you're one up on me.'

Reaching across the desk, he lifted her left hand and examined the ring. 'Am I right in thinking it's Benson you're going to marry?'

'Yes.'

'How long have you been engaged?'

'Eight months.'

He looked surprised. 'And you're not living together.' It was a statement not a question.

Suddenly feeling like some kind of misfit in this modern world, she objected stiffly, 'I'm not sure how you reached that conclusion.'

Ironically, he told her, 'When you were listing your blessings, you said, "*I've* got a place of my own"...'

She bit her lip.

'So why are you playing hard to get? Afraid Benson will change his mind about marrying you if you give him your all?'

Before she could think of any answer, he went on, 'No wonder the poor devil's so edgy if you're keeping him waiting.'

'I'm not keeping him waiting,' she denied sharply. 'And he's not edgy...' But, even as she spoke, she knew he was, and had been for some weeks.

Though it could hardly have been for the reason suggested. Perhaps Dave had seen more clearly than she had what was facing them financially...

'If you're not keeping him waiting, why aren't you living together?' Robert Carrington pursued relentlessly. 'You know what they say about two being able to live as cheaply as one...'

'I really don't see that it's any of your business. And you know what they say about curiosity killing the cat...'

'*Touché*. But I'm afraid we've strayed from the point again.'

Infuriated by his calm effrontery, and the way he had led her by the nose, she said through clenched teeth, 'You mean *you've* strayed from the point.'

'Aha!' he exclaimed softly, 'now you're really starting to hold your own and answer me back. Perhaps you've decided you don't want the job after all?'

Hotly, she said, 'If I have to jump through hoops to get it, the answer's no, I don't want it. You can keep your job.'

He clicked his tongue against his teeth reprovingly. 'Now how do you think Benson will feel about that?'

Eleanor's face grew still and stiff with despair. Why had she allowed this man to bait and torment her until she was rattled enough to throw away the job they needed so badly.

Dave would never forgive her. Never.

'Feel about what?'

Startled, she looked up to find he was standing in the office doorway.

'Did your appointment go well?' Robert Carrington enquired sardonically.

Dave, who was no fool, merely said, 'Very well, thanks. But you were asking how I'd feel about something?'

With a spurious air of confidence he strolled round the desk and, watched by the other man, took the chair Eleanor had vacated for him.

After giving Dave time to get seated, and *her* time to sweat a little—she felt sure—Robert Carrington said, 'Yes…As you're aware, with this job, one of the main stumbling blocks was the length of time it would take to travel between London and Little Meldon each day. Well, that problem has been partially solved…'

As she waited tensely, wondering what he was up to, his eyes caught and held hers. An unmistakable challenge in their tawny depths, he continued smoothly, 'Miss Smith has agreed that she would be quite willing to live at my home, Greyladies Manor, while the work is in progress…'

His words brought a shock of surprise and, mentally reeling, she wondered *why* he had lied.

Common sense told her she should be grateful that he had let her off the hook, but the last thing she wanted was to have to live under his roof.

And somehow he must have guessed as much.

So had he presented it as a *fait accompli* merely to force her hand?

Cocking an eyebrow at her, he waited for her to say something. When she bit her lip and stayed silent, he turned to Dave and went on, 'I was asking Eleanor how *you* would feel about living there?'

'Then you're giving us the job?' Dave burst out eagerly.

'That all depends. To enable the work to be completed as quickly as possible, I'd like you both to be on the spot.'

As Dave opened his mouth to argue, Robert added, 'If you're prepared to meet me on this, all well and good. If you're not...'

He left the sentence hanging in the air, but the threat was plain.

Eleanor looked at Dave, unconsciously holding her breath.

Plainly torn, wanting to tell this arrogant so and so where to get off, but knowing they *needed* the job, he hesitated. It was perhaps twenty seconds before he agreed reluctantly, 'I suppose if that's what you want.'

'It is.'

'Okay.'

'In that case, how soon can you start?'

Regaining some of his cockiness, Dave went into his spiel, 'As it happens, you're lucky. Our next job has been put on hold, so we can make a start as soon as you want us.'

Glancing up unwarily, Eleanor felt herself grow hot as she met Robert Carrington's green-gold eyes once more and read the mockery in them.

'Then suppose you come down to Greyladies tomorrow afternoon?' he suggested briskly. 'Unless you prefer to keep your Saturdays and Sundays free?'

'We're quite used to working weekends,' Dave told him, 'so that's no problem.'

'Good. Then you'll have time to get settled in and size up the job before Monday...

'One of the things we haven't touched on so far is price. When you've seen where I want the new office, and I've explained what I have in mind, you can no doubt work out a rough estimate of how much it's going to cost.'

'I'll be glad to. Oh, and as you've mentioned money, when we start placing orders for equipment we shall need some cash up front.'

Pulling out a cheque book and putting it on the desk, Carrington suggested, 'Say ten thousand?'

'Ten thousand will do fine.'

Dave's voice was casual, but Eleanor knew it was a great deal more than he had expected.

The financier wrote the cheque and passed it to him, before asking, 'You have some transport?'

'Yes, we have our own van. All we need are a few directions so we can find the place.'

'When you reach Dunton Otterly, take the road to Little Meldon. Greyladies is about half a mile south of there.

'Simply follow the main street through the village, and carry on until you come to Grave Lane on the left. The entrance to the manor is about five-hundred yards down the lane, on the right.'

'Got it.'

'You'll see a gatehouse and some tall, wrought-iron gates. Jackson will open them for you.'

Slipping his cheque book and pen into an inside pocket, Robert Carrington rose to his feet.

Dave stood up too, clearly intending to shake hands across the desk, but the older man gave him a perfunctory nod, and held out his hand to Eleanor.

Each time he'd touched her it had been like a small electric shock, but seeing no alternative, she braced herself and took it.

A mocking gleam in his eye, he said, 'Thank you for

your time, Miss Smith. I do hope you think it's been worth it?'

He was as smoothly abrasive as pumice stone, she thought vexedly.

Without waiting for an answer, he released her hand and moved to the door. 'I'll expect you both sometime tomorrow afternoon.' He sketched an ironic salute, and was gone.

Feeling limp, totally wrung out, Eleanor stood and listened to his footsteps receding down the uncarpeted stars.

'Well done, kiddo!' Dave flourished the cheque. 'How did you manage to persuade him?'

'I didn't persuade him,' she admitted.

'So what did you have to promise him?'

'Nothing. The only thing he seemed set on, was that we should stay at Greyladies.'

His ill-humour returning, he said resentfully, 'Well I hope he's damn well satisfied. It's going to be hell stuck in the country in some crumbling old manor house.'

Dave hated the country, she knew. He always said it got on his nerves. A city boy through and through, he was only really happy when there were pavements beneath his feet and a snooker hall handy.

'We'll no doubt be relegated to the servants' quarters and forced to eat with the staff...' He pulled a face. 'But as that's what his lordship's insisting on, we don't have much choice.'

'Can you make a guess as to how long the job might take?' she asked.

'A couple of weeks... If he's paying really well, I might even stretch it to three.'

'Three weeks?' She couldn't keep the dismay out of her voice.

Presuming her objection to be dislike of the country, the same as his, he said, 'Don't worry, I have every intention of coming back to town at the weekends. We can charge the petrol to his lordship.

'Now I'd better get this little beauty paid into our account before the bank closes.' Thrusting the cheque into his pocket, he added, 'I can't wait to see the manager's face, after the way the snooty git talked to me this morning.'

'Dave, you will be…polite, won't you,' she asked anxiously. 'After all, we did have a cheque that bounced.'

'That was yesterday. Today we're riding high with ten thousand in the black.'

'But we still owe Greenlees—'

'Don't worry about Greenlees. I'll call in and explain the situation, give them a post-dated cheque they can cash as soon as Carrington's is cleared.'

He went to fetch his coat. Looking in at the door on his way back, he said, 'I reckon we've earned an early night, so I'm off home as soon as I've sorted that little lot.'

'I thought perhaps we could go out later? Maybe have a meal somewhere?'

'Sorry, kiddo. I've promised to play snooker with Tony and the boys. Pick you up tomorrow about three o'clock. I'll give you a toot, so be ready. Love ya.'

A moment later he was gone, leaving her standing gazing blankly at the closed door.

Surely, if he really loved her, he wouldn't always put ''Tony and the boys'' first?

But it wasn't just a case of putting his friends first, she admitted dismally, apart from when they were working, he never seemed to want to spend any time with her.…

Time…

All thoughts of Dave were abruptly driven out of her mind as once again she heard Robert Carrington's deep voice saying with mocking emphasis, ''Thank you for your time, Miss Smith. I do hope you think it's been worth it?''

Though the time spent in his company had been anything but comfortable, and she had managed, in one way or another, to make a complete fool of herself, she couldn't deny that it had been worth it.

After all, they had been given a job they badly needed, and a substantial cash advance to take them out of the red.

She should be vastly relieved, and of course she *was*. But some still small voice warned that nothing would ever be quite the same again. That just his entry into her life had shifted the balance and changed it in some fundamental way.

She felt a bit like Faust, as though she had sold her soul to the devil to get this job. Oh, don't be a fool! she told herself crossly. All she had done was fail to correct Robert Carrington's lie.

If she'd put his back up by saying she *hadn't* agreed to stay at Greyladies, instead of having a job to look forward to, Smith and Benson might well be finished as a business.

And not only finished, but in debt.

Robert Carrington's visit had changed everything, made all the difference. Not only to the business, *but to her personally*.

That was the rub, the reason for her malaise. His effect on her had been so potent that mingled with the relief was dismay and agitation, an alarming feeling that he had somehow breached her defences.

While Dave always seemed to be retreating from her like an ebb tide, Robert Carrington had swept in and swamped her, got inside her head.

She shivered. Then making a determined effort to put her inner turmoil aside, she went to fetch her mac and bag.

As she locked the office and made her way down the stairs and into the drizzly rain, she thought wistfully that it would have been nice to have done something to celebrate.

Well, she would! But there wasn't much pleasure in going out for a solitary meal, so instead she would buy something to add to her meagre wardrobe, most of which had come from charity shops.

When the previous cheque had been paid into their account, saying he was in need of some new shirts and trousers and a decent jacket, Dave had spent what she had considered to be a serious amount on clothes.

Though there were several things she could have done with, nervous in case their money ran out, she had held back.

But now, though they would be eating with the staff at Greyladies, she would need to have something tidy to change into when the day's work was done.

The nearest department store had just started its summer sale, and she went in to look around. In the lingerie department she bought some cheap, but pretty, undies.

Then, going through to Ladieswear, she chose a skirt and two tops from one of the reduced ranges and, with a sudden, unaccustomed feeling of recklessness, a simple shift in subtle shades of mauve and blue.

On her way out, a pair of sandals caught her eye and, with scarcely a qualm, she added them to her purchases.

By the time she got home, conditioned to *not* spending, she had started to regret her recklessness. But she *wouldn't* feel guilty, she told herself firmly. The lot barely came to what Dave had spent on a jacket, and they now had ten thousand in the bank and a job that should pay well…

Next day dawned fine and, though the sky was still grey and overcast, there were breaks in the clouds. The weather report on the radio suggested that a high-pressure system was moving slowly in, which meant a settled spell was on its way, with soaring temperatures forecast.

Rejoicing at the prospect of seeing a bit of sunshine, even if it was only through some window, Eleanor cleared the small fridge and made herself a salad lunch. Then, having dressed in a patterned skirt and a plain lavender-coloured top, she swirled her hair into a neat knot before finishing her packing.

Dave was late, and it was nearly four-thirty before she heard the sound she'd been waiting for. Grabbing her case, her shoulder bag, and her jacket, she hastily locked up and made her way downstairs.

Outside, the fume-laden air was appreciably warmer, and the pavements were dry for the first time in what seemed weeks.

The white van was waiting by the kerb. Sliding open the rust-spotted door, she pushed her belongings inside, before climbing into the passenger seat.

'I was wondering where *you'd* got to,' Dave looked anything but pleased. 'I'm parked on double yellows.'

'I was wondering where you'd got to,' she found herself saying, as they pulled out to join the traffic stream. 'You're more than an hour late.'

'Had a game of snooker with the boys. It looks like the last bit of fun I'll be getting till next weekend, stuck in some dead-and-alive hole.'

He made it sound as if it was the end of the world, she thought. Then chided herself for being so edgy. She didn't usually criticise Dave in this way.

'But it's worth it, surely?' She made an effort to sound cheerful.

'I suppose so.' Having reached out a hand and patted her knee, he turned on the radio. He liked his pop music loud, which made any kind of conversation virtually impossible.

As usual, the traffic was heavy, and stopping and starting they crawled their way out of London at a snail's pace.

Left with her thoughts, Eleanor made a concentrated effort to steer them towards the—hopefully—not too distant future, when the business was thriving, and she and Dave could be married.

But the more she tried to focus on that future, the more nebulous it became, a kind of mirage that, as she attempted to grasp it, receded steadily, so that it was always out of reach.

The moment she stopped concentrating, her thoughts refocused on Robert Carrington. He had made such an impact on her, that since the previous afternoon she had thought of little else.

Images of his compelling, strong-boned face, his dark-lashed wolf's eyes, his austere, yet oddly sensitive, mouth had filled her head. She remembered his voice and his well-shaped hands, how she had felt when he touched her.

He had flustered and disconcerted her, made her angry and reckless, altogether rattled her; and through it all had run a strong thread of attraction, *fascination* even, that she had refused to admit.

But apart from the way he had affected her, and the fact that he owned Greyladies, she knew nothing about him. Had he a wife? Children?

She recalled him saying, "Someone who loves you? In that case you're one up on me".

Did that mean he had no wife? Or a wife who didn't love him? The media, while admitting that he guarded his privacy fiercely, had apparently dubbed him as a ladies' man.

Of course that didn't necessarily mean he wasn't married... But if he was a philanderer, it might explain *why* his wife didn't love him....

CHAPTER THREE

BY THE time they had left the outskirts of London behind them the traffic had lessened, the sky had cleared, and as they ran into Little Meldon the sun was shining.

The main street was wide, with cobbled areas on either side that sloped gently up to rows of picturesque cottages. In the centre it widened even more to straddle an old stone butter market.

There was a mere handful of shops: an old-fashioned grocers, a bow-fronted butchers, a greengrocers, and a post-office-cum-newsagents.

At the far end was a black and white half-timbered coaching inn, with overhanging eaves and barley-sugar chimneys.

There was hardly any sign of life, and the whole thing could have been lifted straight from Dickens.

'What a dump!' Dave said disgustedly.

Eleanor, who had thought the village delightful and been about to say so, held her tongue. If he was in a bad mood there was no point in antagonising him.

About half a mile further on, as Robert Carrington had said, they came to Grave Lane, and turned down it. On one side was a patchwork of green fields bordered by a ditch and a hawthorn hedge. On the other was a wide expanse of grass, and an old, lichen-covered wall enclosing what appeared to be rolling parkland.

A stone building with gables and turrets and crooked chimneys appeared on their right. A gatehouse in every sense of the word, it spanned a huge, cobbled archway which was guarded by iron gates that put Eleanor in mind of a portcullis.

She gazed at it enthralled. Somewhere, almost certainly in a book, she had seen one just like it.

Grimacing, Dave switched off the radio and touched the horn, and a few seconds later a gnome-like little man appeared in rolled-up shirt sleeves and gardening gloves, and swung open the gates.

'Afternoon,' he said laconically, when Dave rolled the window down. 'Mr Carrington's expecting you.'

As they started up the drive, past a neatly laid-out vegetable and flower garden, he closed the gates behind them and returned to his digging.

For perhaps a quarter of a mile the drive wound serpent-like between banks of flowering rhododendrons and sweet-smelling shrubs, with no sign of a house.

Dave was slumped in his seat, on his face a look of complete boredom, but Eleanor sat up straighter feeling a strange surge of anticipation.

Then, as they rounded the final bend, the manor was suddenly there, like some wonderful surprise.

Only it wasn't a surprise.

A split second before it came into view, she had pictured Greyladies just as it was. As if she had always known it. As if it was as familiar to her as an old friend.

Though long and rambling, the house was a mere two stories, built randomly of old and mellow stone. Creepers climbed its walls and moss grew on its steeply pitched roofs.

It had sturdy chimney-stacks and earthenware chimney pots adorned with cheerful, gargoyle-like faces, and its casement windows were mullioned and leaded, the old, uneven panes catching the light.

An imposing, black-studded front door, the wood of which was almost silver with age, was flanked by long, stained-glass windows, arched at the top, and running from some eighteen inches above the ground almost to the second floor.

High, sun-warmed stone walls, one with a small black door, the other with a wide archway, curved away on both sides.

Bringing the van to a halt on the paved apron, Dave grunted. 'I thought a manor house would be a lot grander, more formal somehow, with pillars and things. This isn't a bit what I expected...'

It was *exactly* what she had expected, and she was lost to it even before she went inside.

As she sat gazing at it speechlessly, he added, 'Better let his lordship know we're here.'

Switching off the ignition, he clambered out, leaving her sitting there.

At that instant the heavy door swung open and Robert Carrington appeared. Casually dressed in stone-coloured trousers and a silk shirt open at the neck, he looked taller and fairer and more striking than ever.

'It must be the butler's day off,' Dave said a trifle too loudly. Adding, 'I bet he's come to direct us round the back to the tradesmen's entrance.'

'Benson...' Nodding coolly to the younger man, Robert Carrington strode across to the van and, opening the passenger door, held out his hand to Eleanor.

Still off balance, thrown by that feeling of *recognition*, she put her hand into his.

His smile holding a hint of mockery, he greeted her as though she was a guest. 'Miss Smith... Welcome to Greyladies.'

The shock of meeting those tawny eyes literally took her breath away, and she was forced to drag in air like a swimmer who's been under water too long, before she could answer, 'Thank you.'

She had tried to tell herself that his effect on her would have faded, that on further acquaintance she would find him ordinary, dull even.

But rather than lessening, his impact was stronger. It made her heart beat uncomfortably fast, set her nerves quivering, and scattered her wits.

Her right hand clasped in his, her skin sensitised by his touch, she fumbled vainly to undo her seat belt with her left hand.

When he reached over to unfasten it for her, he was so close she could see the glitter of his short fair hair as it tried to curl against his temples; see how his dark lashes were tipped with gold, and how tiny laughter lines fanned out from the corners of his eyes.

There were twin creases beside his firm mouth, and above his top lip, a tiny V-shaped scar. His skin was clear and healthy and smelled pleasantly of sun and the fresh masculine scent of aftershave....

He slanted her a gleaming glance from beneath those long lashes.

Feeling a complete idiot because he'd caught her staring at him as though mesmerised, her cheeks flushed with embarrassment.

As he withdrew his hand, it brushed her thigh, and she jumped convulsively.

Perfectly straight faced, he said, 'I do apologise.' Then, 'Allow me…'

Legs trembling, she found herself being helped out of the van.

'Do you need to freshen up?' he asked.

'N-no, thank you.' The moment the words were out she wished she had said yes please. It would have given her time to recover her composure.

'The garages are through the archway and to the right,' he addressed Dave crisply. 'If you'd like to take the luggage straight up to your rooms, my housekeeper will be waiting to show you the way.'

The scowl on Dave's handsome face as he climbed back behind the wheel, told of his annoyance at being ordered about.

That annoyance was tempered to some extent when Robert Carrington added, 'Then perhaps you would care to join us for a pre-dinner drink on the terrace?'

Us... Did that mean there *was* a Mrs Carrington? Eleanor wondered.

A hand cupping her elbow, he led her through the front door and into a panelled hall.

With the feeling that the old house was welcoming her, that she was no stranger here, she stood quite still and looked around, her heart captured and held by the utter rightness of it.

The hall was sparsely furnished with dark old settles and chests, and several suits of armour. There were sconces on the walls, and wrought-iron hoops, the equivalent of the more modern chandelier, hung from the ceiling.

On the left was a huge stone fireplace, now filled with flowers, and on the right, a handsome oak staircase curved up to the first floor.

Sunshine poured through the stained glass windows, carrying with it a wash of colour that made the air glow and shimmer, and spread jewel-bright patterns on the wide, black floorboards.

Spellbound, she heard herself saying in an awestruck whisper, 'It's wonderful! Like living inside a rainbow.'

Then she caught her breath audibly, struck by the conviction that she had said that selfsame thing once before.

'Something wrong?' Robert Carrington enquired.

Confused, thrown by his touch, and by the feeling that she knew this house and it knew her, she pulled free and moved away, stammering, 'N-no... No, I—I just felt as if

I'd been here before. But I haven't, of course, so it must be *déjà vu*.'

But how could *déjà vu* explain the fact that she had known exactly what the house looked like before she had even seen it?

Watching her face, he observed, 'Somehow you don't seem convinced.'

Trying to sound sensible, down-to-earth, she asked, 'What other explanation could there possibly be?'

'You might have seen Greyladies in a magazine.'

'A magazine?'

'The present house was partially built on the foundations of a fourteenth-century priory. Hence the name. Because of its historical interest, a year or two ago when my grandfather was living here, *Our Heritage* did a feature on the place.

'They sent a photographer to take pictures of the gatehouse, the manor itself, the hall, the refectory, the old priory kitchen, and what remains of the ruins of the priory church.'

'That has to be it,' she said, feeling an odd relief that there was some logical explanation. 'Though I don't actually *recall* seeing the magazine, the pictures must have made a big impact.'

'Come and take a look at the refectory and the old kitchen,' he suggested casually. 'See if you recognise them.'

He led the way to the far end of the hall and down a stone corridor, their footsteps echoing hollowly. Opening a door to the left, he told her, 'This is the refectory. As you can probably guess, it's a reconstruction. It was done when the floorboards and panelling were being replaced and the original floor was discovered.'

The refectory was large and severely simple, with rough,

white plaster walls, a beamed ceiling, and a stone-flagged floor worn smooth by the passage of many feet.

There were narrow casement windows, and, ranged against the walls heavy oak sideboards and settles. Above them, at intervals, metal sconces held thick beeswax candles.

A long table ran right down the centre, flanked by high-backed wooden benches. Eleanor could almost see the grey-robed nuns sitting there, silent, ascetic.

The whole thing was austerely beautiful, and totally strange. If she had ever seen a picture of this room, she had absolutely no recollection of it.

'Ring any bells?'

She shook her head. 'None at all, I'm afraid.'

'The old kitchen, which is next door, is mainly notable for its metal-covered well.'

Apart from a couple of deep stone troughs, a massive dresser, and a long, scrubbed table, the kitchen was bare.

One wall was dominated by a huge smoke-blackened inglenook fireplace. On the wide hearth was a trivet, and a roasting spit. An iron rod stretched from side to side, from which dangled several large hooks.

'No?' He raised an eyebrow.

'No.'

Nodding as if satisfied, he asked, 'Now what about that pre-dinner drink?'

Although she was anything but comfortable in his company, the urge to see the rest of the house was strong, and she had been hoping he would offer to take her round.

As though picking up her disappointment, he went on smoothly, 'If you're interested in seeing any more, after dinner I'll give you a guided tour of the house and grounds.'

'Oh, yes please!' Then wishing she hadn't sounded quite

so eager, she added a shade awkwardly, 'That would be nice.'

He grinned fleetingly at her schoolgirl politeness, making her wish she had said nothing, before escorting her back across the hall and into a panelled living-room.

Furnished with a soft leather suite the colour of burnt honey, and antiques that bore the gleaming patina of age, it was dominated by a fireplace she could have stood erect in. Propped against the stone was a long-handled toasting fork.

As she gazed at it, totally absorbed, her face full of dreams, he said, 'Tell me what you're thinking.'

Glancing up, she met his eyes. They held a look that surprised her into admitting, 'It made me think of winter nights... Frost and snow and blizzards, crackling logs and roaring flames...'

'Very poetic,' he commented.

It could have been a jeer, but somehow she didn't think it was.

'You sound as if you enjoy an open fire?' He made it into a question.

'I'm sure I will one day.' Her grey eyes unconsciously wistful, she added, 'All I have at the moment are two small radiators.'

'Radiators do tend to lack aesthetic appeal,' he agreed. 'Though I've no objection to central heating if it's kept hidden. In fact for the greater part of the year it's *necessary* in a house like this.'

Opening the French windows, he ushered her onto a broad, flagged terrace that appeared to run the entire length of the house. It was deserted except for a small tiger-striped tabby cat sleeping in the sun on what seemed to be an old stone mounting-block.

Several comfortable-looking recliners were grouped

around a low table, and he stooped to pull one of them forward for her.

When she was seated, he dropped into a chair alongside her, and went on, 'I'm pleased to say that Josh, my grandfather, regarded Greyladies as a home rather than a showplace.

'So while a good half of the manor has been kept more or less as it was, you'll find the half that's lived in has been brought up to date, and we now have *en suite* bathrooms and all modern amenities.

'We are, however, sadly lacking when it comes to modern technology. Until the new office is set up, the telephone is our only means of communication....'

Only half listening as she covertly studied his face, she found herself thinking that his kind of bone structure would make him good-looking even when he was old.

'Though Josh was a businessman, he preferred to travel backwards and forwards to town most days rather than instal ''computers and suchlike''. And I must admit that when I came to visit him, it was a pleasure to get away from such things...'

Just as he finished speaking, an elderly butler appeared from a small door at the far end of the terrace wheeling a drinks trolley.

'Would you like me to pour, sir?'

'No thanks, Tompkins. You can leave it.'

As the man moved away, Eleanor asked the question that had been lurking at the back of her mind. 'Will Mrs Carrington be joining us?'

Robert Carrington's eyes met hers, a glint of mockery in their green-gold depths, before he answered smoothly, 'I'm afraid not. As a matter of fact, my stepmother lives in Canada.'

Rising to his feet, he queried politely, 'So what is it to be?'

Unused to drinking, she hesitated.

'A dry Martini perhaps?' he suggested.

'Oh, yes, that would be lovely,' she agreed quickly.

Having filled two cocktail glasses and passed one to her, he was just about to resume his seat when the manservant reappeared.

'I'm sorry to disturb you, sir, but you're wanted on the telephone.'

'Who is it, Tompkins?'

'A Mr Marshall, sir. He apologised for calling on a Saturday evening, but said he had some very urgent business to discuss with you.'

'Very well, I'll be right in.' Then to Eleanor, 'If you'll excuse me?'

'Of course.'

He set his glass down on the trolley and vanished through the French windows.

Putting her own untouched drink on the table, Eleanor looked around, what she saw filling her with a quiet pleasure.

From the edge of the terrace sloping green lawns studded with an occasional beech or larch ran down to gardens that formed a semi-circle, providing a perfect setting for the house.

A soft breeze carried the scent of rosemary and thyme and the sweet smell of basil. She had always loved herbs, and she sniffed appreciatively.

Lying on the stone mounting block, paws placed daintily together, tail curled neatly around its thin body, the cat stirred and turned its head to stare at her with unblinking green eyes.

The *contre-jour* lighting picked out the fur round its ears and turned its whiskers to fine gold wires.

Though she had never had a pet of her own, Eleanor

liked animals. 'Hello, Puss,' she said softly. 'What's your name?'

It rose to its feet and stretched, arching its back, before jumping down and padding over to wind sinuously around her ankles.

When she had stroked behind its ears, it jumped onto her knee and lifted its face to hers, rubbing its head against her chin. Then, having paddled for a moment or two with velvet paws, it settled itself in her lap, purring like a small steam engine.

Feeling completely at peace, she closed her eyes and lifted her face to the sun, unconsciously smiling as she thought how lovely it would be to live in a place like this. No wonder Robert Carrington preferred it to London....

'So there you are.' Dave's voice broke into her reverie. 'Where's the lord of the manor?'

Opening her eyes, she answered, 'Robert is indoors. Taking a phone call.'

Dropping into a chair, he went on grudgingly, 'I can't deny he's done us proud. We've got a big bedroom and bathroom each, and our own sitting-room with a tv.'

Eleanor was just sending up a silent prayer of thanks that he was satisfied, when he added, 'But the whole damn place is like a morgue. It gives me the creeps. I don't know how I'm going to stand days at a time in this God-forsaken spot.'

He looked longingly at the trolley. 'I could do with a drink. I suppose it's okay if I help myself.'

'I don't think you should,' she objected.

'It's all right for you, you've got one.'

'You can have it if you like.'

'I was thinking of a real drink, not that stuff,' he said ungraciously.

'Well, I don't suppose he'll be long.'

'It's no use *supposing*.' Dave got up and helped himself to a liberal amount of whisky.

Taking a long swallow, he sat down again and scowled at the cat. 'What the devil are you nursing that mangy flea-ridden thing for?

'Hellfire!' He jumped a mile, spilling some of his drink down his trousers, as a large black and tan Rottweiler padded through the French windows.

'He won't hurt you,' Robert Carrington assured him, following the dog out. 'You'll find he's very docile and good-natured once you've made friends.'

His face the colour of putty, Dave said, 'I'd rather you just kept him well away from me.'

Signalling the dog to stay where he was, their host turned to Eleanor. 'How about you, Miss Smith? Are you afraid of dogs?'

'No. I'd be happy to make friends with him.'

At a nod from his master, the dog approached, sturdy tail waving.

She held out her hand for him to sniff at, before stroking him. 'What's his name?'

'Paddington. Paddy for short.'

Indicating the cat, who had made no attempt to move, he added, 'And that's Jessie. The pair of them are good friends and play together. Occasionally Jessie sends him packing if he gets a bit rough.'

Snuffling and wriggling his thick body in ecstasy at being petted, Paddington leaned his not inconsiderable weight against Eleanor's legs.

Laughing, she said, 'I do believe you're just an old softy.'

'He is indeed. Though he's a rescue dog who was starved and ill treated, it hasn't made him nasty. He still likes people.'

Feeling his tail whack against the chair, she said, 'I've

just realised what's different about him. In all the pictures I've seen of Rottweilers their tails have been docked. It always seemed such a shame.'

'I agree. It's a practice I've never approved of. I gather you like animals?'

'Yes, I do.'

'But you don't keep a pet?'

'No. I've always wanted one. I'd love to have a dog, but in a London flat, and when I'm out so much, it just wouldn't be fair.'

'I couldn't agree more. During the week while I'm in town, Paddington stays here with my housekeeper, Mrs Tompkins, who dotes on him...

'Another spot of Dutch courage, Benson? You seem to have spilt most of that.'

Though resenting the smooth mockery, Dave held out his glass and, having received a generous refill, said a grudging, 'Ta.'

Picking up his own drink, Robert Carrington sat down and asked urbanely, 'How was your journey here? Much traffic?'

'Not bad at all once we were clear of London.'

'I take it you had no trouble finding the place?'

'No,' Dave admitted. 'Though I hadn't expected it to be quite so far off the beaten track.'

'Oh, I wouldn't say it was that far,' the other man objected mildly. 'Little Meldon is barely half a mile away.'

When Dave's expression showed only too clearly what he'd thought of the village, Robert Carrington enquired civilly, 'I hope you're happy with your rooms?'

'They're fine.' Then with a touch of belligerence, 'But I really don't see *why* it's necessary to stay here. It would be perfectly possible to—'

'I've already made it clear that I prefer you to be on the

spot. It makes a lot more sense than wasting time travelling each day.'

'Well, so long as it's *our* time we're wasting and not yours…. Going backwards and forwards has to be a lot better than being stuck here in the middle of nowhere.'

His voice like polished steel, Robert Carrington said quietly, 'If you're not prepared to abide by our agreement, please feel free to return my cheque and leave at once.'

Dave blanched. 'I didn't mean I wasn't prepared to abide by it…. Of course I'll stay and do the job….'

'In that case, as you hate the county so much, the sooner you can get the work done, the better.

'Before we go into dinner I'll show you the room I'm hoping to use as an office, and give you a brief idea of what I want in it. That way you can start planning immediately.'

At that moment, to Eleanor's great relief, the butler appeared and, having cleared his throat, announced, 'Dinner is ready when you are, sir.'

'Thank you, Tompkins. We'll be in shortly.'

Paddington, who had been sitting like a ton weight on Eleanor's feet, stirred himself, and making little grunting noises followed the black-coated manservant back inside.

'It's his suppertime,' Robert Carrington explained. 'Mrs Tompkins always feeds him in the kitchen.'

When Dave had tossed back the rest of his whisky, and Eleanor had lifted the cat from her lap and set it gently on its feet, their host led the way through the French windows and into the hall.

Indicating a door set in the panelling, he suggested wryly, 'As you've been nursing my mangy, flea-ridden cat, you might like to wash your hands before we eat?'

'Thank you.' Wishing fervently that Dave would be a great deal more careful with what he said, she fled into the well-appointed cloakroom.

When she emerged, the two men were returning across the hall. Dave's dark, handsome face wore a sullen expression, while Robert Carrington looked coldly displeased.

'You won't forget what I said about lighting?' The older man's voice held a note of warning.

'No, I won't forget,' Dave said shortly. 'But I thought you were paying me to give you advice—'

'I'm paying you to give me what I want.'

Oh, Lord, she thought, discord already.

Without another word their host led the way to an elegant and beautifully furnished dining-room, where a table that would have seated twenty or more, was set for three with monogrammed linen and fine crystal. A centrepiece of fresh roses filled the air with fragrance.

Having pulled out Eleanor's chair with grave courtesy, he waved the younger man to a seat opposite, before taking his own place at the head of the table.

Dave, looking totally out of his depth, overwhelmed by the formality of his surroundings, fidgeted uncomfortably.

She felt a quick sympathy for him.

Good manners requiring it, Robert Carrington put aside his displeasure and essayed a few general remarks.

Eleanor did her best to respond, but Dave's gloom acted like a wet blanket, and each attempt at polite conversation fizzled out.

The first course was served and eaten in a silence broken only by the ticking of a long-case clock, and the scrape of Dave's soup spoon.

By the time the second course arrived, she could tell by the tight, closed look on his face and the growing clumsiness of his movements, that he was getting thoroughly rattled.

In the event it was a pity they weren't eating in the servants' hall, she thought. They would no doubt have been a great deal happier there.

Sipping her wine, she tried to think of something to say to ease the tension, but her mind, stubbornly refusing to cooperate, remained a total blank.

A moment later, reaching for the salt, Dave knocked his fork off his plate. With a muttered oath he stooped to pick it up, and was just about to wipe it on his table napkin, when Robert Carrington signalled the hovering manservant to replace it.

With a show of bravado she could only admire, Dave remarked, 'I'm afraid we don't really belong in here. We were expecting to eat with the servants in the servants' hall.'

Robert Carrington smiled slightly. 'I hope you're not disappointed, but we no longer have a servants' hall as such.

'It's called progress. At one time there was a large enough staff to need a servants' hall, and my grandfather always used to dress for dinner.

'These days, however, things are a great deal more informal. I only dress for dinner on special occasions, and the live-in staff have been reduced to three. Jackson, who occupies the gatehouse, and Tompkins and his wife who have a self-contained flat above the kitchens.'

'That doesn't seem a lot of staff for a place this size.' Eleanor made a valiant effort to keep the conversation going.

Reaching to refill her glass, he told her, 'Though there's still enough land to require several estate workers and a manager to run it, the manor itself doesn't need a lot of staff. For one thing, I'm in town all week...'

'Of course.'

'And as I mentioned earlier, only half the house is lived in, with a total of five guest bedrooms, and they're not often in use.

'Mrs Tompkins has daily help come in from the village, and Jackson does the same with regard to the gardens...'

For the remainder of the meal they talked about the house and the estate, while Dave looked bored and uncomfortable.

The moment the cheese plates had been cleared, he pushed back his chair and rose to his feet with undisguised eagerness.

'Now I know more or less what you want, I'll go and make a start on the office layout. As you say, the sooner we get the job done the better.'

Eleanor was about to excuse herself and go with him, when Robert Carrington said, 'You won't need Miss Smith, I take it? I was intending to show her around the rest of the house.'

Dave shook his head. 'It's just a case of deciding what goes where, and what we need to order first. A couple of hours hard work should do it.'

'Sure you won't have coffee before you go?'

'No thanks.' He eyed the cut-glass decanter on the sideboard. 'Though I wouldn't mind taking a brandy with me.'

'Do help yourself.'

Ignoring the dryness of the invitation, Dave splashed a goodly amount of brandy into a goblet and took himself off without another word, leaving Eleanor with mixed emotions.

She wanted to see the house, but she didn't want to be left alone with Robert Carrington. He was altogether too formidable and unsettling.

'As it's such a nice evening, perhaps you'd like to have coffee on the terrace?' he suggested.

Not sorry to leave the dignified formality of the dining-room, she agreed, 'Oh, yes, that would be lovely.'

He rose to pull back her chair just as the butler appeared with a large silver tray. 'We'll have it on the terrace, please, Tompkins.'

'Certainly, sir.'

Outside the evening was mild and golden, the air full of birdsong and the sweet scent of newly mown grass. It was a benediction after the wet and miserably cold spring.

Settled in one of the recliners, sipping the rich and fragrant coffee, Eleanor felt her earlier mood of quiet pleasure flowing back. This time, however, beneath the smooth and peaceful surface swirled a current of *awareness*.

She felt a pull of excitement, a kind of dangerous intoxication that she knew had less to do with the amount she had drunk, than the presence of the man by her side.

When she was engaged to be married to the man she loved, how could she be so disturbed, so affected by a man she didn't even like?

Glancing up unwarily, she found his eyes were fixed on her, a gleam in their tawny depths that suggested he knew exactly what she was thinking.

Making a great effort to appear cool and collected, she looked away without undue haste. Unless she was willing to let him have a good laugh at her expense, she would *have* to keep cool and find some way to hide that unwanted and inconvenient attraction.

When their coffee was finished and she had refused a second cup, he asked, 'About ready for the grand tour?'

Summoning all her composure, she nodded and rose to her feet.

'What would you like to see first?'

As he stood beside her she was very conscious of his height, his sheer *maleness*, and her voice sounded squeaky in her own ears, as she answered, 'I really don't mind.'

Leading the way inside, he said, 'Then suppose we start with the lived-in bit, and leave the fun bit until later?'

'Sounds fine,' she agreed lightly.

CHAPTER FOUR

THE "lived-in bit", with its black oak floors and white walls, was serenely beautiful, and Eleanor basked in the feeling that the old house welcomed her with open arms, like a mother.

But all the time she was aware that, as though trying to gauge her reactions, Robert Carrington had scarcely taken his eyes off her face. The knowledge made her tongue-tied and awkward with him.

When she said nothing, as though determined to make her voice her feelings, he remarked, 'I get the impression you like Greyladies?'

'I love it.' Then wondering if her response had sounded too fulsome, she wished she had been more restrained.

But he smiled at her, as though her enthusiasm had pleased him.

They had almost completed their tour of that part of the manor, when Robert Carrington opened a door into a long, bare room quite unlike the rest of the house.

'This was my grandfather's studio,' he explained.

Clearly a much later addition, it was a single storey, with skylights. The north-facing wall had windows for most of its length, and along the other walls were wooden workbenches and slatted shelves on which canvases were stacked. At the far end, an empty easel stood forlornly on the tiled floor.

'Though Josh was no Van Gogh, he painted for most of his adult life, in fact until a couple of years before he died. I believe he got a lot of pleasure from it.'

'What did he paint?' she asked.

'Landscapes, still life, portraits. Some of his portraits were pretty good. This one, for instance. Though he never hung it.'

He lifted down a package from the nearest shelf and unwrapped it to display the portrait of a girl with a heart-shaped face, widely spaced grey eyes, and dark hair falling almost to her waist.

Her head tilted a little to one side, she was smiling brilliantly.

'Though the actual technique leaves a lot to be desired, he's somehow managed to capture the feeling of youth and joy, don't you think?'

Eleanor could only agree. The picture fairly radiated happiness.

She was staring at it enthralled, when he asked, 'Does anything else strike you about it?'

'It could almost be me,' she said slowly. 'The eyes are alike, but my hair has never been that long, and the clothes must date from the 1950s...'

And this joyous young girl had no scar.

Swallowing hard, she queried, 'Have you any idea who she is?'

'Her name was Jenny Linton.'

The name meant nothing to her.

While he rewrapped the picture and replaced it carefully on the shelf, he observed dispassionately, 'Though your eyes are the same almond shape, the colour isn't right. If Josh got it exact, her eyes are blue-grey, while yours are a true grey with a darker rim of charcoal and no hint of blue.'

She was surprised and oddly disconcerted that he knew the colour of her eyes so precisely. Beyond the fact that they were grey, Dave probably wouldn't have a clue.

As they made their way back to the hall, he went on, 'Another one of his portraits that I always thought was particularly good, hangs in the library, which is on the second floor.'

As Eleanor began to climb the imposing oak staircase, her hand recognising the smooth feel of the banister and her feet finding the wooden treads familiar, she was seized by the strangest conviction that it wasn't the first time she had climbed these stairs.

'*Déjà vu* again?' Robert Carrington suggested.

Flustered by the fact that he seemed to know exactly what she was thinking and feeling, she said a shade defensively, 'I don't really know how else to describe it.'

'A feeling of being accepted? A kind of natural affinity with the place?' he suggested.

'Yes… That's it exactly.'

Her face lighting up, she smiled at him, and he had to restrain a sudden impulse to take her in his arms and kiss her.

'It's as if the house likes me too,' she went on. Then added uncertainly, 'Though I don't see how it possibly can…'

'Why not? A house this old is more than just stone and timber. You could almost say that as well as atmosphere and ghosts, it has a soul.'

'Does it have ghosts?' she asked, wide-eyed.

'I've no doubt there are plenty, in the sense of memories and feelings that linger on. But the only *real* ghost we can lay claim to, if you'll forgive the contradiction in terms, is our own Grey Lady.

'But I'll tell you all about her later, and show you where she's said to walk.'

Reaching the top of the stairs they crossed the wide landing and turned right down a corridor.

'Along here is the library and the suite of rooms I occupy now,' he told her. 'They used to be Grandfather's.

'When Josh suffered his first stroke and became partially

paralysed, rather then stay downstairs, or have a chair-lift put in, he decided to live up here.

'He always said he preferred the view from the upper floor, and he had the room adjoining his bedroom converted into a private sitting-room-cum-study, so he could be next door to his beloved library.'

The library was a handsome room, with black leather furniture, a wine-coloured carpet, matching velvet curtains at its mullioned windows, and a little pulpit-staircase. Three of its walls were book lined, the fourth panelled in dark oak.

Above the stone fireplace hung the portrait of a woman with a straight nose, a generous mouth, and widely spaced eyes beneath winged brows. Her gaze was steady and direct, and her smile had a singular sweetness, like that of a child.

Her soft dark hair, liberally threaded with silver, was taken up into a coil, and there were fine lines around her mouth and eyes.

Profoundly moved, though she couldn't have said why, Eleanor queried, 'Surely that's the same woman?'

'Yes, that's Jenny Linton. Of course it was painted when she was a great deal older.'

'Was she a member of the family?'

'No. Apparently she was a lifelong friend of Grandfather's.'

'Did you ever meet her?'

He shook his head. 'No, never. I rather wish I had. Ready to go on?'

The portrait fascinated her and she would have liked to have lingered, but she said politely, 'Yes, of course,' and allowed herself to be ushered out of the library.

As they headed back towards the stairs, indicating a trio of closed doors, he told her, 'Those are the rooms that Mrs

Tompkins prepared for you and Benson. There's a central sitting-room with a bedroom on either side....

'Having no great opinion of people's behaviour these days, and being somewhat strait-laced, she was pleased that I'd specified separate bedrooms.... Though of course it doesn't necessarily follow,' he added cryptically, and smiled slightly as a tinge of colour rose in his companion's cheeks.

By tacit consent they walked straight past the doors. The strident sound of a television gameshow followed them, suggesting that Dave had found something other than work to occupy him.

Eleanor felt irritated that he wasn't doing what he'd promised. But then *she* wasn't working, so who was she to criticise?

'Are you a television fan?' Robert Carrington queried.

She shook her head. 'I don't even own one.' Then almost apologetically, 'I'm afraid in this day and age that must make me seem a bit odd.'

'Not at all. I find it most refreshing. So what do you do for enjoyment?'

'I like reading and listening to music.'

'What do you read?'

'Almost anything that comes to hand,' she admitted. 'I have catholic tastes.'

'What about music?'

'Classical, middle-of-the-road, a little pop, some jazz.'

'Quite wide-ranging,' he approved. 'Do you like opera?'

'Yes.'

'Ever get to see any?'

She shook her head.

'Why is that?'

'I don't really...' About to admit she didn't have the money, she changed it to, 'I don't really have the time.'

'Is there a composer you particularly like?'

'Puccini.'

'I might have guessed. Any other?'

'Wagner.'

'Now I admit to being surprised. A lot of people find him heavy.'

'Do you?'

'No. Wagner happens to be one of my favourites.'

Steering her down a corridor to the left, he changed the subject. 'This, I think you'll find, is the fun bit of the house.'

The 'fun bit' with its many twists and turns, its small rooms that led straight into each other, its cubby-holes and ramifications, delighted her.

She loved the way two steps went up and three went down, the passages that seemed to lead nowhere, and the narrow, twisting staircases with their galleries and landings.

They were descending one of the staircases when she paused part way down to look through a tiny window. 'I can see the ruins you mentioned,' she told him excitedly. 'I hadn't realised they were so close.'

'This part of the house is actually built on the foundations of the old priory, which was destroyed by fire in the early fifteen hundreds.'

Bracing his hands on the stone wall each side of her head, effectively trapping her there, he bent to peer over her shoulder. 'If you look past the big beech tree you can just glimpse the remains of the outer wall.'

He wasn't touching her, but he was so close she could feel the warmth of his breath on her nape. If he turned his head a little, his lips would brush the side of her neck...

Her nerve snapping suddenly, she swung round.

He straightened, but though his face was only inches from hers, he made no effort to move back.

As, frozen into immobility, she stared at him, his eyes

on the silver thread of scar-tissue, he asked, 'How did you get your scar?'

All her colour draining away to leave her face paper-white, she said hoarsely, 'I don't like to talk about it.'

'Why does it bother you so much?'

'Because it's ugly.'

With the tip of one finger he traced the fine, jagged line, as he had done at their first meeting, before saying seriously, 'I don't think it's ugly.'

Dave certainly did.

As though reading the thought, he said, 'And I can't believe Benson does.'

'You mean if he did, he wouldn't want to marry me?'

'I don't mean anything of the kind. If he doesn't want to marry you I'm sure it has nothing to do with the scar.'

'He *does* want to marry me.'

Unless he'd changed his mind.

Walking right into her head with stunning ease, Robert Carrington asked, 'What will you do if he doesn't? How will you fight for him?'

She had never really learned how to fight, only to propitiate, provide, enable... And suppose that wasn't enough?

All at once she was terribly afraid.

Watching her face, and seeing that fear, he drew back a little and said, 'But we're wasting a perfectly lovely evening. Let's forget about Benson and go and take a closer look at the ruins.... Tell you what, instead of going the short route, we'll walk through the old walled garden.'

Somehow she found her voice, and pointed out, 'It's starting to get dark.'

'Don't you think that's the time gardens have a special magic...? And later, there's always the chance you might see our Grey Lady. Have you ever seen a ghost?'

'No.' Gathering herself, she added drily, 'And I'm not terribly sure I want to.'

'Don't worry,' he said cheerfully, 'I promise I'll hold your hand.'

Rather than comforting her, the assurance panicked her. She fought back. 'Promise *not* to, and I might consider it.'

He laughed, and she was amazed to see how it softened his hard face and made his green-gold eyes dance. 'Very well,' he agreed. 'Though if we see anything really scary, *you* might have to hold *my* hand.'

Aware that it would have been a lot more sensible to have insisted on joining Dave, and hardly knowing why she hadn't, Eleanor allowed herself to be led down the rest of the stairs and through a side door.

Outside, the evening air was fresh and sweet. A balmy breeze stirred the trailing creeper and carried the scent of honeysuckle and sun-sated flowers.

Though twilight was spreading its gauzy blue veils, the sky was still brushed in the west with turquoise and pink and fine trails of golden cloud like mermaid's hair.

Walking side by side, without touching, they crossed a smooth sweep of green lawn and went under an arch of clipped yew into the Elizabethan walled garden.

Eleanor caught her breath. In the fading light, the old pink bricks that made up the walls seemed to glow softly, and the climbing roses had an almost unearthly radiance.

As though voices might spoil the magic, neither spoke, but strolled in silence along crazy-paving paths bordered with herbs and flowers, until they reached a small door that led through to the ruins of the old church.

Most of the foundations were visible, grass growing through the stones, and one huge archway and part of the south transept were still standing.

During the time they had been walking, the dusk had stealthily deepened, and now the sky was a clear dark blue pricked with stars. Above the archway a full moon was rising, bathing the ruins in an eerie silver light.

Drawing her down onto a stone bench that still held the memory of the sun's warmth, Robert Carrington told her softly, 'That's what my grandfather used to call a Wolf Moon… And it's just the right sort of night for our ghost to walk.'

'I would have thought any self-respecting ghost would have chosen a dark, stormy night.'

'Not the Grey Lady.'

'You said you'd tell me about her.'

'Her name was Theresa. Apparently she was the youngest daughter of a nobleman who, growing increasingly impatient with her wild ways, banished her to the priory.

'The tale goes that, a most reluctant novice, she used to steal out at night to meet her lover.

'After a while, discovering she was pregnant, and desperate to escape from the priory, she begged him to bring a spare horse the following night, so they could run away together.

'She waited for him that moonlit night, but he never came. When dawn approached, knowing she couldn't go back, she stole the horse belonging to a visiting church dignitary and set off to find her lover. But she had barely gone half a mile, when the beast stumbled and threw her, and she broke her neck.

'According to some old records, she was buried just where she died. Whether that's true or not, the track became known as Grave Lane.

'Since then there have been countless stories that on moonlit nights she appears near the priory, and waits for her lover to come for her.'

After a long silence, Eleanor asked seriously, 'Do you think there *are* such things as ghosts?'

'Only, as I said earlier, in the sense of memories and feelings that linger on and create a certain mood. A kind of atmosphere that some people seem able to feel more strongly than others. Can you pick up any aura of unhappiness or tragedy here?'

She shook her head. 'Though I suppose tragic things must have happened at some time, all I can feel is a kind of peace and…' Reminding herself that she was only here to do a job, and unwilling to sound pushy, she let the words tail off.

'An affinity with the place?'

'Yes.'

'And that means a lot to you?'

A little uncomfortably, she asked, 'What makes you say that?'

'When I suggested it earlier, you smiled at me as if I'd said something lovely, something wonderful and special, just to please you. It made me want to take you in my arms and kiss you.'

Watching her freeze, he added, 'But bearing in mind you have a fiancé you apparently love, I resisted the temptation.'

Despite all her efforts, her voice shook a little, as she said, 'I'm glad about that.'

'Are you really? That's a pity, because I find I can't restrain the urge any longer.'

Unable to say a word, she sat quite still, her eyes on his face, her breathing becoming rapid and shallow.

In the moonlight, she saw him smile. 'You should just see your face! If the Grey Lady had come gliding up you couldn't look more petrified. Do I take it you aren't too keen on being kissed?'

She said thickly, 'As far as I'm concerned a ghost would be preferable.'

'How can you possibly judge? On your own admission you've never seen a ghost. And though you've no doubt been kissed, you've never been kissed by me. Until now, that is…'

Without holding her in any way, he leaned forward and brushed his lips against hers. It was the briefest of kisses, a thistledown touch.

'There, that wasn't so bad, was it?' he asked teasingly.

Her pounding heart made speech impossible.

Sliding a warm hand round the back of her neck to cup her nape, he bent his head and covered her mouth with his own.

Though his kiss was still light and undemanding, the sheer physical force of him struck her like a blow in the solar plexus, leaving her limp, and driving all the breath from her body.

She felt a rush of pure sexual desire for him and when, his mouth moving against hers, he deepened the kiss, the world ceased to exist.

There was nothing but this man and what he was making her feel, and by the time he reluctantly called a halt and released her, she was lost and mindless.

For a few seconds, her eyes closed, she sat motionless, afraid to move, feeling as though she was poised on the edge of some precipice with nothing to hold on to.

When she finally opened eyes still bemused and dazed with desire, it was to find he was studying her face in the moonlight. With a gesture that was curiously tender, he brushed a strand of dark hair away from her cheek and tucked it behind her ear.

'I think we'd better take the long way back,' he commented drily. 'If Benson sees you looking like that, you'll be lucky if he doesn't batter your bedroom door down.'

Remembering Dave's apparent lack of interest, she said, 'I'll be lucky if he does.' Then realising too late how very revealing her words had been, she bit her lip.

His mouth tightening, Robert Carrington remarked grimly, 'In my opinion, the man's a fool.'

'I shouldn't have said that,' she muttered uncomfortably. 'It's really nothing to do with you.'

'Yes, it is,' he disagreed.

'How can it be?'

'I think you could well use your imagination on that one.'

Wishing she hadn't asked, she shivered.

Noticing the involuntary movement, he queried, 'Is that shiver caused by excitement or cold?'

'Cold,' she lied.

'Perhaps you'd like me to forget that you're engaged, and warm you up?'

'No, I wouldn't!'

She felt agitated and dismayed that she was letting Dave down so badly, and angry that Robert Carrington apparently regarded her as an easy conquest.

But of course it was her own fault. In spite of loving Dave, and wearing his ring on her finger, she had *acted* like an easy conquest. And, in so doing, she had almost certainly jeopardised their chances of successfully completing the job they had come to the manor to do.

If she didn't set the record straight right now, things would never work, and her position here would be untenable.

She was searching for the right words, when her companion rose, and taking both her hands pulled her to her feet. 'Then we'd better be starting back. The air's getting appreciably cooler.'

As they turned to retrace their steps, he tucked her hand through his arm.

Pulling it free, she began jerkily, 'I really don't think…' Letting that go, she tried again. 'As things are, I don't think you should…we should…be acting in this way.'

'Because you're engaged?'

'Yes. But not only that…'

'You don't think I should be making a pass at one of my house guests?'

'What you do with your *guests* is your own business. But I don't regard myself as a guest.'

'Why not, when I'm happy to treat you as one? Would you still have a problem if we'd met socially and I'd invited you here?'

'But we would never have met socially. We come from quite different worlds.'

'I'm not so sure about that. In any case, it doesn't bother me.'

'Well it bothers me.'

'Inverted snobbery?'

'Call it what you like,' she said recklessly. Then regretting her outburst, she went on more carefully, 'But it doesn't alter the fact that I'm not here as a guest, Mr Carrington, I'm here to work.'

He winced. 'Don't you think, now we've kissed each other, we could dispense with the formality. You could call me Robert, and I could call you Eleanor.'

Sidetracked, she said, 'No one calls me Eleanor. It always gets shortened Ella.'

'I'd much prefer to call you Eleanor. It's a beautiful name.'

She had never cared much for the name Eleanor, but somehow it sounded like poetry when he said it.

Pulling herself together, she tried to get back to the point. 'I'd prefer you to call me Miss Smith,' she informed him coolly. 'As I said, I'm here to work, and I'd like our relationship to be kept on a...' Having almost blued it, she hesitated, feeling the need to be diplomatic.

'A distant, business-like footing?' he hazarded. 'Exactly.' She breathed a sigh of relief. If he was willing to forget what had just happened and stick to that, things might still work out.

Her hopes took a knock, when he shook his head. 'It's a little late for distant and business-like, don't you think? I'd say our relationship has moved on to up close and personal.'

'That's what I've been trying to say... In the circumstances it *shouldn't* have done any such thing.'

'So you'd like me to back off?'

'Yes, I would.' Then with difficulty, 'I'm sorry I behaved so foolishly.'

'Perhaps we should blame it all on the moonlight?' he suggested.

For the rest of the way back they walked a good foot apart and in silence, each seemingly busy with their thoughts.

Having retrieved the situation and done what she had hoped to do, Eleanor should have been reasonably settled and satisfied, relieved that she had called a halt in time.

Instead, she felt an aching sense of loss. A longing for what might have been.

But what on earth was she thinking of? It would have been utter madness to have jeopardised her future with Dave for a man who only wanted a brief fling; a man who would no doubt have felt nothing but contempt for her afterwards.

Or pity.

And pity would be almost worse than contempt.

So now she had succeeded in distancing herself, she must stay close to Dave and refuse to be tempted. Keep out of Robert Carrington's way as much as possible....

They were nearing the house when Paddington came ambling to meet them, making little puffing noises of excitement, tail wagging a greeting.

'Well, hello...' Eleanor stooped to pat him.

'You've made a conquest there,' Robert Carrington remarked. 'Though he's gentle and good-natured, there are very few people he actually makes a fuss of.'

Eleanor felt obscurely pleased.

As, the dog walking between them, they made their way to the terrace now lit by lanterns, and in through the French windows, he asked, 'Would you like a milky drink, or maybe a nightcap before you go to bed?'

'No, thank you.'

'You're sure there's nothing I can do for you to help you sleep?' he suggested wickedly.

'Quite sure.' She looked anywhere but at him.

'Then allow me to see you up.'

'Please don't bother,' she said hastily.

'It's no bother,' he assured her, with smooth politeness. 'I'm going to bed myself.'

While they climbed the stairs, the dog's claws clicking on the old oak treads, he explained, 'Some urgent business has cropped up. I've an eight o'clock breakfast appointment in town.'

'On a Sunday?'

'I'm afraid so.'

'Oh,' she said a little blankly. 'Does that mean you'll be in town all week?'

'I'm not sure. Certainly for a few days.'

She should be happy he was going, she told herself. It made everything so much easier. But instead of feeling happy, she felt a hollow disappointment.

His eyes were on her face, and afraid he would pick up that disappointment, she explained hastily, 'I was asking because of the work to be done.'

'Of course,' he said gravely. 'Though I had intended to be here at least for the initial stages, I don't want my absence to make any difference to the project going ahead. Before I leave tomorrow I'll get everything down on paper that you and Benson will need to know, and give you my phone number so you can contact me if any snags crop up....'

When they reached the rooms he had pointed out as being hers and Dave's, the television was still going full belt.

Making no comment apart from a raised eyebrow, he went on, 'While I'm away, Mrs Tompkins will take care of you and provide anything you may need. 'What you choose to do with regard to meals etc., is of course up to you, but as far as the staff are concerned you have guest status. Benson will no doubt appreciate that, even if you don't.'

Remembering how Dave had helped himself to whisky, she cringed inwardly.

'If you would like to borrow any books from the library, please feel free, and there's a music centre in the living-room with a selection of tapes and CDs that I think you'll like.'

'Thank you.'

With a hint of dry self-mockery that told her he was enjoying playing the courteous host, he told her, 'You're more than welcome.'

Then formally, 'Well, goodnight, Miss Smith. I'll see you sometime towards the end of next week.'

'Goodnight,' she answered, and was annoyed with herself because instead of the words sounding cool and distant, as she had intended, they had sounded almost forlorn.

A gleam of mockery in those green-gold eyes, he added, 'I'm sure you'll be able to sleep a good deal easier now you know you won't have to think up ways to avoid me.'

Watching her colour deepen, he smiled a little before trailing a finger down her hot cheek. A moment later he was walking away, Paddington at his heels.

Gathering herself, she turned and opened the door into an attractive living-room, where a blast of sound hit her.

Dave was sprawled on the settee in front of the television, a lock of dark hair falling over his forehead making him look like a moody Elvis.

Eyes glued to the late film he was watching, he said, 'I was beginning to wonder where the devil you'd got to. Surely it doesn't take all evening to look around a house?'

'We went to have a look at the r-ruins of the old priory church…'

Memory filled her with guilt, making her stammer a little and deepening the colour in her cheeks, but engrossed in his film, which looked violent and unpleasant, Dave merely grunted.

Raising her voice so she could be heard over the gunfight taking place, she told him, 'I'm a bit tired, so I think I'll go straight to bed. Which is my room?'

She held her breath wondering if, now they were living under the same roof, he would suggest sleeping together, and suddenly finding herself far from happy with the idea.

But without taking his eyes off the screen, he pointed to the door on the right. 'There was nothing to choose, so I've put your case in there.'

'Thank you…. Goodnight.' She stooped to kiss his cheek.

'Night, night.' He made no effort to kiss her back.

Her room was large, with white walls, dark oak floor-boards, and a beautiful oriental rug in softly glowing colours.

The furniture, which was antique and well-polished, included a handsome bow-fronted chest of drawers, and a large double bed.

Which meant they *could* have slept together.

But once again the idea was anything but welcome, and she felt surprised and puzzled by her own reluctance.

Her case was on a low chest and, opening it, she found her toilet bag and night things, and went through to a modern, nicely appointed bathroom.

While she showered and cleaned her teeth, she made an effort to rationalise her feelings.

In the end it proved to be easy. She hadn't been able to contemplate starting the more intimate side of their life together, while her head was still full of thoughts of Robert Carrington, and her mouth was still remembering his kiss.

There! she thought triumphantly, as she brushed her long dark hair, now that was sorted out to her satisfaction, she could relax and stop worrying about it. Put Robert Carrington out of her mind.

Climbing into the high, comfortable bed, she attempted to do just that.

But if she had fondly imagined that rationalising how she felt would make everything right, she soon discovered her mistake.

While her mind stubbornly refused to banish his image, and her flesh still cried out for him, she tossed and turned restlessly.

But it was nothing to do with him *personally*, she assured herself firmly. Like any young, healthy woman, she had needs that, because of Dave's concerns, were unfulfilled. Needs Robert Carrington had managed to arouse.

If she and Dave *had* been sleeping together, it would never have happened.

Frustration had made her vulnerable.

She felt somewhat comforted.

Tomorrow, when they got back into their normal working routine, and without Robert Carrington's disturbing presence, she would return to her usual calm, untroubled self.

But tonight she was unable to feel either calm or untroubled. In spite of all her efforts, a frame by frame replay of the evening's events kept her awake until a rosy dawn was breaking.

CHAPTER FIVE

SHE had failed to draw the curtains the previous night, and sunshine slanting in through the leaded panes and lying warm on her closed lids, awoke her.

A glance at her watch showed it had turned eight-thirty. Robert Carrington would be safely in London by now, and having breakfast.

Far from cheering her, the realisation brought a strange feeling of emptiness that she did her best to ignore.

One of the latticed windows had been left partly open and, jumping out of bed, she pushed it wider and leaned out.

The morning air was full of sunshine and birdsong. Dew sparkled like diamonds on the grass, and in one of the shallow stone troughs a thrush was taking his morning bath.

Normally her heart would have rejoiced at such a lovely scene, but today gladness was mingled with another more poignant emotion, a sense of loss that she didn't want to either identify or admit to.

When she had showered and dressed, finding no sign of Dave in their living-room or his bedroom, she made her way downstairs.

As she reached the hall, a neatly dressed, matronly figure appeared and bade her a polite and smiling, 'Good morning, miss.'

'Good morning.' Eleanor returned the smile. 'You must be Mrs Tompkins.'

'That I am, miss. I was just coming up to see if you would prefer to have breakfast in your room?'

Eleanor shook her head. 'Thank you, but I'm quite happy to have it downstairs.'

Looking relieved, the housekeeper said, 'I set today's breakfast in the morning-room. Mr Benson's already there, if you'd like to join him? Do you know where it is?'

'Yes, thank you. Mr Carrington showed me around last night.'

Just saying his name gave Eleanor a funny feeling.

When she reached the sun-filled, oak-panelled morning-room, Dave was seated at the table halfway through a substantial breakfast.

Glancing up from the Sunday paper propped in front of him, he said grumpily, 'I presume you knew his lordship wouldn't be here?'

'Yes, he said he had business in London.'

'You might have told me last night. I could have had a lie-in.'

'I'm sorry, I didn't think.'

Indicating a couple of sheets of paper tossed carelessly on the white cloth, he said, 'I've just been wading through the instructions he's left. There's a great load of them, and the swine didn't forget to mention that he expects us to *stay here* as agreed.'

Resentfully, he went on, 'I daresay he's instructed the servants to spy on us and make sure we do. Any idea how long he'll be away?'

'A few days, he said.'

Dave grunted. 'It can't be long enough as far as I'm concerned. Well as soon as you've finished eating, we might as well make a start.'

His handsome face impatient, he added, 'The faster we get the job done, the better. This whole damned place gives me the willies.'

Over the next two or three days, using the latest catalogues, they began to select precisely what they would need to order. Then, having measured the available office space, they worked out where to site the various pieces of furniture and equipment to provide maximum efficiency.

At least Eleanor did.

Having said several times that the sooner they got the job done, the better, Dave showed little sign of actually getting down to it. He slept late, so it was mid-morning before he made a start and seeming moody and on edge, unable to concentrate, stopped work early and went to sit in front of the television in their room.

He refused to either set foot in the dining-room, or eat on the terrace, saying he'd rather have dinner in their own suite. But, concerned for the elderly butler, Eleanor had dug her toes in and vetoed any suggestion of trays being carried up and down the stairs.

Annoyed at being overruled, he demanded peevishly, 'So what do you expect me to do, starve?'

Ignoring his childish behaviour, she merely queried, 'Would you like me to ask Mrs Tompkins if we can have dinner served in the morning-room, as well as breakfast and lunch?'

'Yeah, I suppose that'll do.'

Though the food and wine at dinner were invariably excellent, and Tompkins waited on them with grave efficiency, Dave usually managed to find something to complain loudly about.

Putting his ill-humour down to his hatred of the country, and sympathising to some extent, Eleanor had tried to cheer him up.

To no avail.

While invariably smiling and friendly towards Eleanor, Mrs Tompkins served Dave breakfast and lunch in silence, obeying his curt orders with tight-lipped politeness.

After one such lunchtime incident, when the housekeeper

had gone, Eleanor protested uneasily, 'I don't think you should talk to her like that.'

He looked genuinely surprised, 'Why not? Servants are used to obeying orders.'

'Mrs Tompkins is the *housekeeper*.'

'So what's a housekeeper but a servant?'

'Well, at least try to be a little more polite. Robert Carrington always is.'

'Well, of course *his lordship* can do no wrong,' Dave sneered. 'And it seems I can do no right...'

Eleanor felt sorry she'd made the comparison. Robert Carrington had been born with every advantage, while Dave had had virtually nothing.

With a muttered oath, he pushed back his chair. 'I'm damn well fed up! Nothing but criticism. Today I'm being rude to the servants. Last night I was drinking too much.'

'Well, you were,' she said quietly. 'You had almost half a decanter of brandy.'

'What do you expect me to do when the booze is free, drink lemonade?'

'No, of course I don't... I didn't mean to criticise.... It's just that—'

Without waiting to hear any more, he turned on his heel and stormed out.

Eleanor sighed. She had always hated any discord between them. But this job, which they had needed so badly, and which *should* have been a godsend, had always had a downside.

In some ways it was a pity they had ever taken it, but what else could they have done? And if they hadn't accepted the job, she would never have seen Greyladies. Never have felt this fierce love for the old place—for love was what it was—never felt this sense of *belonging*.

Though of course she *didn't* belong here and never

would. When the job was done, she would have to turn her back and walk away for ever.

A coil of sadness wound itself around her heart and tightened. But at least she would have memories, she reminded herself. Memories not only of the house but of its owner....

Though her feelings for him, strong as they were, were much less easy to define. All she knew was, he had thrown her completely off balance, got under her skin and disturbed her body and soul.

Since he had gone, she had tried hard not to think about him, but whenever her mind wasn't fixed firmly on work, images of his attractive, hard-boned face had crept in.... The straight nose, the thickly lashed tawny eyes, the mouth that was both austere and passionate....

She kept recalling the sound of his voice, the touch of his hand, his ironic smile, the way he'd made her feel...

Sighing, she made an effort to pull herself together. Instead of sitting here thinking about Robert Carrington she should be trying to heal the rift between herself and Dave.

No matter what her heart said, her head told her that the sooner they could get the work done and leave here, the better. Dave hated the place, while she loved it too much.

Squaring her shoulders, she rose and went in search of her fiancé. She found him where she had expected to find him, slumped in front of the television.

He looked so misunderstood and downcast that her heart smote her. Sinking to her knees by his chair, she covered his hand with hers. 'I'm sorry, love... I know this job isn't to your taste—'

'You're damn right, it isn't.'

'But there's no point in us falling out, is there?'

'Suppose not,' he admitted grudgingly. 'It's just that never moving out of the house is getting on my nerves.'

'Then why don't you go out? There's...' About to say

'some nice country around here' she changed it to, 'A nice pub in the village—'

'You must be joking!'

'It wouldn't do any harm to try it. You can always have a drink there and—'

'I can have a drink *here*, if you'd stop nagging.'

Though feeling uncomfortable about the amount of his host's liquor he was consuming, she promised, 'Very well, I won't say another word.'

He grunted. 'But that's only part of it. I miss London, being able to go out with the boys and have a game of snooker.'

She forbore to point out that they had only been here a few days, and said, 'I suppose you must do.'

Then more positively, 'But most of the preliminary work has already been done. If we finish it this afternoon, surely by tomorrow we can start to order the equipment?'

Perking up, he said, 'You're right! God knows I could do with a trip up to town, and as it's *necessary*, even his lordship won't be able to argue. Tell you what, if you can ask for our dinner to be served early tonight, I'll set off straight after the meal and spend the night in town. That way I'll be able to visit the suppliers first thing in the morning and arrange for immediate delivery of the essentials.'

For the rest of the afternoon, buoyed up by the prospect of getting away, he was a great deal more cheerful.

It had been a hot day and, just before dinner, feeling rather sticky and grubby, Eleanor slipped upstairs to take a quick shower and change into a light, button-through skirt and silky, olive-green sleeveless top.

When she hurried down, her hair loose around her shoulders, Dave was waiting, but for once he made no complaint, and the meal passed without a cross word being spoken.

The moment his coffee-cup was empty he collected the

case he had already packed and left standing in the hall, and tossed it into the waiting van.

Following him out into the sunshine, Eleanor asked, 'When will you be back?'

'Tomorrow sometime,' he said vaguely, and, giving her a quick peck on the cheek, drove away without a backward glance.

The heatwave having held, when Eleanor wasn't working, or taking a stroll through the gardens, she had found herself a book and sat outside. Unwilling to use the main terrace, she had chosen to sit in a corner of the side terrace—usually with Paddington by her side, or Jessie in her lap—where there were several loungers and a small table.

Now she hesitated between her usual spot which, facing west, would still be a suntrap, or taking a stroll in the sunken garden that, screened by a handsome row of Spanish chestnuts, would lie largely in the shade.

Though she loved the walled garden, she had assiduously avoided walking there, knowing it would evoke too many memories of its owner.

Deciding on the terrace, she went upstairs to fetch her book. So far she had lacked the courage to go into the living-room and play Robert Carrington's CDs, but she had eagerly availed herself of his permission to use the library.

It was one of her favourite rooms. It had a warmth, an atmosphere of tranquility, that seemed to draw and enfold her. Several times she had lingered there, looking at the books, gazing at the portrait above the fireplace, or just sitting savouring the sense of peace it gave her.

Returning with a beautifully illustrated edition of *The Ingoldsby Legends*, she went down the back stairs and out through a small side door. The warm evening air was sweetly scented, the sun thick and golden as melted honey.

She was barely seated in one of the cushioned loungers, when Paddington came ambling up, and with a contented grunt settled himself at her feet. A moment later, as if by magic, Jessie appeared and, having been fussed, made herself comfortable in Eleanor's lap, purring contently.

Finding the low sun was blinding her, and unwilling to disturb the animals by getting up and moving her chair, Eleanor put the book carefully on the nearby table and closed her eyes.

Enjoying the warmth on her face and bare arms she was half asleep, encased in a soft cocoon of seductive idleness quite foreign to her nature, when something brushed her lips.

She opened bemused eyes. So close that the image was blurred, she saw long-lashed tawny eyes set deep under level, well-marked brows, thick, wheat-coloured hair, and a long, mobile mouth.

Robert Carrington, his hands resting on the arms of her chair, was bending over her, his lean, tanned face only inches from hers.

He murmured something she didn't catch and, moving even closer, so she was forced to shut her eyes again, he kissed her once more.

This time, though still light and not invasive, no one could have called that kiss merely friendly. It teased and coaxed and titillated and went on and on.

When he finally drew back, roused from her sleep, Jessie jumped down and, tail in the air, stalked away, affronted.

For what seemed an age, Eleanor was speechless, then her breathing quick and shallow, she managed in a rush, 'I thought we'd agreed on *distant* and *businesslike*, Mr Carrington.'

'Sorry,' he said mendaciously. 'I just couldn't help myself. You are quite irresistible.'

Dave never seemed to find her irresistible, and with her hair tumbled anyhow, and her face shiny and innocent of make-up, she was only too surprised that a man like Robert Carrington did.

Dressed in a light-weight business suit, he looked powerfully attractive, and she found it hard to take her eyes off him as, shrugging out of his jacket, he tossed it onto a spare chair and tugged at his tie to loosen it.

Then dropping into a lounger alongside her own, he rolled up his shirt sleeves to expose tanned, muscular arms lightly sprinkled with golden hair, before going on, 'However if you want *businesslike* I'll try. How is the job going?'

'Very well…' Annoyed to find she still sounded shaken, she paused to gather herself, then continued, 'All the preliminary planning is done, and we're ready to move on to the next stage.'

At that moment the door opened and the butler appeared with a tray on which was a tall graceful jug and two glasses.

'Ah, here's the Pimms I asked for…. Thanks, Tompkins, I'll pour.' Then to Eleanor, 'You'll find Tompkins makes the best Pimms you've ever tasted.'

Looking gratified, Tompkins inclined his head slightly, and took himself off.

Having filled two glasses and handed her one, Robert Carrington waited until she had taken a sip of the cool, fruity drink before enquiring, 'So what do you think?'

'Mmm…it's lovely.'

'But not the best Pimms you've ever tasted?'

'It's the *only* Pimms I've ever tasted,' she admitted.

Setting his glass down on the table, he crossed his ankles, rested his elbows on the arms of the chair, and leaned back.

All his movements held a kind of lithe, masculine grace, and she found it a pleasure to watch him. She was gazing at him surreptitiously from beneath long lashes, when it occurred to her that she had better explain Dave's absence, before he got round to asking.

'Dave's gone up to London.' She tried to sound casual.

'Has he now? I thought he'd go tomorrow.'

'It made sense to go tonight,' she explained hastily. 'He'll be able to visit the suppliers first thing in the morning and arrange for immediate delivery of the furniture and equipment we need to make a start.'

'When you put it like that, it does sound very sensible,' Robert Carrington agreed evenly.

Then with a change of subject that totally threw her, 'Tell me about yourself.'

'W-what?' she stammered.

'Well to say I've kissed you on no less than two separate occasions, I know very little about you.'

'There's nothing *to* know,' she said uncomfortably. 'My life's been quite dull and ordinary.'

'Then tell me about *you*. How you feel about your day-to-day living... What things you find easy to cope with. What your hang-ups are.'

'You'd only be bored.'

'Try me. I might be absolutely fascinated.'

'I very much doubt it.'

'Go on,' he teased. 'You show me your psyche and I'll show you mine.'

While she desperately cast about for some way to change the subject, he reached over and took her hand. 'Well if you find that too difficult at the moment, we'll start with practical things. Tell me how long you've known Benson, and where you met him.'

Flustered by his touch, she said distractedly, 'I've known him since we were quite young. We were at Sunnyside together.' As he waited quietly, she explained, 'Sunnyside is a children's home.'

'Why was he there?'

Having expected him to ask, "Why were *you* there?" she breathed a sigh of relief. It was a great deal easier to talk about Dave, than herself.

Withdrawing her hand, she answered levelly, 'When he was just a toddler he was found abandoned. For a time he was fostered, then he went for adoption. After a while his adoptive parents split up and he found himself back in care. They tried fostering again, but by this time he was classed as disturbed, and it didn't work…'

His voice calm, interested, Robert Carrington said, 'So you got to know each other?'

'Dave was a year or two older, so we didn't really know each other all that well.' Awkwardly, she added, 'But I missed him when he left.'

Nodding, as if he understood what had been left unspoken, he asked, 'Did you keep in touch?'

'No. We met again quite by chance. I was working at a supermarket checkout and we recognised each other. We both had plans for the future, and—'

'What were *your* plans?'

Remembering how contemptuous Dave had been of those plans, she hesitated. But if Robert Carrington proved to be equally contemptuous, what did it matter?

'I was hoping to run a second-hand bookshop, or maybe a tearoom,' she admitted. 'But perhaps you think that kind of thing is only for old maids?'

'Why should I think that?' When she didn't answer, he went on, 'Though I imagine both would have been hard work, I'm sure you could have made a success of either. But you changed your mind?'

'Dave said he could do with a partner.'

'And that was when he suggested you take a business course?'

Surprised that he'd remembered, she said, 'Yes.'

'What was he doing at the time?'

'He was still at college, with another year to go.'

'Full time?'

'Yes.'

'Did he have a grant?'

She shook her head. 'He didn't want to mortgage his future.'

'It couldn't have been easy to support himself?'

'He managed,' she said briefly.

'With your help?'

Her refusal to answer was answer enough.

'When we talked before,' he pursued, 'you mentioned keeping your *hotel* job, but you've just told me you worked in a supermarket?'

'I worked in a hotel during the day and the supermarket when I had weekends or evenings free.'

'You must have worked all hours. For how long?'

'About four years.'

He muttered something that sounded like, 'Dear God.' Then, almost savagely, he demanded, 'Didn't you take any time off?'

She shook her head. 'I needed the money.'

'Of course,' he said slowly. 'Anyone needs money to start a business. Tell me, who put up the money to start Smith and Benson?'

Lifting her chin, she objected, 'I don't see that's anything to do with you.'

She heard the breath hiss through his teeth, before he remarked bitterly, 'A man like Benson *would* get there on the back of a woman.'

Jumping to her feet, she burst out furiously, 'How dare you sneer at Dave! Though he had none of your advantages, he's twice the man you are! At least he had enough gumption to want, and to work for, a better future.

'You were born with a silver spoon in your mouth. People like you haven't the faintest idea what it's like to be grindingly poor. To be unwanted and abandoned. To be brought up in a children's home with no family and no one to love you or care what happens to you...'

Choked, blinded by angry tears, she turned to run. But without appearing to move, Robert Carrington was ahead of her, blocking her way, so that she blundered into his arms and felt them close around her.

Half sobbing, she tried to struggle free.

He refused to let her go. Holding her gently but firmly, he kept her exactly where he wanted her until, admitting defeat, she stood quite still, head down, making no further attempt to escape.

'That's better.' Lifting her chin, he used his handkerchief to wipe away the tears, before saying softly, 'Look at me, Eleanor.'

She obeyed.

Meeting her hurt, accusing eyes, he said, 'Forgive me. I didn't mean to upset you.'

Then, taking her hand, his fingers threaded through hers, he urged, 'Come for a walk in the garden. You need to dissipate some of that adrenalin.'

As he led her across the lawn towards the arch of clipped yew, Paddington at their heels, she said jerkily, 'You had no right to stand in judgement on Dave. You made him sound like a sponger, and he's nothing of the kind.'

'While I can't alter my opinion of Benson, perhaps I should, for the moment at least, have kept that opinion to myself.'

'You've misjudged him completely,' she insisted, determinedly freeing her hand. 'Your attack on him wasn't justified.'

As they began to stroll down a path bordered with clumps of pinks and sweet-smelling lavender, he asked, 'What about your attack on me? Admittedly I've never been grindingly poor, nor have I been abandoned, but I do know what it's like to be unloved and unwanted. At least by my parents.'

Startled, she asked, 'Your parents didn't want you?'

'No. From being a very young child I was always aware of that, without really knowing why. It wasn't until I was much older that my grandfather told me.

'It seems my mother, who was a social butterfly without an ounce of maternal feeling, had never wanted a family, and it was my father who, needing a son and heir, talked her into having a child.

'They were an oddly matched pair. She was barely five feet tall, beautiful and vibrant and always full of life and fun. My father, who was quiet and serious, well over six feet and, like most Carrington males, far from handsome, absolutely adored her.

'The birth was a difficult one, and I was handed straight over to a nanny without my mother even holding me.

'Though she recovered physically, she was never the same again. She went into what's now called postnatal depression, and seemed unable to throw it off.

'She refused to go out of the house or meet people, and for long periods at a time, as though focused inside herself, she simply sat and stared into space.

'Depression is a terrible thing.

'My father, apparently blaming himself for wanting a child, turned against me to such an extent that he couldn't bear the sight of me, and I was cared for by a succession of nannies, until I was old enough to be sent away to boarding school.

'During the school holidays I was pushed off on school friends or passed from relative to relative like an unwanted parcel, until Josh found out. After that I went to stay with him. He gave me the only affection I'd ever known.

'When I was eleven, after all those years of being only half-alive, my mother died from an overdose of sleeping pills. I don't know to this day whether it really *was* an accident, though it was treated as one.'

Reaching a bench that was still in the sun, by tacit consent they sat down, while Paddington, panting a little in the heat, flopped at their feet.

'A year later,' Robert Carrington went on, 'my father married again. Miriam, who came from Canada, was big and cheerful and bouncy. The widow of a rancher, she had two young sons and a daughter, and for a little while I cherished hopes of being part of a happy family.

'But while Miriam would have gladly accepted me, my father couldn't, and when they went to live in Canada so he could run her late husband's ranch, I was left behind. That was when my grandfather explained things to me.'

He had been speaking coolly, dispassionately, with no hint of self-pity, yet Eleanor could sense a kind of inner desolation, and her heart went out to him.

'I'm sorry.'

Impulsively, she put a hand on his arm. It was the first time she had voluntarily touched him, and the shock of the warm, sinewy flesh and hair-roughened skin beneath her palm, made her remove it instantly.

'There's no need to waste your pity on me,' he told her almost curtly. 'As you pointed out, I'm one of the lucky ones. I was born with a silver spoon in my mouth.'

'I'm sorry,' she said again. 'I do know that material things can't make up for lack of love. Or being alone.'

'I've rarely been alone in the physical sense. In fact,' he added with a wry grin, 'I had a great time when I discovered girls. But I imagine you mean spiritually alone?'

She nodded.

'Yes,' he said quietly, 'there is no way to describe such emptiness. But being brought up in a children's home, you must know a lot more about that than I do....'

Realising that he *understood*, some of the remembered pain loosened its grip.

'At least I had a grandfather who was fond of me.'

'You must have been very sad when he died.'

'Yes, I was. I still miss him. But that's enough of doom and gloom. Compared to an awful lot of people's lives, mine has been a bed of roses....'

Uncoiling his length in one fluid movement, he took both her hands and pulled her to her feet. 'And I'm hoping it will soon get even better.'

With no attempt to elaborate on that, he suggested, 'Come on, I'll show you the lake.'

'You've got a lake?'

'Though it's always referred to as "the lake" I suppose it's more of a pond really... You can give me your verdict when you see it.'

All at once the atmosphere between them was easy and relaxed. Knowing about his childhood had given her a better understanding, altering their relationship, moving it forward, so that she felt far more comfortable with him.

In a companionable silence, they left the walled garden behind them and walked across rolling green parkland studded with clumps of trees.

The sun was just slipping reluctantly below the horizon. Its last rays bathed everything in a golden light, turning the grass into myriad shining spears and making the sturdy oaks cast blue-black, elongated shadows.

While Paddington ambled off to investigate the nearest stand of trees, they walked a little way until a smallish body of water came into view.

Serene and enchanted, as though caught in a spell, its mirror-smooth surface reflected the blues and pinks, the lilac and green and gold of the late-evening sky. Around its edges stretched beds of pale, feathery reeds, and in the centre was a small, humped-backed island with a single pine tree.

'What do you think?' he queried, cocking an eyebrow at her.

'Oh, definitely a lake.'

'How can you tell?'

'No ducks.'

As she spoke, a dabble of ducks left the cover of the reeds and, silent and stealthy as an Indian war party, paddled away across the water leaving V-shaped ripples in their wake.

They both burst out laughing simultaneously.

As their laughter died away, his eyes fixed on her face, he said huskily, 'You're completely enchanting when you laugh.'

A moment later, without knowing quite how she got there, Eleanor found herself in his arms, being kissed with a skill and thoroughness that took her breath away and made her pulses race.

CHAPTER SIX

HER legs refusing to support her, she melted against him, while the muscular warmth of his body, and his lips moving against hers, drove every sane thought from her mind.

She was opening her mouth helplessly in response to his urging, when a sharp whack on her ankle brought her to her senses.

Pulling herself free, she looked dazedly at Paddington who was prancing around them, a long stick clenched in his jaws.

If Robert Carrington was annoyed by the interruption, he gave no sign of it, merely saying ruefully, 'Saved by the bell. Or in this case, the dog. I can see where he caught you. Does it hurt?'

'No, not really.'

And in any case it was worth it, to be saved from her own weakness. If it hadn't been for Paddington she would have been lost, only too ready to let Robert Carrington keep on kissing her until—

Snapping off the thought, she turned and began to retrace her steps, unconsciously hurrying, angry that she had made a fool of herself yet again.

Catching her up, he walked by her side without further comment, stooping from time to time to pick up the stick and throw it for the dog.

What on earth had got into her? she wondered desperately, as they left the park and headed back through the garden. It was as if she could no longer govern either her feelings or her responses.

All her adult life her wants and needs had been leashed,

kept in check, subjugated by the necessity to work for the future. *She had been in control.*

So why wasn't she now?

Once again she tried to rationalise things, to tell herself that her instinctive response had been due simply to sexual attraction and an underlying frustration.

But it wasn't as if she was particularly ardent or hot-blooded. Even her longing for Dave had been as much mental as physical.

She had yearned for the warmth and comfort of his presence, someone to *be* there, to say goodnight and good morning to, someone to have breakfast with, rather than merely share a bed.

Wanting a homely, comfortable relationship based as much on companionship as on sex, she had never once thought of herself as a passionate woman.

So why was it that when Robert Carrington laid so much as a finger on her, she went into meltdown?

'We may as well go in this way.'

His voice broke into her thoughts, and she found herself blushing as though he could read them.

Leaving Paddington enthusiastically, but futilely, chasing after a large furry moth, they went in through the French windows.

As they left the living-room to cross the hall, the light from the nearest chandelier fell on her face. Proving he never missed a thing, he remarked teasingly, 'All this hurrying has made you look positively flushed.'

'It's a warm night,' she muttered, on the defensive.

Ignoring that, he queried, 'Tell me, why *did* you walk so fast?'

When, hastening up the stairs, she failed to answer, he suggested, 'I thought you might have been trying to run away from temptation?'

'Not at all.' She made an attempt to sound haughty. 'I just wanted to go to bed.'

'My sentiments exactly. So is it to be your bed or mine?'

Stopping outside her door, and suddenly finding she was breathless, she told him, 'My own bed, and alone!'

He sighed. 'I could quote Andrew Marvell.'

Her blush deepening, she said crisply, 'I'd rather you didn't.'

'Okay,' he agreed accommodatingly. 'I promise not to mention anything about long-preserved virginity if you promise not to go without giving me at least a goodnight kiss.'

Suddenly panic-stricken, she took a step backwards and felt for the door handle. It moved under her hand and the door opened a few inches.

'There's no need to look quite so scared,' he objected mildly. 'I said a kiss, and that's what I meant. I've no intention of following you in there and forcing myself on you.'

The assurance only quickened her pulse rate and made her feel hollow inside. *If he did follow her in he wouldn't need to force himself on her.*

'In fact you'll have to ask me.'

With a flash of spirit, she announced, 'Well, in that case, I'm safe enough.'

'Safe enough to risk a kiss?'

'I don't happen to want to kiss you.'

'Liar,' he said equably.

Putting a light hand on her nape, he drew her towards him.

Like someone under a spell, she stared at him, unable to take her eyes off his mouth as it moved closer.

His face blurred, out of focus, and a second later his lips were touching hers, quite gently, but the effect was the same as throwing a lighted match into a pool of petrol.

Her whole being ignited, and once again pride, self-control, scruples, were all gone, lost in the excitement of his kiss. Without conscious volition, her lips parted beneath his, and her arms wound around his neck.

Only some tiny part of her mind struggled to hang on to a shred of sanity, to warn her that she was engaged to be married, and that this man only wanted a bit of fun at her expense.

In response to that warning she made a valiant effort to back away. But while her legs obeyed her, her arms, reluctant to free themselves, were still around his neck, and her mouth was still clinging to his, so that as the door swung wider, he moved into the room with her.

Apparently regarding her actions as an invitation, he closed the door with his foot. Then, setting her back to the panels, he continued to kiss her while his free hand travelled slowly over her body, learning the exact shape and size of her.

When it moved to cup the soft curve of her breast and his thumb brushed lightly across the sensitive nipple, her stomach clenched and shudders of delight started to run through her.

As he continued to tease, every nerve in her body tightened in response and her blood began to flow through her veins sluggish and hot as lava.

Unable to fight against her own needs she was being drawn steadily and relentlessly into a state of blind desire from which there could be no possible return, when he lifted his head and asked huskily, 'Quite sure you want this?'

His question broke the spell, and while her body screamed *yes*! her mind battled for control and won. Tearing herself away, she cried, 'No! No I don't! All I really want is to be left alone.'

'That wasn't my impression.' His face was calm, but he

was breathing fast, and she realised that though he was hiding it a great deal better, he was equally aroused.

'I—I was thinking of Dave,' she stammered.

'Benson's not here, and you gave every sign of wanting me.'

Recalling how she'd clung to him, she took a deep shuddering breath, and said, 'I'm sorry... I didn't mean to lead you on.... Please go.... Though Dave's not here, he's still my fiancé. I don't want to let him down.'

'What do you imagine your fiancé will be doing now?'

'He won't be with another woman, if that's what you're implying.'

'Are you quite certain about that?'

'Quite certain, so don't bother trying to malign him.'

'I wasn't trying to malign him. I was merely pointing out that he's—'

'I don't want you to point anything out. I just want you to go...' *Before she weakened.*

When he made no move, she added desperately, 'You said you had no intention of forcing yourself on me....'

'I also said you'd have to *ask*, and I meant both. Goodnight, Eleanor.'

He waited for her response.

She swallowed hard. 'Goodnight, Mr—'

A finger to her lips, he stopped her, and his voice wry, remarked, 'The way you insist on calling me *mister* makes me feel like a character from one of Jane Austen's novels. Couldn't you manage Robert just this once?'

Only too anxious for him to go, she said, 'Very well... *Robert.*'

'Not all that painful, was it?' He touched his mouth to hers, and a second later the door had closed quietly behind him.

His kiss, though the briefest of salutes, had been purposeful, proprietary, as if, in spite of her protestations, he'd kissed her *by right*, as if she *belonged* to him.

Somehow the notion of belonging to him affected her in the strangest way, leaving her weak-limbed, and trembling.

Taking a few steps, she sank limply onto the couch. If only she knew why he was behaving in this way. What his intentions really were.

But there were so many uncertainties, so many unanswered questions about the whole situation.

With other, well-established firms to choose from, why had he come to them in the first place? And finding how small and relatively inexperienced they were, why had he employed them?

Had he only given them the job and insisted on them staying at Greyladies so he could seduce her? A kind of *droit de seigneur*?

Oh, don't be a fool, she scolded herself crossly, of course he hadn't. Whatever his reason for insisting they stay here—if he had a reason apart from the stated one—it wouldn't be that. Why should he go to so much trouble over someone like her when he could probably have almost any woman he fancied?

Yet there was *something*… Something she could neither pin down nor understand. He had never treated her as just someone hired to do a job of work….

But perhaps it was all her fault? Maybe it was *her* reaction to *him* that had caused the problem in the first place? Had he picked up her helpless fascination and, intrigued by it, decided to see how far she would go in spite of being engaged?

He wouldn't care about wrecking her engagement, or about hurting Dave. The two had been at daggers drawn since the word go….

So why had he given them the job…?

Her thoughts having come full circle, she made a determined effort to put the whole thing out of her mind. But with her emotions still in a state of turmoil, it was a little while before she was able to pull herself together enough to go through to her bathroom.

When she had showered, cleaned her teeth, and brushed her hair, she donned a fine-cotton nightie before climbing into bed.

Feeling too agitated to settle, she reached for the book she had been reading, only to find it wasn't there. So much had happened, that it was a moment or two before she recalled taking it outside and leaving it on the patio table.

Thank the Lord she'd remembered in time, she thought fervently, as she jumped out of bed and pulled on her towelling robe. If the book had been left out all night, the dew would have ruined it.

Having knotted the belt of her robe she wriggled her feet into her slippers and, dark silky hair tumbling around her shoulders, crept quietly across the landing and down the back stairs. The moon shone so brightly through the leaded windows that she needed no other light.

The side door was locked and securely bolted top and bottom. But the big, ornate key turned easily in the lock, and both the bolts slid back with only a faint rattle.

Leaving the door slightly ajar, she crossed the moon-silvered terrace, only to find the book was no longer on the table. Whoever had locked up had obviously noticed it and taken it in.

The sky was a clear dark blue and pricked with stars, the air balmy and full of the perfume of night-scented stocks. A faint breeze stirred the leaves on the beech tree, and somewhere close at hand an owl hooted with melancholy mirth.

It was such a magical night that she was tempted to linger, but common sense reminded her that tomorrow Dave would be back and there would be work to do. She should at least *try* to get some rest.

Reluctantly she went back inside and, having locked and bolted the door behind her, made her way upstairs.

Still she felt restless, so instead of going straight back to her room, she headed for the library in search of a book to read.

As she moved on slippered feet down the moonlit corridor, high in one corner and almost hidden by a wooden beam, the little red eye of some electronic device blinked at her.

Wary of the fact that Robert Carrington's suite of rooms was close by, she opened the library door and closed it quietly behind her, before switching on the light.

As always, she stood for a moment or two looking at the portrait that hung above the hearth. Then, smiling at the face that was now as familiar to her as an old friend's, she moved to select a book.

She had almost decided on *The Forsyte Saga* when, though there hadn't been a sound, a prickle of *awareness*, a feeling that she wasn't alone, made her glance round.

Her heart stood still. A small door in the panelling—a door that she had never really noticed before—was open, and leaning against the jamb, watching her silently between half closed lids, was Robert Carrington.

He was barefoot and wearing a short, navy silk dressing gown that showed his straight legs were tanned and muscular and lightly furred with soft gold fuzz. His hair was damp and slightly ruffled, as if he was fresh from the shower.

Though only too aware of the sexual promise implicit in those brilliant, heavy-lidded eyes, and that tough male body, and recognising the danger, she couldn't seem to will her gaze away from him.

A tawny hawk of a man, with a bony nose and a beautiful

mouth, he looked self-assured and very virile, at once ter-
rifying and alluring.

His well-shaped head was tilted a little to one side, his
expression intent, almost abstracted, as if he was mentally
making love to her.

Just the thought filled her with a sizzling heat.

Lifting a questioning brow, he asked, 'Unable to sleep
for some reason?'

'I—I couldn't find the book I was reading,' she stammered, 'so I decided to choose another one.'

'And have you? Chosen another one, I mean.'

'Yes.' Taking *The Forsyte Saga* from the shelf she
hugged it to her. 'I'm sorry if I disturbed you. I was trying
to be quiet.'

'I'm sure you succeeded. But the night-security system,
as well as warning when any outside door or downstairs
window is opened, picks up movement and pinpoints any
unwelcome intruder's position. Though of course you
couldn't be called an intruder... Or *unwelcome*...'

A gleam in his eye, he went on silkily, 'I was just about
to make myself some coffee, so perhaps you'd like to stay
and share it?'

'No!' Hearing the panic in her own voice, she made an
effort to speak more moderately, 'No, I wouldn't, thank
you.'

'Well, if you don't fancy the idea of decaffeinated coffee
laced with brandy, I'm sure I can think of *something* that
will help you sleep.'

Her voice shaking, betraying her awareness of the double
meaning in his words, she managed, 'Thank you, but no,'
while her brain warned how imperative it was that she
should escape without delay.

Her eyes fixed on him as though he was some dangerous
animal, she began to back away, babbling, 'There'll be lots

to do tomorrow, so I'd better go and try to get some sleep....'

Her words ended in a gasp as she misjudged the direction and, the edge of the settee catching her behind the knees, sat down with a bump.

'Decided to stay after all?' Without having seemed to move, he was by her side.

'You know perfectly well I haven't.'

Laughing at her flustered, indignant tone, he offered, 'Then let me give you a hand up.'

Taking her free hand he pulled her to her feet, then lifting her hand to his lips dropped a kiss into the palm. All sensation left her body and moved to the hand that seemed to hold the imprint of his lips like a brand.

Caught and held by the same kind of magnetic force that holds an iron filing to a lodestone, she stood as though turned into a statue, clutching the book tightly to her chest while she gazed up at him with wide grey eyes.

They were so close she could smell the tangy freshness of his shower gel and feel the warmth of his body. She fancied she could hear both their heartbeats. They even seemed to be breathing in unison.

He smiled a little and, as though claiming his own, bent his head and kissed her mouth. A gentle, yet searching kiss, it almost immediately evoked a tearing need that shook her to her very soul.

When her lips parted beneath his he deepened the kiss, exploring her mouth delicately, experimentally, kissing her with a kind of leashed, yet hungry passion that inflamed her even further.

Suddenly there was no yesterday, no tomorrow, only the here and now. All she could feel was an intense pleasure, and a kind of surging excitement that swept her along. Passion rolled in, enveloping her like a fog bank, cutting her off from the outside world.

The Forsyte Saga thudded to the floor unnoticed.

When, continuing to kiss her, he unfastened the belt of her robe, she freed her arms and allowed it to fall to the floor, finding the feel of his hard, muscular body through their thin layers of clothing, mind-blowing.

Totally lost now, she made not the slightest protest when he slid the straps of her nightdress from her shoulders and, easing it down past her waist, sent it to puddle at her feet.

Then, as his mouth continued to ravish hers, he slid his fingers into her long, silky hair to cradle the back of her head, while his free hand made a tactile exploration of the soft curves he had exposed.

Inviting his touch, her nipples grew firm, and when he rolled one gently between his finger and thumb she began to make soft mewling sounds deep in her throat.

Those little whimpers had a powerful effect on him, and drawing back abruptly he said, 'If you don't want me to make love to you, you'd better tell me so now, while I can still stop.'

Eyes closed, she swayed, and he gripped her upper arms to steady her. 'Well?'

Beyond speech, she simply leaned against him, her face pressed against the warm column of his throat.

Holding her a little away, he ordered, 'Look at me, Eleanor.'

When she opened grey eyes so clouded with passion that they appeared almost black, he asked, 'Do you want me to make love to you?'

She nodded.

'Not good enough.' His face was cruel, implacable. 'I want to hear you ask me.'

'Please...'

'Are you asking?'

'Yes... I'm asking,' she said thickly, and with a brief

flash of icy cold lucidity wondered if, now he had won, he would reject her and walk away.

But with a little murmur of triumph, he swept her into his arms and carried her through the door in the panelling, shouldering it shut behind them.

His sitting-room was at once simple and spacious, with panelled walls and black, polished floorboards on which were spread some beautiful old rugs, their subtle blend of colours delighting the eye.

The bedroom, almost as large, was dominated by a lovely old four-poster with a woven blue and gold canopy. The patchwork counterpane, its once vivid squares now comfortably faded, had been turned back.

Despite the soft, balmy air coming in through the open window, there was a faint lingering scent of pot-pourri.

Carrying her over to the bed, he laid her gently on it, and stood looking down at her, studying her small, beautifully shaped breasts, her curving hips and long, slender legs.

She would have been embarrassed by her own nakedness if the flame in his eyes hadn't told her clearly that he liked what he saw.

Shrugging off his dressing gown, he tossed it over the nearest chair.

Just the sight of him affected her more than she would ever have believed possible. Tall and lean and clean-limbed, he had wide shoulders and narrow hips and a clear skin that bore the sheen of health. He was every woman's dream, with a masculine beauty that made her heart throw itself against her ribs and her throat go so dry, she found it difficult to breathe.

Or was it that the air was thick with the smoke of burning bridges? Whatever, having come this far, there was no power on earth that could have made her turn back.

As he stretched out on the bed beside her, putting her

arms round his neck, she pulled his face down to her own and they kissed with a mutual urgency and need.

While they kissed he explored her body, running a hand from her slender waist down over her flat stomach to the soft nest of dark curls and the silken skin of her inner thighs.

When he touched her and she gasped, instinctively lifting herself, he instantly withdrew his hand.

Kissing away her little murmur of disappointment, he said softly, 'Don't worry, my love, I intend to give you every pleasure, but I don't want to spoil things.'

He nuzzled his face against her breasts, and she could feel his mouth warm and smiling against her skin as he added, 'We'll take this *very* slowly.'

She roused in the very early morning to the dawn chorus, a feeling that the world was a wonderful place, and the comforting knowledge that she wasn't alone.

Though he wasn't touching her she could feel his presence at her back as palpably as if he had been. She was aware of every bone and muscle in his body, his heartbeat, strong and steady, the whisper of his breath on her hair.

The warmth of him spread through her like the sun's rays, bestowing a blessing. She ached to look at him. But she didn't want to wake him. Moving with the greatest care, she turned slowly to face him.

He was lying on his side, his thick, gold-tipped lashes spread like fans on his hard cheeks, his mouth, controlled yet passionate, relaxed in sleep.

A golden stubble adorned his upper lip and jaw. She had never seen him unshaven before, and she thought how virile and sexy it made him look.

The night had been a very warm one and the bedclothes had been pushed back, showing a long sprawl of tanned and sinewy arms and legs sprinkled with a light fuzz of hair.

Oh, but he was *gorgeous*, and his lovemaking had been... But she could find no words to express the pleasure and delight he had given her.

Not just once, but several times, joyous and passionate, in control of his body and hers, he had caught her up and flown her to the heavens until she had seen shooting stars and heard the angels singing and discovered rapture.

She sighed, and at the same instant saw that he was awake and watching her, brilliant green-gold eyes narrowed against the dawning day.

Reaching out, he drew her towards him, snuggling her close. 'What was the sigh for? Were you disappointed? If you were, I could always try again.' Her cheek resting comfortably at the juncture where chest and shoulder meet, she said, 'I wasn't disappointed.' Shyly, she added, 'It was heavenly.'

His hand caressing her breast, he said, 'Well in that case perhaps I should make sure I haven't lost my touch.'

He hadn't.

When she drifted to the surface again, sunshine was streaming in. Only half awake, still enshrouded by a golden fog of slumber and bliss, she reached out a hand and found she was alone in the big four-poster.

Relaxed and languid, sated with pleasure and the abandonment of self that sleep brings, it was a little while before the mist started to clear and her world began gradually to come into focus.

When it did, suddenly the picture was all wrong.

Oh, dear God, what had she done?

Shocked into awareness, she had just pushed herself into a sitting position when the sound of a light rap made her freeze.

How could she face Mrs Tompkins? Resisting the temptation to cower under the bedclothes like a child, she pulled them up to her chin and braced herself for the accusing eyes.

But it was Robert Carrington who came in from the adjoining room, carrying a round tray balanced on one hand. He looked clear-eyed and healthy, and a great deal too attractive.

Obviously freshly showered and shaved, he was smartly dressed in light trousers and a dark silk shirt open at the neck.

While she was naked and dishevelled.

She felt her face flame.

What must he think of her?

No doubt he thought her easy. At least as far as *he* was concerned... But surely he must know that she wasn't promiscuous?

'Good morning.' He smiled at her. 'I thought you might be ready for some coffee, so I made this with my own fair hands.'

Struck dumb, she failed to answer.

Putting the tray on the bedside table, he stooped to touch his lips to hers as if it was the most natural thing in the world, before enquiring, 'Just milk?'

'Please.' In her own ears her voice sounded thin and weak as if it came from a long way away.

He filled a cup and handed it to her, then pouring another for himself, sat down on the side of the bed.

In any other circumstances that sense of sharing and companionship would have delighted her. As it was, she felt agitated and ashamed, uncomfortable in the extreme.

As she gulped the coffee which was hot and strong, just how she liked it, she tried to think of something to say.

But what could she say? There was nothing that would excuse her behaviour. She had acted like a wanton, and they both knew it.

Biting her lip, she heard the long-case clock in the library began to chime the hour…nine…ten…eleven…twelve…

No, surely it couldn't be!

She put her cup down on the saucer with a rattle and looked at her watch. Twelve o'clock! Dave would almost certainly be back by now, and here she was, still lying in another man's bed.

Galvanised into action, she pushed back the clothes and made an effort to get out the far side.

His hand on her arm prevented her.

Keeping her where she was with infuriating ease, he asked, 'Something wrong?'

Her face, drained of all colour now, she demanded urgently, 'Is Dave back yet?'

'No, he isn't.' Then levelly, 'I take it you're starting to regret what happened?'

'Of course I regret it,' she cried.

He sighed. 'I wondered how long it would be before you'd start giving yourself hell.'

But scarcely hearing, she almost wailed, 'How could I have treated Dave like that?'

'Don't you think he might be to blame?'

'How on earth could *he* be to blame?'

Then, realising what he was driving at, she flushed. Robert Carrington was not only experienced but needle-sharp when it came to putting two and two together. Finding she was still a virgin, he had reached pretty much the same conclusion that she herself had come to.

Frustration had made her vulnerable.

But that didn't mean she could forgive herself, or that Dave would forgive her.

'I'm happy to say you're a very passionate woman,' he went on. 'So much so, that it puzzles me how you managed to hold out against temptation until you met Benson.'

Without thinking, she spoke the exact truth. 'I'd never really been tempted.'

Then realising too late how very revealing that was, she stammered, 'F-for one thing I never had *time* for boy-friends. I was always too busy working.'

'Well at least *some* good came of all that hard work. Virginity is a rare gift these days.'

Only she had given it to the wrong man.

As though reading her thoughts, his smile caustic, he added, 'A gift I enjoyed receiving, even if I *was* only a stand-in for Benson.'

Feeling as if she had been kicked in the solar plexus, she hit back. 'I hadn't thought of you as a man who would enjoy deflowering virgins.'

Mockingly, he agreed, 'I'm not, unless I have their full-est cooperation.'

'Which in my case, you did,' she admitted bitterly.

Then her voice harsh with self-recrimination, 'I must have been mad! I don't know how I'm going to break it to Dave.'

'Then you intend to tell him?'

'It wouldn't be fair not to,' she said miserably.

'Is he always fair to you?'

'Yes, he is! Now will you please let me get up.'

Without moving, he said conversationally, 'Thursday is the day Mrs Tompkins cleans the library…'

Remembering her abandoned nightdress and robe, Eleanor cringed.

'So when you looked like sleeping in,' he continued blandly, 'in order to save everyone's blushes, I took your night things back to your room and brought you some clothes. You'll find them in the bathroom.'

'Thank you.' Dreadfully embarrassed by the thought of Robert Carrington going through her cheap and skimpy wardrobe, she eased herself past him and fled.

She had reached for the handle of the bathroom door, before she realized there *was* no door in that corner of the room. Yet her brain insisted that that was where it should be.

Disconcerted, and for a moment or two completely disorientated, she stood exactly where she was, before glancing around her, at a loss.

Robert Carrington had risen to his feet and was standing watching her, his face intent, a kind of stillness radiating from him.

Gripped by an illogical panic, and very conscious of her own nakedness, she felt her face grow heated.

Picking up his short silk robe, he helped her into it, tied the belt, and rolled up the sleeves which fell over her hands, before enquiring, 'What's the problem?'

'I'm afraid I got confused,' she said raggedly. 'For some reason I imagined the door to the bathroom was in that corner.'

'It used to be. But when my grandfather decided to have the rooms altered, it was moved over there—' he indicated a door to her right '—next to his dressing-room.'

'Oh,' she murmured blankly.

'You must have second sight.'

Oddly discomforted by the idea, she denied, 'I doubt it, I'm much too ordinary. I must have been thinking of my own room, and where the bathroom door is in relation to the bed.'

'That could be it,' he agreed.

Then, dismissing the puzzle, he went on prosaically, 'As it's such a lovely day, I thought when you're ready we might have lunch on the terrace?'

She would sooner have run a mile than eat lunch with him but, needing to return to some kind of workable footing, she said carefully, 'Thank you, but if Dave's back he might want to just snatch a sandwich and get straight to work.'

'*If* he's back.' On his way to the door, he added, 'But I doubt very much if he will be.'

CHAPTER SEVEN

THE instant the latch had clicked quietly behind him, anxious to get out of his suite, she showered with all speed.

Even after the shared intimacy of the previous night, it seemed strange to be using his shower gel, seeing his toilet things and his shaving kit on the shelf, borrowing his comb.

As soon as she had dried herself, she dressed in the undies he'd selected for her, pulled on the simple cotton dress, and slid the sandals onto her bare feet.

Then she listened carefully for any sounds of movement either in the library or the corridor outside.

The last thing she wanted to do was run straight into Mrs Tompkins. But having heard nothing, and recalling that it was lunchtime so the housekeeper would doubtless be busy, she ventured out.

Finding the coast was clear, she hurried along to the rooms she and Dave had been given. If he *did* happen to be back…

But if he was, though she needed to unburden herself, to get it off her conscience, she could hardly just blurt out her perfidy. She would have to wait until the right time.

Though would there ever be a right time?

Hating Robert Carrington as he did, it would be a double blow. It would put him in an impossible position. He would probably insist on throwing up the job and leaving straight away.

But that would mean returning the cheque they'd been given, and then where would they be?

In deep trouble.

Perhaps it made more sense not to tell him, at least until the job was finished, for both of their sakes.

Uncertain which she needed most, his presence, or a breathing space, she didn't know whether to be pleased or sorry to find there was no sign of him either in their living-room or his bedroom. Nor could she see the bag he had taken.

But thinking about it logically, and recalling how delighted he had been to get away, he was hardly likely to hurry back to a house he hated.

No doubt from his point of view, it would be a much better option to stay and have a lunchtime pie and pint and a game of snooker with the boys.

Well at least it would give her time to decide what to do for the best.

With a cowardly feeling of reprieve, she made her way down the stairs and out onto the sunny terrace, where a table was set for a cold lunch.

Robert Carrington, who was stretched in a lounger, rose to his feet at her approach.

She was surprised to see he had put on a tie.

He smiled at her. A lover's smile, that made her pulse rate quicken.

But somehow she must ignore his smile and the effect it had on her. Find some way to refute that intimacy, to distance herself.

She was trying hard to appear cool and aloof, when Paddington, his tail waving like a banner, came to greet her as if she was some long-lost friend.

'Well, hello.' She stooped to pat him.

When she straightened, her cheeks a little pink, Robert Carrington pulled out a chair and settled her at the table, before taking his own seat opposite.

Despite her resolve, such cosseting gave her a warm feeling of being cared for and cherished, and though she knew that feeling was spurious, on one level his outmoded courtesy still warmed her pleasurably.

Having helped her to quiche and salad, he queried, 'A glass of wine?'

'No, thank you. I'd prefer water. But please don't let me stop you.'

'I wasn't intending to have wine. I thought this afternoon I'd take you out for a drive. Show you a little of the countryside.'

She began to shake her head. 'Thank you, but I really—'

'Or perhaps you don't like the countryside?'

'Yes, I do.'

'Then what's the problem?'

The problem was, she needed to avoid his company.

Stiffly, she said, 'As Dave might be back any time, I don't think it's a good idea.'

Pulling a face at her formality, he challenged, 'Do you seriously believe Benson will come rushing back?'

Unwilling to lie, she changed tack. 'In any case, I don't want to keep you from your work and I have work to do!'

'I've decided to take the day off and give you a day off.' Wickedly, he added, 'I'm not as young as I used to be, and my energy is somewhat depleted.'

When, blushing furiously, she relapsed into silence, he said with satisfaction, 'So that's settled. Now is there anywhere in particular you'd like to go?'

'No, I—'

'Then I suggest Cromford Edge. The view from there is reputed to be one of the best locally, and I understand we can get an excellent pot of tea at the Cromford Arms...'

Though her sensible side knew quite well that she should refuse, she badly wanted to go with him.

'How does that sound?'

Undermined by the ambivalence of her own feelings, she somehow found herself agreeing weakly, 'Fine.'

'Good.'

For a while they ate in silence then, with a suddenness that caught her by surprise, he asked, 'How old were you when you were taken into care?'

'I don't know for sure,' she answered reluctantly. 'Seven or eight, they thought.'

'Then you remember your parents?'

'No.'

'Surely at that age you must remember who you lived with?'

She bent her head, so that a dark, silky curtain of hair fell forward, partially screening her face. 'I couldn't remember anything.'

'Why not?'

Losing colour, she said, 'It's something I don't like to talk about.'

'So the two are connected?'

When she looked up at him blankly, he reminded her, 'You told me you didn't like to talk about your scar, which seems to indicate a connection.'

Reaching across the table, he took her hand. 'It's quite obvious that something traumatic happened... But it's better to bring things out into the light of day and take a good look at them, rather than let them lurk in the dark and breed chimeras.'

He was right, of course, and the warmth of his hand holding hers gave her the courage to joke, 'You tell me your secrets and I'll tell you mine?'

'That's my girl.'

Giving her slim fingers a squeeze, he released them and helped her to strawberry mousse, before pursuing, 'So what *do* you remember?'

'The first thing I can recall is waking up in hospital with absolutely no idea of who I was, or how I got there.

'For a while I drifted in and out of consciousness, only

vaguely aware of doctors and nurses taking care of me. When I came to fully, a policewoman was waiting to talk to me. She said her name was Jackie, and asked what my name was. I didn't know.

'She asked a lot of questions, none of which I could answer. Then she told me I'd been found unconscious and bleeding from a head wound, some little distance away from a burnt-out car.

'When I asked her why I couldn't remember, she said I was suffering from amnesia, and as soon as that was better I'd get my memory back. In the meantime, they would ask the Press to help.

'When the story, and a picture of me, went into the papers it was hoped someone would come forward who recognised me.

'No one did.

'Though a nurse told me that one day, while I was asleep, a young woman came who *thought* she might know me. But she was mistaken, and she went away again before I woke up.'

Watching Robert Carrington's jaw tighten, she went on, 'The wound to my temple and face healed, but after several weeks I still couldn't recall a thing.

'When it was time for me to leave hospital, and no one had come forward to claim me, I was put into care. One of the first things I remember about Sunnyside is the matron remarking, "It's a pity she's got that ugly scar".'

He muttered something under his breath that sounded suspiciously like an oath, before urging, 'Go on.'

'I had to have a name, so they decided to call me Eleanor Smith, after one of the home's founders, and they chose April the seventh, the day I went there, to be my birthday.

'At first, presumably to spare my feelings, no one would talk about the accident or answer my questions. But I *needed* to know, so I kept on asking.

'I'd started to have nightmares where I was lost and alone in the dark, and haunted by something terrible I couldn't see.

'My screams disturbed the other children, so after a few days they decided it might be better if I knew the truth, and the same policewoman came to see me.'

She had started to tremble, and once again he took her hand and held it.

Oddly reassured, Eleanor went on, 'She told me it had been a February night, and below freezing, when the accident happened on a quiet country road.

'They thought that the car had skidded on some black ice, glanced off a tree, and rolled down the steep hillside, before landing upright.

'No other vehicle was involved.

'The remains of a woman they presumed to be the driver, were found in the burnt-out wreck. But the fire had been so fierce that, with virtually nothing to go on, they were unable to identify her.

'At first the police were puzzled because I'd been found quite a little distance away from the car, and it seemed unlikely, to say the least, that I'd got there on my own.

'Then, because the woman's remains were found in the *back* of the car, they came to the conclusion that she must have dragged me clear, then returned to get something, maybe a first-aid kit or a blanket. They believe she had just crawled back into the wreck when the petrol tank exploded.

'I thanked her politely for telling me, but all the same I was disappointed. I'd hoped that *knowing* what had happened would bring my memory back. It didn't. The nightmares changed to burning cars and charred bones, but eventually they stopped.'

'Dear God,' he said quietly. 'You poor thing.'

'Everyone was very kind to me, and it wasn't their fault that I felt so empty and alien, so *alone*.

'As time went on, and no one came forward to report a missing child, they tried sending me to foster-parents.

'My foster-mother was very nice, and I was just starting to feel at home and wanted, when I overheard her saying, "I wouldn't mind keeping the child, if only they could have something done about that dreadful scar...."

'I ran out of the house and went to hide in the park. When they eventually found me I refused to go home with them. I kicked up such a fuss that they were forced to send me back to Sunnyside.

'I'm sure now that she meant it kindly, but at the time I just saw it as a rejection. I felt as if no one would ever love me, as if I wasn't *worth* loving, because I was ugly.'

'Everyone is worth loving,' he said firmly. 'And as I've already told you, the scar *doesn't* make you ugly.'

'It's faded a lot over the years,' she admitted.

He shook his head. 'Even if it hadn't, it could never have made you ugly. The shape of your face, your eyes, your mouth, are all lovely now, and they must have been then. In any case a lot of beauty comes from the *inside*.'

'Ah, but you see there *was* no inside. Because I couldn't remember, I felt as though half of me was gone, and what remained was so lacking in substance that people could look right through me. The invisible child. It took me a long, long time to begin to fill that empty space.'

'How did you fill it?'

'Books mainly.'

'Not the company of the other children?'

She shook her head. 'I never really got to know any of them. I always felt like a ghost who could stand and watch, but wasn't able to join in.'

'You got to know Benson.'

'I didn't actually get to *know* him, I just worshipped him from afar,' she admitted drily. 'When he left without a word, I was quite devastated.'

'So what did you do then?'

'I began to plan my future. How I would work and save and one day start my own business.'

Her voice softening, she added, 'I could never have envisaged then that Dave and I would start a business together, or that he would ask me to marry him.'

Letting go of her hand, his expression suddenly bleak, Robert Carrington asked, 'Then you really do love him?'

'Of course I love him.' Almost to herself, she said, 'I can only hope that last night's stupidity won't have spoilt everything.'

Sighing, he assured her, 'Believe me, last night's *stupidity*, as you call it, won't have made the slightest bit of difference.'

He sounded so certain, that she was somewhat reassured.

If Dave really did love her—and now a man like Robert Carrington had found her attractive enough to take to bed she could almost believe he did—surely he would forgive her, rather than throw away their future together as a team?

Watching as her expression cleared somewhat, he asked, 'How are the bogeymen doing?'

She answered, 'There's nothing like the light of day for cutting them down to size.' And found it was the truth. Once spoken of, the painful past had miraculously lost its sting.

As she finished speaking, Mrs Tompkins appeared with a tray of coffee.

'I do hope I'm not rushing you? Only it's my afternoon to go into Claybourne and visit my sister.'

He gave Eleanor an enquiring glance. 'I believe we're both finished?'

'Yes, quite finished, thank you.'

Turning to the housekeeper, he asked, 'Do you need a lift into Claybourne, Mrs Tompkins? Miss Smith and I will be going that way shortly.'

'No, thank you,' that good lady said cheerily. 'As soon as I've cleared lunch away and stacked the dishwasher, Mr Tompkins will take me.

'Once a month, regular as clockwork, he drops me off at my sister Nancy's. Then when her son gets home from work, he drives me back.'

'That sounds like an excellent arrangement. Perhaps you'll ask Tompkins to bring the convertible round before you go?'

'That I will, Mr Robert.' Beaming at them both, she departed.

His voice full of triumph, he said, 'There, you see! Even Mrs Tompkins doesn't do it.'

'Do what?'

'Call me *Mr Carrington*.'

Suddenly feeling her spirits lift, Eleanor grinned at him impishly, 'Well I can call you *Mr Robert* if you'd really like me to.'

All at once he was on his feet, dangerously close, a gleam in his eye. 'And at the risk of scandalising Mrs Tompkins, I can carry you upstairs and make love to you until you've agreed to drop the mister.'

Feeling her throat go dry, and deciding to take the light approach, she said hurriedly, 'I'm sure you can't afford to deplete your energy any further.'

He grinned. 'I can always spend the remainder of the afternoon in bed. Though as you'll be with me, I'm sure I can think of something much more exciting to do than rest.'

'You said you were taking me to Cromford Edge,' her voice cracked.

Looking down at her from beneath ridiculously long lashes, he asked, 'So which destination do you prefer, Cromford Edge or Heaven?'

Only too aware of how badly she had behaved, she had thought herself in no further danger of repeating her mistake. But just for a split second she was sorely tempted to throw caution to the winds and choose heaven.

Shaken to the core that she sat mentally castigating herself.

'Finding it hard to choose?' he suggested.

She gathered her wits and, rising to her feet, denied, 'Not at all. I'd like to go to Cromford Edge, please, *Robert.*'

He sighed. 'Ah, well, victory of a sort, I suppose.'

Picking up a smart jacket that was tossed over a chair, he queried, 'Do you need to fetch a coat or anything?'

'No, thank you.' Then anxiously, 'We won't be out too long, will we? You mentioned having a pot of tea, and if Dave gets back and finds I'm not here…'

'That won't happen.'

How he could be so certain?

Needing reassurance, she persisted, 'You promise we won't be late?'

'I promise we'll be home before Benson gets back.'

She breathed a sigh of relief.

Taking her hand, he asked, 'About ready?'

Caught between a quick excitement and a nagging certainty that she was doing totally the wrong thing, she said, 'Yes.'

'Then let's go.' The jacket slung over his shoulder and held by one crooked finger, he smiled at her, and gave her hand a squeeze.

His smile filled his face with charm, making him all but irresistible, and her heart began to race.

As they walked round to the front of the house, where the white convertible was waiting, its hood down, she found herself thinking how vastly different Dave and Robert Carrington were.

Though tough and powerful-looking, the last man she would have suspected of being in any way soft, he seemed to enjoy looking at her and holding her hand, while Dave rarely did either.

But she mustn't allow Robert Carrington's undeniable charm to beguile her. She must stay cool and composed, and keep her feelings well under control.

Having settled her into the front passenger seat, he tossed his jacket in the back, slid behind the wheel, and reached across to fasten her safety belt.

Just his shoulder touching hers quickened her breathing and sent little shivers through her, making her realise that staying cool and composed was easier said than done.

When they approached the gatehouse, Jackson, who was working in the garden, put down a ball of green twine, and came to open the gates for them.

'How are the sweet peas doing?' Robert called.

'Coming on apace with this bit of sunshine,' Jackson answered cheerfully. 'Should easily beat last year's.'

As they drew away he gave them a salute, which Robert answered with a wave.

Keeping to the back roads, so they met scarcely any traffic, they drove through pleasant, rolling countryside, where the pasture was bright with buttercups, streams and ponds flashed silver, and oaks and chestnuts stood in their own shade.

Eleanor could never remember feeling so carefree, so glowing with happiness. Even the dangerous knowledge that most of her happiness sprang from the man beside her, his companionship, the warmth of his presence, wasn't enough to dim that glow.

A balmy breeze blowing her long hair into silken strands, she lifted her face to the sun, a smile on her lips.

After a sidelong glance at her rapt expression, he flicked a switch and the soaring adagio from *Spartacus* filled the car.

While it added yet another dimension to her pleasure, the

lovely, passionate music brought with it memories of the previous night. Memories that, refusing to be banished, made her go hot all over and threatened to destroy her hard-won composure.

It was almost a relief when the music ended, and a minute later having been climbing steadily for some time, they reached Cromford Edge.

The look-out point was clearly a popular spot. There were a lot of vehicles already parked, and quite a few people coming and going.

She wondered briefly why he'd elected to come here. It wasn't at all the kind of place she would have expected him to choose.

Drawing the car into one of the few vacant spaces, he jumped out and came round to open her door. Then hand in hand, like lovers, they strolled to the edge of the bluff.

As he had said, the view was superb, and they stood for a while admiring it before turning to walk back to the car.

When he had slipped into his jacket, they strolled the few hundred yards to the Cromford Arms, which was a long, black and white half-timbered building with climbing roses and overhanging eaves.

Inside it was quietly luxurious. An air of gracious living, and a discreet notice requesting that gentlemen going through to the lounge and dining-room, should wear jackets, seemed to place it firmly in a more conventional, tranquil era.

A white-coated waiter met them at the entrance to a pleasant, sunny lounge, where tea was being served. With a stately air he led them to some chintz-covered chairs grouped around a low table, and set in front of a stone fireplace filled with flowers.

They had been seated only a moment or two when a beautiful, well-dressed woman, her dark hair taken up into an elegant chignon, was shown in.

Apparently catching sight of them, she waved the waiter aside, and started in their direction.

But as she approached their table, as if uncertain whether or not she had made a mistake, her steps faltered and she hesitated, her manner now totally at odds with her imperious gesture to the waiter.

Robert Carrington rose to his feet and said, 'Good afternoon Lady Allenby... How nice to see you again.'

There was courtesy in the greeting, but no warmth, and his face looked curiously taut.

'May I introduce Miss Smith...'

Her blue eyes fixed on Eleanor's face, the woman gave a little nod of acknowledgement and moistened her lips.

'Eleanor, my dear, this is Lady Sarah Allenby, wife of Sir John Allenby, Chairman of the Allenby Whitehead Corporation.'

Tall and fashionably thin, Lady Allenby was expertly made-up and wore diamond earrings and a broach on her silk jacket that, if real, must have cost a small fortune.

Feeling out of place in her simple cotton dress and sandals, and with wind-tangled hair, Eleanor murmured, 'How do you do?' Then thinking how tense and uncomfortable the older woman appeared, gave her a friendly smile.

'Won't you join us?' Robert invited.

'Thank you.' Her voice was low and husky, and sounded oddly impeded.

He pulled forward a chair for the newcomer.

Sitting down, she smoothed her skirt over her knees, and fiddled with the catch of her bag.

The waiter came up and, having distributed large, leather-covered menus, informed them, 'In addition, to our usual range of sandwiches and cakes, we have freshly made smoked salmon pâté, local strawberries, and some excellent Danish pastries.'

Lady Allenby shook her head. 'Just tea. Earl Grey.'

'Eleanor?' Robert enquired.

She would have much preferred coffee, but there was no mention of anything but tea on the menu and, unwilling to disturb what appeared to be a sacred ritual, she said, 'I'll have the same, please.'

The order given, Robert explained to their unexpected guest, 'Eleanor is staying at the manor for the time being.'

'So what do you think of Greyladies, Miss Smith?'

Clear grey eyes glowing, Eleanor answered, 'It's absolutely lovely.'

Her still-beautiful face pale, and holding a look of strain, Lady Allenby opened her mouth as if to say something further, then closed it again, leaving her question unasked.

There followed an awkward silence which lengthened until Robert enquired civilly, 'How is Sir John keeping these days?'

While his manner was faultless, Eleanor got the distinct impression that he neither liked nor approved of Lady Allenby.

'He's fine. The doctors said his heart attack was a mild one, and more in the nature of a warning.'

'I heard a rumour in the City that he was thinking of retiring.'

'It's true he's been thinking about it...'

Eleanor was surprised, she had put Lady Allenby down as no more than forty-one or two, possibly even younger. If her husband was thinking of retiring, there must be a big age gap.

'But I'm rather hoping he won't. Even now John has so much drive and energy. I simply can't imagine what he'll *do* with himself all day if he retires. Especially if he insists on living in the country....'

Looking ill at ease, she was conversing jerkily, abstractedly, her gaze returning repeatedly to Eleanor's face.

At length, she asked, 'How long will you be staying at Greyladies, Miss Smith?'

'I'm not quite sure. A week, possibly two. It all depends on how soon we can—' She stopped speaking as their tea arrived on an ornate silver tray.

Having carefully set out the delicate bone china cups and saucers, the waiter placed the silver teapot in front of Lady Allenby, before departing.

She lifted the heavy pot then, her well-manicured hand shaking visibly, put it down again with a thud.

'Perhaps you'd like me to pour?' Eleanor suggested impulsively.

'If you wouldn't mind?'

'Of course not.'

At the younger woman's assurance, she surrendered the task with obvious relief.

As Eleanor began to fill the cups, she caught Robert's glance and found herself recalling how she had spilt tea into his lap.

He was obviously recalling the same, for though his face remained still and grave, his eyes danced, and one lid flickered in the ghost of a conspiratorial wink.

They were as one, sharing a private joke. She felt a rush of pleasure, a sweet confusion.

When she had passed them each a cup, Lady Allenby remarked a shade stiltedly, 'I understand you live in London, Miss Smith?'

Wondering how she knew, Eleanor answered, 'Yes.'

'It must be quiet at Greyladies… Don't you miss the hustle and bustle of town, and long to get back there?'

'No, not at all.'

'You surely don't dislike London?'

'No. In some ways it's a wonderful place. But I don't care much for the traffic jams, the packed buses and tube trains, or the expensive and overcrowded accommodation.'

Brushing such things aside, Lady Allenby said, 'I'm willing to ignore the problems. I always think that in spite of the crowds, London is so much more inviting and civilised than the country.'

His voice cool, dispassionate, Robert observed, 'I believe you have a nicely situated mansion near Mayfair?'

'Yes. Allenby House overlooks Hyde Park.'

'And a chauffeur-driven Rolls?'

Looking a little surprised, she agreed, 'Yes...' Adding, 'And thankfully, Thornton is very good in traffic.'

'Then it must be easy to ignore the problems. Perhaps if you found yourself living in a cramped bed-sit in one of the less affluent areas, and had to fight your way on and off crowded public transport, London wouldn't seem quite so inviting and civilised.'

Though his tone had been perfectly pleasant, even slightly jocular, Eleanor saw that the older woman looked distinctly disconcerted.

Feeling sorry for her, she said quickly, 'My fiancé loves London. He wouldn't live anywhere else.'

'I can only wish John felt the same way.'

Lady Allenby got to her feet abruptly. 'Well, if you'll excuse me, I really must be going.'

As Robert rose politely, she added, 'My husband likes me to be at home when he gets back...

'Well, goodbye.' Clutching her bag, she turned and hurried away, leaving her tea untouched.

Resuming his seat, Robert observed to Eleanor, 'Your tea looks cold. Would you like a fresh cup?'

'No, thank you.' In a rush, she confessed, 'I don't usually drink tea. I much prefer coffee.'

'Why didn't you say so?'

'I didn't like to.'

'It isn't a crime. I must admit that I prefer coffee myself.'

Then thoughtfully, 'I presume the aversion to tea is something to do with Sunnyside?'

'They used to give us cups of pale grey, lukewarm liquid that they called tea.' She shuddered at the unpleasant memory.

A look on his face that could have passed for tenderness, he observed, 'No wonder it put you off. Would you like me to order some coffee?'

Shaken by that look, it was a moment or two before she could find her voice to protest, 'Oh, no, please don't bother.'

'It's no bother.'

'But I'm sure it's not the done thing to ask for coffee at teatime.'

'Then we'll shock them, and be Philistines.'

Signalling the waiter, he asked for a pot of coffee for two.

'*Coffee*, sir?'

'Coffee,' Robert said firmly.

As, looking distinctly put out, the man went to do his bidding, Robert turned to Eleanor and asked, 'So what was your impression of Lady Allenby?'

'I thought that despite her position, she seemed very on-edge and nervous.'

'Did you like her?'

'I felt sorry for her,' Eleanor said slowly.

'You felt *sorry* for her?' he repeated, clearly taken aback.

Eleanor flushed. 'It must seem sheer impertinence on my part to feel sorry for someone who probably has everything she wants, but all the same I did. She doesn't look at all happy.'

'I doubt very much if she is,' he agreed flatly. 'Sir John has always had a reputation for being extremely difficult, a man who likes to rule both his business empire and his home with a rod of iron. But though there was an age gap of over twenty years, she still chose to marry him.'

Convinced that Robert was a compassionate man, Eleanor was surprised by how harsh and unsympathetic he sounded.

'Well if they loved each other…'

'I'm quite sure love never came into it. At least on *her* side.'

'Maybe she didn't know what he was like until it was too late.'

'By her own admission, she knew *exactly* what he was like—ruthless and egotistical, a petty dictator. It was widely rumoured that his first wife had always lived under his thumb.'

'But if she knew that, why do you suppose she married him?' Eleanor spoke the thought aloud.

'I don't need to *suppose*,' Robert said. 'She told me exactly what had motivated her.'

CHAPTER EIGHT

'IT WAS the old, old story. She married him for his money—apparently while she's toeing his line he's generous enough—a position in top society, and a title.

'He *may* have loved her, but it seems more likely that he married her for her youth and beauty, and for the son and heir he desperately wanted, and his first wife hadn't managed to provide...'

Robert broke off as the waiter appeared with a tray of coffee and, setting it down as though it soiled his hands, walked away.

'We'll probably be blacklisted after this,' he remarked with a grin.

His cheerful unconcern made her feel a lot easier.

Reaching for the cafetière, he pressed the plunger and poured the steaming liquid.

'Thank you.' Accepting a cup, Eleanor sipped gratefully, before asking, 'So they have children?'

'No. After sixteen years of marriage they're still childless, so it seems very unlikely that he'll get his heart's desire now.'

His expression suddenly wintry, he added, 'I wonder if they both still think it was worth it.'

'Surely they must do. Their marriage has lasted.'

'Only just. She told me that a few years ago, when he blamed her for their childless state, she was so miserable that she offered him an uncontested divorce in exchange for a reasonable settlement.

'But he doesn't believe in letting go of what is his, and

paranoid about any breath of scandal, he refused to even consider it.'

'If she was so unhappy, I'm surprised she didn't leave him.'

'Sir John must have known, or at least guessed, why she was marrying him. Before their wedding day, he insisted that she signed a marriage contract to the effect that if she left him, or tried to divorce him, she wouldn't get a penny of his money....'

Watching as Robert leaned forward to refill her cup, Eleanor found herself puzzling over his relationship with Lady Allenby.

It seemed to be a most curious one. His manner towards the woman had been cool and distant, anything but *friendly*, yet she had apparently told him things that surely she wouldn't have passed on to a mere acquaintance?

Her smooth forehead creased into a frown, Eleanor remarked, 'You must know Sir John and Lady Allenby very well?'

He shook his head. 'I've known Sir John distantly, and in a business capacity, for a number of years, but I only met Lady Allenby recently.'

Seeing her surprise, he explained, 'The first occasion was somewhat fraught, and I doubt if she would have been quite so honest if she hadn't had rather too much to drink. You must know the old saying, *in vino veritas*...'

Eleanor felt a quiver of mingled distaste and disappointment. Though Robert had a quick, clever tongue, he was usually neither unkind nor malicious. The only person she had known him verbally scourge, was Dave. She would never have suspected him of being a man who would gossip like a fishwife.

Yet here he was repeating Lady Allenby's tipsy confidences to *her*—a perfect stranger—almost as if she had a *right* to hear them.

On Eleanor's wavelength, as he often seemed to be, he met her gaze squarely. 'Needless to say, had the circumstances been different, I would have respected her ladyship's revelations....'

There was biting scorn in the words, *her ladyship*.

Still not fully understanding, but knowing with certainty that she had misjudged him, her eyes fell beneath that steady regard.

After a moment he went on, 'I may even have felt a little sorry for her....'

'But you didn't?' she asked huskily.

'No, I didn't. Had I been able to feel any sympathy whatsoever, it would probably have gone to Sir John.'

'To *Sir John*? But he doesn't sound a very nice man.'

'I'm sure he isn't...'

Watching her face, he said, 'And before you accuse me of simply sticking up for my own sex, it has nothing to do with the fact that we're both males.'

As she waited, he continued bleakly, 'I can pity anyone who is just married for their money. Especially if they happen to be in love with their opposite number. Although that probably *wasn't* the case as far as Sir John was concerned.'

Knowing instinctively that Robert was speaking from personal experience, she blurted out, 'But it *was* with you?'

'You're very quick,' he commented approvingly. 'And yes, I loved Zoe.'

Feeling as though her heart had stopped, she protested, 'When I mentioned *Mrs* Carrington, you said your stepmother was in Canada. I didn't realise you had a wife.'

'I haven't. Though it was a very near thing. All the wedding arrangements had been made when we broke up.' Shrugging, he added, 'But it's a while ago now.'

She was wondering just how long ago it *had* been, when she caught sight of the glass-cased carriage clock on the mantelpiece.

Nearly ten minutes to five! Oh, Lord! Dave would almost certainly be back by now, and no doubt he'd be anything but pleased to find she wasn't there.

'Just look at the time!' she exclaimed. 'Shouldn't we be getting home?'

'There's no rush,' Robert answered comfortably. 'You haven't finished your coffee yet.'

Vexed by his laid-back attitude, she said shortly, 'I don't want any more, thank you... And you promised we wouldn't be late.'

'I promised we would be home before Benson got back,' he corrected.

Agitation brought her to her feet. 'But it's nearly five o'clock. He's sure to be back by now.'

Robert rose, towering over her. 'It's unlikely, to say the least. In fact I'm willing to bet a kiss to a kick that he won't be.'

'We still have a longish drive,' she pointed out.

Seeing her genuine anxiety, he touched her cheek with a gentle finger. 'Very well, if it'll make you feel any happier we'll start back at once, and take the shortest route.'

Though it was almost six o'clock by the time Robert drove through the archway at Greyladies and came to a stop in front of the garages, to Eleanor's chagrin, there was no sign of the van.

'It seems I won the bet,' he said, as he helped her out, 'so I'll collect.'

Before she could make any objection, he had bent his head and touched his lips to hers.

He wasn't holding her at all. The only contact between them was their mouths, and she could easily have moved away.

But somehow she didn't. Instead she stood as if rooted

to the spot, while he kissed her with a gentle, persuasive warmth.

As his mouth moved against hers, her heart began to pound, her stomach folded in on itself, and the warmth between them turned to red-hot passion.

When his arms went around her and moulded her close, thigh to thigh, hip to hip, her whole body melted, soft female contours against hard male bone and muscle.

She was being drawn irresistibly into a whirlpool of delight and passion, when the sound of a vehicle approaching brought her to her senses, and made her pull away guiltily.

But it wasn't Dave's white van that appeared through the archway, it was a blue saloon with a strange young man at the wheel, and Mrs Tompkins sitting beside him.

'Sorry I'm late,' the housekeeper apologised, climbing out. 'But Tim was held up at work, and then he had to stop for petrol.'

'That's all right,' Robert said easily, 'we're only just back ourselves.'

Waving to her nephew as he drove off, she asked, 'Would you mind if dinner is a bit later than usual?'

'Not at all, in fact it…'

Without waiting to hear the rest of Robert's reply, Eleanor slipped away and hurried up to the privacy of her room on shaking legs.

Sinking down on the bed, racked with shame for the desire she had felt, she flayed herself for being so weak and foolish.

If she couldn't exercise more self-control than this, perhaps it would be better to tell Dave the truth as soon as he got back, and suggest leaving straight away.

Though if she did, and Robert insisted on having his money back immediately, which he had every right to do…

She sighed. It came back to that every time. Talk about being in a muddle!

If only she hadn't got herself into this mess. But she had, and it was much too late to cry over spilt milk. All she could do now was bitterly regret her behaviour and try to steer clear of further temptation.

By tomorrow it should be less of a problem. As soon as Dave was back, and the new equipment had been delivered, she would be working too hard to have either the time, or the opportunity, to weaken.

But where *was* Dave, she wondered worriedly. With no legitimate excuse to stay away another night, he should have been back ages ago.

She found a change of clothing, and went into the bathroom to shower and shampoo her hair. When she had blow-dried it, she put on fresh undies, a cream and grey silky sheath, and a pair of light sandals.

It wasn't until she had applied a touch of make-up, and was twisting her hair into a dark, shining knot on top of her head, that the most obvious reason for his failure to arrive struck her.

If he hadn't left early enough, he had most likely been caught up in the rush-hour traffic. It could be absolute murder getting out of London at that time of day.... But even if he *had* hit rush hour, he should be with them by dinnertime.

Feeling somewhat more cheerful, she made her way downstairs. She had just reached the terrace when Jessie came strolling in from the garden with what appeared to be a live vole in her mouth.

Sorry for the poor little creature and wondering if she could save it, Eleanor called the cat, which came obediently and wound round her ankles.

Stooping to stroke behind the velvet ears, she coaxed Jessie to give up her prize. The cat paddled for a while with

her front paws before relinquishing the vole which, too terrified to run, simply crouched there.

It appeared to be unharmed and Eleanor picked it up,
holding the warm pulsing body carefully between her
palms.

Jessie, who had apparently lost interest, settled herself
on one of the loungers while Eleanor set off towards the
walled garden.

Choosing a place where there was plenty of ground
cover, she leaned down and opened her hands to release
the tiny creature. For a second or two it remained quite
still, half hidden by the leaves, then like a flash, it was
gone.

The little incident made her think of a field mouse that
had lived in the bare garden at Sunnyside, and she walked
back to the house and washed her hands abstractedly, remembering how, in the winter, she had saved scraps of food
for it.

But one day Matron had spotted what she was up to, and
told her firmly that mice were vermin, and she mustn't
encourage them. It was the nearest she had ever come to
having a pet and, loving it, she had mourned its loss for a
long time.

Eleanor had just returned to the terrace, which apart from
the sleeping cat was still deserted, when Tompkins appeared with the pre-dinner drinks trolley.

'Good evening, miss,' he said with grave politeness.

'Good evening, Tompkins.'

'The master asked me to give you his apologies, and say
he'll be with you shortly.'

When she was seated in a lounger, he queried, 'May I
pour you a drink, miss?'

'I don't think so, thank you, Tompkins. I'd rather wait
for the others.'

Then, in the hope that Dave had returned while she was

in the garden, she asked, 'Have you any idea if Mr Benson has arrived back yet?'

'Not to the best of my knowledge, miss.'

'Has there been any message from him?'

'No, miss.' Clearing his throat, Tompkins added persuasively, 'May I mention that there is a jug of freshly made Pimms.'

He was so eager to please, that unwilling to hurt his feelings, she said, 'That does sound nice. Maybe I'll change my mind and have a drink after all.'

He filled a tall glass and, careful to observe the niceties, offered it to her on a small, round, silver tray.

She took it and while he watched her a shade anxiously, sipped some of the cool, fruity concoction. 'Mmm…that really is delicious. Thank you, Tompkins.'

Looking pleased, he bowed his head and departed.

Sitting in the sun, she sipped her drink and waited for the men, hoping against hope that Dave would be the first to arrive.

But it was Robert who appeared through the French windows. He had changed into casual trousers, and a white linen shirt, and looked vitally attractive.

'Sorry about that. A badly timed phone call. I hope Tompkins gave you a drink?'

'Yes.'

Looking at his lean, hard-boned face she found herself wondering how, at their first meeting, she had thought him far from handsome. Now she considered him the best-looking man she had ever met. Barring Dave of course, she tacked on somewhat guiltily.

'Would you like a refill?'

'No, thank you.'

Pouring himself a glass of Pimms, he sat down next to her, and stared into the middle distance, a frown drawing his well-marked brows together.

That brooding look was so unlike him, that she wondered if his phone call had upset him in some way.

When he continued to sit in silence, deciding she had better broach the subject first, she said, 'I'm afraid Dave still isn't back. He must have got a late start and been caught in the rush-hour traffic.'

'It's seven-thirty,' Robert pointed out quietly. 'Even if that was the case, he should be here by now. If he was *intending* to come back, that is.'

'Of course he's intending to come back,' she insisted. 'How could he possibly do otherwise?'

Then, suddenly realising that beneath his quiet exterior Robert was furiously angry, she caught her lower lip between her teeth, and said no more.

The silence was stretching uncomfortably when the butler reappeared, and said, 'I'm sorry to disturb you sir, but a lady has called and is insisting on seeing you.'

Frowning, Robert asked, 'Who is it, Tompkins? What does she want?'

The butler looked pained. 'I'm afraid I don't know, sir. She declined either to give her name or state her business, though she did assure me that she wasn't from the Press.'

Robert rose and, turning to Eleanor, said, 'If you'll excuse me, I'd better see what this is all about.'

Watching him walk away, it occurred to her that the lady in question might be Lady Allenby. There seemed to be some strange connection between Sir John's wife and Robert, that she couldn't begin to understand.

But when, after a short absence, he returned, it wasn't Lady Allenby he had with him, but a willowy blonde.

In her late twenties or early thirties, Eleanor guessed, and only an inch or two shorter than Robert himself, she was undeniably attractive, and possessed a stunning figure.

For a moment the newcomer looked put out to see another woman present, clearly wondering who she was, and what she was doing there. Then her critical gaze assessing Eleanor's looks and clothes, and finding her no competition, she relaxed.

His face expressionless, Robert said briefly, 'Eleanor, may I introduce Miss Hamlin... Zoe, this is Miss Smith.'

Zoe... Hearing the name came as an unpleasant shock, and feeling her heart contract, Eleanor somehow managed, 'How do you do?'

So this was the woman he had once loved, *and maybe still did*, she thought bleakly. How strange that she should turn up unexpectedly, when only that afternoon he had been talking about her.

She wondered if Robert was thinking the same.

His manner towards the blonde giving nothing away, he invited courteously, 'Won't you sit down?'

When Zoe had lowered herself with feline grace into one of the loungers, and crossed her slim, silk-clad ankles, he asked, 'Can I get you a drink?'

'A gin and tonic, please.'

'Ice and lemon?'

With a charming grimace, she protested, 'Darling, surely you remember? It's not that long ago.'

'On the contrary,' he said coolly, 'a year is quite a long time.'

So it was a year.

'Too long,' she agreed, smiling up at him from beneath false lashes.

He handed her the drink and, remaining on his feet, asked, 'So what are you doing in these parts?'

'I've been working on one of the sitting-rooms at Meddlecome Hall.'

'Zoe is an interior designer,' Robert explained to Eleanor, as he moved to stand by her side.

'I could never catch you at your flat,' the blonde complained. 'So when I realised I was quite close to Greyladies,

I decided to pop in on my way back to London and see if by any chance you were here.'

His tone polite, but detached, he queried, 'Did you want me for anything special?'

If she was disconcerted by his apparent lack of interest, she hid it well. 'I thought I'd just say hello, for old times' sake.'

'I see.' Then like a rattlesnake striking, 'Why did you refuse to give Tompkins your name?'

She darted Eleanor a swift, resentful glance. 'I'm afraid I don't find it easy to talk in front of someone else…'

'I'll go and see if Dave is back yet.' Eleanor started to rise.

A restraining hand on her shoulder, Robert said, 'There's really no reason for you to leave.'

Turning to the blonde, he assured her, 'Eleanor knows about our past relationship, so you can talk freely in front of her.'

Just for a moment Zoe's anger and disappointment showed, as she struggled visibly for control.

'You were about to explain why you didn't tell Tompkins who you were,' Robert pursued.

Mistress of herself again, she gave him a rueful smile. 'Well I know you can be…hasty…and I thought if you knew who it was in advance, you might refuse to see me.'

'Now why on earth should you think that?'

Determinedly ignoring the sarcasm, she added gaily, 'That's why I decided to surprise you.'

'I must admit you have. You would never come with me to Greyladies when I wanted to visit Josh.'

'Darling, I'm a town girl.' She made a face. 'You know how much I loathe and detest the country.

'I wouldn't consider working in it, if it wasn't absolutely necessary. I'd much prefer all my commissions to be in town.'

Then coaxingly, 'Please don't look so cross. I know what happened in the past was all my fault, and I've been wanting to tell you how sorry I was to have made such a mess of things.'

'Why did you leave it this long?'

'You were so angry, I knew you'd need time to get over it....'

When he said nothing, she added, 'But I was hoping that by now you would be ready to forgive me....'

'How is Simon? I understand you went back to him.'

'Yes, I did,' she admitted. 'But I couldn't get you out of my mind, and we finally split up.'

'Perhaps that's just as well. I heard he'd recently been posted to the back of beyond. Not at all your cup of tea.'

Ignoring that, she got back to the point. 'If you knew just how much I've regretted my stupidity, I'm sure you *would* forgive me.'

He raised a level brow. 'Stupidity?'

'It wasn't until it was too late that I realised how I really felt about you... And still do.'

'And how *do* you feel about me?'

'Surely you must know.'

'All I know for sure is what you told Bridget.'

'I made a bad mistake. That's what I'm trying to tell you now.' Her blue eyes were appealing. 'It isn't easy to say this in front of someone else....'

When he gave her neither help nor encouragement, she let that go, and suggested, 'Maybe when you're in town we could have a meal together?'

Just as she stopped speaking, Tompkins appeared and, having coughed gently, announced, 'Dinner is served, sir.'

Turning to the blonde, Robert invited politely, 'If you haven't already eaten, perhaps you'd care to stay and dine with us?'

She gave him a brilliant smile. 'As it happens, I haven't, so that would be lovely.'

'I'll see that another place is set.' Tompkins anticipated his instructions.

'There should be no need,' Robert said briskly. 'If you've set a place for Mr Benson, Miss Hamlin can have that.'

'Certainly, sir.' The butler bowed his head and retreated.

Eleanor bit her lip. As Dave still wasn't back, there was really nothing she could say.

As though it was something she had done often, Zoe made as if to take Robert's arm.

But, moving away a little, he indicated politely that she should precede him and, smiling down at Eleanor, asked, 'About ready to eat, my love?'

Reaching for her hand, he pulled her to her feet and dropped a light kiss on her lips, before escorting the two women through to the dining-room.

Angry and flustered, but unwilling to cause a scene, Eleanor went with the greatest reluctance. The last thing she wanted was to be used to make the other woman jealous, and conscious of Zoe's eyes burning into her she wished fervently that she could find some excuse to escape.

But her mind remained a blank.

As soon as they were seated, with herself on Robert's right and Zoe on his left, a melon starter was served.

Both the women, for different reasons, said little and, after an attempt at general conversation ground to a halt, the remainder of the meal—poached salmon followed by a light summer pudding—was eaten in silence.

The cheeseboard had been brought before Zoe, who seemed to have rallied somewhat, asked, 'Do you live locally, Miss Smith?'

'No, I live in London.'

'If by any chance you need a lift back to town...'

'Thank you, but—'

'Eleanor is staying here,' Robert informed her.

'Oh, I see.' Turning her attention back to the other woman, Zoe queried, 'Do I take it that you're on holiday?'

Determined to speak the exact truth, Eleanor said, 'No, I'm not on holiday.'

'Oh? May I ask what you do for a living?'

'I help to instal computer and communication networks.'

'Good gracious!' Zoe exclaimed. 'I hadn't appreciated that I was talking to someone so clever.'

'I can't claim to be that, I'm afraid. Dave does the really clever bits.'

'The Dave you mentioned earlier?'

'Yes. We're in partnership.'

Zoe was nothing if not quick. 'So you're actually working at the manor?'

'Eleanor is staying here as my guest.' Robert broke smoothly into the conversation.

'Dave too?' she asked, as Tompkins appeared with the coffee.

His tone repressive, Robert informed her, 'Benson has returned to London.'

'But a place at the table was laid for him, so you must be expecting him back?'

'No, I'm not expecting him back.'

Eleanor again was shaken by his certainty. He just *had* to be wrong. Of course Dave was coming back. He wouldn't stay away a second night without letting her know.

Returning to the fray, Zoe queried, 'How long will *you* be staying here, Miss Smith?'

Before Eleanor could answer, Robert reached for her hand and raised it to his lips. 'I have every hope that from now on Eleanor will be making Greyladies her home.'

Though she knew he was only tormenting Zoe, he

sounded sincere, and suddenly it was more than she could bear.

Aware how she felt about the manor, and knowing she had never had a real home, how could he say things like that? How could he be so cruel?

Leaving her coffee untouched, she stood up abruptly and pushed back her chair. 'If you'll excuse me—' she was surprised by how steady her voice sounded '—I have a nasty headache.'

She turned away and, half blinded by a rush of tears, hurried upstairs to the privacy of her own sitting-room.

Closing the door behind her, she sank down on the couch and stared sightlessly into space, while the tears continued to flow. Though aware she meant less than nothing to him, she was still bitterly hurt that he could treat her like this. But perhaps in his desire to make Zoe jealous he hadn't realised how unkind he was being?

But why did he *need* to make Zoe jealous? It was quite obvious that she would go back to him like a shot. So if he still loved her, why didn't he just say so?

Or was it his intention to try and teach her a lesson before he took her back?

If it was, *she* wanted no part of it.

The angry tears rolled down her cheeks even faster, dripping off her chin and falling onto the knuckles of her left hand—the hand that Robert had kissed.

As she clumsily wiped them away, she was shocked to discover that her third finger was bare. She was no longer wearing her engagement ring.

But though it was a little loose, she *always* wore it. Like some talisman, she had never taken it off since Dave had put it on her finger.

Now it was missing.

She jumped to her feet utterly panic-stricken. Where on earth could it be?

A quick search of the couch failed to locate it. Perhaps she'd lost it in the dining-room?

Hurrying to the door, she was just about to pull it open when there was a knock.

Robert was standing on the threshold, barring her way. He looked tough and formidable.

'Please go away,' she begged huskily.

After a glance at her swollen eyes and wet, blotchy face, he muttered something half under his breath and gathered her into his arms.

His concern was more than she could bear, and completely overwrought, she began to sob.

Cradling her head to his chest, his cheek against her hair, he held her, murmuring little inarticulate words of comfort, until the sobs died away.

As, sniffing, she struggled free, he handed her a spotless hankie and, his voice tender, said, 'I could see you were upset, but I'm sure there's no need to take on like this.'

'There's every need,' she choked, blowing her nose and scrubbing at her face.

'I'm sorry, I never meant to—'

Pride coming to her aid, unwilling to let him see just how much he'd hurt her, she broke in fiercely, 'It has nothing to do with you. I've lost my ring.'

'You've what?' He sounded startled.

'I've lost my engagement ring.'

'Oh, hell!'

Usually he was quietly spoken, and she was surprised by his vehemence.

'Have you any idea where it might be?' he asked after a moment.

'No, none. Unless I lost it in the dining-room.'

His voice curiously flat, he said, 'I noticed you weren't wearing it when we had our drinks on the terrace, but I assumed you'd taken it off.'

'I never take it off.'

Looking at her ravished face, his jaw tight, he asked, 'Can you remember when you last noticed it?'

She shook her head helplessly. 'I'm so used to wearing it, I tend *not* to notice, to simply accept that it's there.'

'Try thinking back.'

She went back in her mind.

'Yes! I was wearing it when I showered and changed for dinner. I remember because as I was coiling my hair up, a strand got caught and tugged a bit.'

'Go on from there.'

'And I still had it on when I picked up the vole...' The sun had made the small zircons sparkle.

'When you picked up the vole?'

She explained, adding, 'I took it into the walled garden and let it go... Of course! My ring must have slipped off then, and because of all the ground cover, I didn't notice it.'

'Can you remember the exact place?'

'More or less.'

'Then let's go and find it.' Taking her hand he hurried her down the stairs and out into the garden.

'This is it, I think,' she said a shade breathlessly, as they reached what she judged to be the approximate spot. 'Though I wasn't paying a great deal of attention, I seem to remember that big clump of pink hollyhocks by the wall.'

In front of the taller herbaceous flowers, the delphiniums and cornflowers, the golden rod and glowing red-hot-pokers, was a riot of periwinkle, and an extensive carpet of close, ground-hugging plants.

Her heart sinking as she realised just what they were up against, she said anxiously, 'I'm afraid it's going to be like looking for the proverbial needle in a haystack.'

'It's a devil of a place to lose it,' he agreed. 'But we'll see what we can do. Now where do you suggest we begin?'

'About here, I think.'

Starting from that spot, they fanned out, and on their hands and knees began to search every inch of the ground.

At first the late sun was on their backs, then it disappeared behind the wall, leaving the evening air blessedly cooler. They worked on, parting the leaves and peering between each plant, fingers feeling in the soil around the base.

A grey-lilac dusk was hampering their efforts before Eleanor, her hair untidy and dirt on her knees, got up stiffly and, close to despair, said, 'It's no use, we're never going to find it.'

'Not tonight, maybe, but never's a long time.'

As Robert rose to his feet, brushing leaf-mould off his trousers, she saw that his corn-coloured hair was rumpled and there was a broad smear of dust across his right cheek.

He looked oddly boyish and she felt a sudden rush of almost maternal tenderness. She wondered if Zoe had ever seen him this dishevelled, and her heart constricted painfully at the thought of the woman he had once wanted to marry. Maybe still did.

His eyes on her expressive face, and attributing her desolation to their failure to find the ring, he urged, 'Cheer up! We will find it, I promise.

'Now let's go and tidy up and have a nightcap.' He tucked her grubby hand through his arm.

Feeling too low in spirits to object, she left it there, and they walked back to the house in the gathering dusk.

CHAPTER NINE

As THEY reached the hall, the butler appeared. If he noticed their disordered state, he gave no sign, merely said, 'Your nightcap, sir, would you like it served indoors or on the terrace?'

Turning to Eleanor, Robert queried, 'Do you have any preference?'

She shook her head. 'I won't have a nightcap if you don't mind.... Dave's sure to be back by now and he'll expect me to—'

'If you'll pardon me, miss,' Tompkins broke in respect-fully, 'Mr Benson hasn't yet returned.'

'He hasn't?' She heard the dismay in her own voice.

'No, miss.'

'You're quite sure about that?'

'Quite sure, miss.'

As she bit her lip, Robert said briskly, 'Thank you, Tompkins. Don't bother with a nightcap. I'll get anything we may need.'

'Very good, sir.' The manservant moved away on silent feet.

Together, Eleanor and Robert crossed the hall and climbed the stairs. When they reached her door, he paused to say, 'As soon as you're ready we'll have coffee and brandy in my sitting-room.'

She had opened her mouth to refuse, when he added firmly, 'I need to talk to you.'

Her heart sank. If it was Zoe he wanted to talk about, she'd rather not hear. It was too painful. 'I really don't—'

With a sigh, he warned, 'If you're not there in ten minutes, I'll be forced to come and fetch you.'

It seemed she was to have little choice in the matter, unless by some miracle Dave *was* back.

But everywhere was silent, and all the rooms were empty. Her heart sank even lower. In spite of the butler's assurance, she had clung to the desperate hope that he might have slipped in unnoticed.

Where on earth could he be? she wondered, as she showered quickly, and brushed out her hair. If there was some problem, surely he would have phoned?

If she had been staying here she wouldn't have bothered to dress again but, unwilling to go to Robert's suite in her night things, she put on fresh undies and a light, button-through shirtwaister.

She was about to re-pin her hair, when a quick glance at her watch showed that her allotted ten minutes was up.

Unwilling to be *fetched* like some recalcitrant child, she left it loose, a dark silky cloud around her shoulders and, making her way along to Robert's suite, tapped at the door.

'Come on in,' he called.

She obeyed, and was met by the welcome aroma of coffee. As she closed the door behind her, he came out of the bedroom, and she was startled to see that he was wearing nothing but a short, white-towelling robe.

Grinning wryly at the look on her face, he said, 'It didn't seem worth getting dressed again, but don't worry, I'm quite decent.'

He might be decent, but his lack of clothing did nothing for her composure.

'Come and sit down.'

Looking anywhere but at him, she took a seat on the couch. Only when she'd committed herself, did she realise it would have been better to have sat in a chair.

Having filled two coffee-cups, he put hers on the small

table beside her, and reached for the cut-glass brandy decanter.

'Not for me, thank you,' she said decidedly.

'You may find that you need one.' He poured two generous measures.

'Why should I need one?'

He came to sit beside her, turning a little to face her. 'Let's say for medicinal purposes.

'In the last twenty-four hours quite a few things have happened. One thing in particular was *wonderful*, the rest, not so good...'

She could only agree.

Waking in Robert Carrington's bed and having to face the fact that she had let down the man she loved, had been far from good. Then there had been Dave's continuing absence, and losing her ring...

But somehow none of those things had upset her half as much as Zoe's unexpected arrival. Though admitting she had absolutely no claim on Robert, the way he had tried to use her to make the blonde jealous, had caused her a lot of anguish.

To hear him describe Zoe's advent as *wonderful*, added immeasurably to that anguish and, her emotions dangerously close to the surface, she felt her eyes fill with tears.

As she tried desperately not to blink, to her chagrin a single bright teardrop escaped and rolled down her cheek.

'Don't cry,' he said, his voice tight. 'Please don't cry.'

'I'm sorry, I never do as a rule, it's just that—' Pulling herself up, she stopped short.

Wiping away the tear with the ball of his thumb, he assured her, 'We'll find it, I promise...'

So he thought she was still upset over the ring. Well that was better than him knowing the truth.

'If it means so much to you, I'll have Jackson clear the site completely in the morning.'

'It does mean a lot to me.'

She watched his jaw clench, and guessing he saw her as childish, pathetic even, she tried to explain. 'In all my life no one had ever really loved or wanted me. When Dave gave me the ring, it was like a symbol, a talisman, a hope for the future. That's why I always wore it....'

He got up abruptly and walked across to the window. The curtains hadn't been pulled to, and he stood quite still, his back to the room, gazing out over the dusky garden.

She could see the tension in his neck and broad shoulders, and the long, elegant line of his spine. His normally corn-coloured hair was darkened with water, and curling damply into his nape. She thought how virile and attractive he looked.

No wonder Zoe still wanted him.

Even the back of his well-shaped head with its neatly set ears was exciting, and she couldn't take her eyes off him as, for what seemed an age, he stood gazing through the leaded panes.

She was just wondering what he was thinking, when he swung round, his face set and decided, and returned to sit beside her.

'I said just now that in the last twenty-four hours a lot has happened, some of it not so good... And I'm afraid there's worse to come.'

Losing colour, she whispered, 'Are you trying to tell me that Dave's been involved in an accident?'

'No, that's *not* what I'm trying to tell you.'

'But something *must* have happened to him,' she insisted raggedly. 'Otherwise he would have been back by now.'

Then her voice rising a little with dread, 'He might be lying unconscious in some hospital... Or worse even... dead...'

Robert's mouth tightened, before he said with quiet emphasis, 'I can assure you categorically that Benson is alive and well.'

She was about to ask how he could be so certain, when he went on, 'But I think it's time you faced the fact that he isn't going to come back. He's gone for good.'

'No, you're wrong,' she cried. 'He'll come back.'

As Robert began to shake his head, she took a deep breath and blurted out the truth. 'He *has* to come back. You see the last cheque I wrote bounced, and we couldn't pay our suppliers. If you hadn't given us an advance of ten thousand pounds, we would be in terrible trouble.

'We *have* to do this job. For one thing, some of your money will already have been spent. If Dave had to pay cash for the things he ordered this morning, there may not be much more than five thousand left.'

'There's none left.'

'What?'

'The minute the cheque was cleared, as prearranged, the whole of the ten thousand was taken out in cash.'

'I don't know why,' she said blankly. 'We didn't need that much. We only owed Greenlees one thousand five hundred, and Dave said he was going to give them a post-dated cheque.

'Even if he gave them cash instead and paid in advance for the stuff he ordered this morning, it shouldn't have come to much more than five thousand.'

'He didn't pay in advance for anything.'

'You don't understand, he may have *had* to. Because their confidence had been shaken, Greenlees might have refused to deliver anything that hadn't been paid for.'

'He didn't *order* anything.'

'But that's what he went to London for.'

'That's what he *said* he was going for. What he *actually* went for was to pick up the cash, and run. All the money has gone. If he did give your suppliers a post-dated cheque that will bounce too.'

'This is ridiculous,' she said shakily. 'I know you've never liked him, but you're making him sound like a criminal.'

'Technically, he is.'

'That isn't true. It *can't* be.'

His tawny eyes serious, he said, 'Believe me, I wouldn't be telling you all this if I didn't know it was the truth.'

'*How* do you know?'

'As well as hiring a private investigator to watch his every move, I've done quite a lot of digging into his past.'

While she sat still and stunned, Robert continued, 'When I first started to check back I discovered he'd been in prison for fraud and deception. He was released just days before you met him.'

She felt a crazy sense of relief. 'No, no, you're quite mistaken. You've somehow got the wrong man. When I met Dave he was at college. He'd already been there for two years, and was just about to start his final year.'

'Benson never went to college,' Robert told her positively.

'Of course he did.... Where else would he have learnt so much about computers and communications? And he really does know an awful lot.'

'I'm sure he does, but most of it he picked up while he was in prison. With rehabilitation a priority, they run special technology courses. He was clever enough to grab, and make the most of, every single opportunity that came his way.

'That's something he's adept at, exploiting both situations and people. It's one of the things that makes him a good con man.'

'I don't believe it,' she said forcefully. 'Have you any hard facts?'

'Plenty. It's a fact that since he left the children's home he hasn't worked for more than a week or so at a time. He's made a practice of living off women, mainly young girls who fell for his good looks and charm.

'It's a fact that, finding most girls didn't have enough money to cover his needs, he latched on to an elderly widow. Unfortunately she trusted him completely, and it didn't take him long to con her out of her small amount of life savings. But it was stealing her credit card and trying a spot of fraud, that finally landed him in prison.'

Needing to grasp the full enormity of what he was telling her, she questioned, 'And you say he'd only been released a matter of days when he met me?'

'Yes. He was cock-a-hoop when he discovered you had some money. But knowing how hard you'd worked for it, and aware that you were more intelligent than most of the women he'd conned, he realised he'd have to move with care.

'Your idea of starting a business seemed to make sense, and even though it meant waiting a year, he decided that so long as it was what *he* wanted to do, and you kept supporting him, he'd go along with it.'

'You don't think the spell in prison might have changed him? That by the time he met me he really wanted to go straight?'

'No, I don't,' Robert answered flatly. '*Possibly* he saw it as a chance to make something of himself. Though I very much doubt it.'

'What makes you say that?' she challenged.

'Why do you think he suggested you should be the senior partner?'

'You'd better tell me.'

'As you *knew* who he was, he was forced to use his real name, so he was hoping that if things went wrong, you would be the one to have to carry the can.

'However, going into partnership with you was a con-
structive move, and it might well have meant a decent future, if he'd been willing to do his share of work—'

'Oh, but he *was*,' she broke in eagerly.

Looking grim and unconvinced, Robert asked, 'Who did
all the work on the office you found?'

'Well as it happens I did, but Dave was always out trying
to get orders—'

'I've no doubt he was always out, but his time was spent
in snooker halls rather than making any effort to drum up
business. Even so, with your input, the partnership might
still have worked if he hadn't given in to temptation and
started syphoning money off.'

So that must be why Greenlees' cheque had bounced in
the first place. She had been sure there was enough in the
account to cover it....

But if Dave had needed more money why hadn't he told
her? How could he have taken it behind her back, then lied
to her, if he'd *cared* at all?

Feeling curiously empty, hollow, she said carefully, 'You
seem to know pretty well everything, but there's one aspect
you haven't yet touched on. The personal side... Did he
really love me? Intend to—' Unable to go on, she stopped
and swallowed hard.

A long silence followed. Then, with a sigh, Robert said,
'Because I know how much it means to you I'd *like* to be
able to tell you that you were special, that he was on the
level as far as you were concerned. But I'm afraid he just
used you as ruthlessly as he used all those other women.'

Her hands balled into fists and, not wanting to believe
it, she began to shake her head.

'Think it out for yourself,' he urged. 'If he'd loved you,
would he have kept *taking* in such a selfish way? What has
he ever *given* you?'

'An engagement ring.'

'Which meant less than nothing as far as *he* was concerned. When you were ill did he care for you? When you were sad did he comfort you? When you were lonely was he there for you?'

'No,' she admitted quietly.

'Then I'm surprised you didn't see it sooner.'

'Perhaps because I was afraid, I've been trying *not* to see it. I didn't want to think he cared nothing for me.... I *had* to believe he loved me, *had* to believe he wanted to marry me... Maybe he—'

Almost angrily, Robert said, 'It's time to stop clinging to false hopes and face the fact that he didn't love you, and he certainly never had any intention of marrying you.'

Rattled, she cried, 'How can you be so sure about that?'

'Because he already has a wife.'

'No, he can't have!'

'I'm sorry to have to break it to you so brutally, but he's been married for almost three years....'

So he had been married even when he was talking about extending their partnership to include marriage. And the engagement ring *had* been just a sop.

'Her name's Tony...'

Eleanor bit her inner lip until she tasted the warm saltiness of blood. How many times had Dave mentioned Tony but, gullible to the last, she had assumed that his flatmate was a man.

For a moment or two, while she assimilated the news, she spiralled in circles of pain like something mortally wounded. Dave was the only one who had ever loved her...

Only he hadn't.

'One of the reasons he didn't want leave town and live at Greyladies,' Robert went on, 'was that his wife doesn't like to be alone, and she kicked up a tremendous fuss about being left.'

In a dead voice, Eleanor asked, 'If you knew all this,

why did you insist on us living at Greyladies? You must have had a reason.'

After a glance at her pale face, Robert answered, 'Yes, I did. I wanted him out of the way while Marshall, my private detective, finished gathering all the facts.

'On Saturday night, having heard Marshall's latest report, I decided to go to London and check the more personal things out for myself.

'I went to see his wife and we had a long and very frank discussion.

'In return for certain assurances, she told me a lot about her husband's activities that I couldn't otherwise have known. In particular, exactly how he had *used* you.

'I found myself appalled by his capacity for meanness and deceit and callous insensitivity. When I came back home on Wednesday evening I was so furious, that if Benson had still been here, I might have felt tempted to break his neck.'

'Instead you took me to bed. Was that because you felt sorry for me?'

'No, it wasn't,' he said curtly. 'I don't take women to bed because I feel sorry for them. And if you can't tell the difference between sympathy and sexual desire, you have a problem.'

Seeing he was seriously angry, she moistened her dry lips and apologised. 'I'm sorry, I shouldn't have said that.' All at once she was close to tears, and her voice shook betrayingly, as she tried to go on. 'It's just that I'm...'

He reached out and, taking her hand, gave it a squeeze. 'It's all right. Don't worry about it. I know how shattered you must feel. It's a terrible shock to learn that someone you love has treated you so shabbily.'

Swallowing, she asked, 'What about his...wife?' In spite of her efforts she stumbled a little over the word. 'Does she...?'

'Yes, though he's never tried to keep anything from her, and she knows exactly what he's like, she still loves him. And I believe that in his own way he cares about her.

'She told me he's been worried to death about her health over the past two or three months. After you first mentioned he was edgy, I realised you were right. He obviously had something on his mind. Though I had no idea what...'

After hesitating, as if wondering how much it was going to hurt her, Robert said, 'The fact is, she's expecting a baby, and it's proving to be a difficult, and costly pregnancy.

'They've lost one child—she was pregnant when they got married—and she needs some specialised treatment. Treatment that has to be paid for, and is extremely expensive.

'That seems to be the main reason he decided to take the ten thousand and disappear.'

'His wife knows about it?'

'Oh, yes, she knew the plan. As soon as Benson had his hands on the money, they were intending to do a moonlight flit.

'Although the flat they have is small and shabby, it's fairly cheap for London, and she wasn't looking forward to having to move, but they thought for ten thousand it was worth it.

'They appear to be two of a kind. Though she didn't want him to have to do anything *criminal* in case he was caught, she had absolutely no qualms about living off other women.

'In fact she seemed quite proud of the way he'd conned you into supporting them both by pretending he was at college.

'The only thing she does jealously insist on, is that he stays faithful to her.'

Her voice tight, Eleanor said, 'I see. How lucky for me.'

'For us both. When it seemed as if you and Benson might *not* be going to bed together after all, I began to live in hope. When I discovered for a fact that you weren't lovers, I couldn't believe my luck.'

'No doubt you wouldn't have wanted another man's cast-offs,' she remarked bitterly, and knew she was being unfair.

'I would have wanted you any way I could get you,' he corrected. 'I still can't imagine how Benson managed to keep his hands off you.'

'Even if he hadn't had a jealous wife I doubt if he would have found me sufficiently attractive to want to take to bed.'

'Don't be foolish, my love...'

She wanted to cry, *don't call me that*! It hurt too much when he didn't mean it.

'There's no man in his right mind who wouldn't want to take you to bed.'

'*He* certainly didn't. In fact he never seemed to want to touch me at all.

'I tried to tell myself that because of the way he'd been brought up, he was undemonstrative. That he kept his feelings hidden deep inside, as I did. But in my heart of hearts I think I knew he felt nothing for me. Not even lust. But our future together, was the only dream I had to cling to....'

And now that dream had come to an abrupt end.

As though reading her mind, Robert said, 'There was no point in it dragging on. You wouldn't have wanted it to, would you?'

'No,' she said. 'It's better to face the truth than live in a fool's paradise.'

Only now she had nothing. No Dave... No future together to look forward to... No money... No business...

She felt a great desolation of spirit.

'Thank you for telling me.'

As she jumped up and turned blindly away, he rose to his feet and spoke her name. 'Eleanor...'

Turning back, she went into his arms like someone coming home, and feeling their warmth close around her, put her head on his shoulder, not *wanting* his compassion, but *needing* it.

Making no attempt to kiss her, he simply stood and held her quietly.

For a while she allowed herself to lean against him, absorbing the comfort, gathering his strength, mentally steeling herself to the point where she would be able to leave the haven of his arms and walk away.

Finally, knowing that if she didn't move now she would lose the will to go, she pulled free and headed for the door, stumbling a little.

He reached it first.

When she refused to look at him, he put a hand beneath her chin and lifted her face. 'Why don't you stay?'

Her grey eyes darkened almost to charcoal, she said harshly, 'I don't want your pity.'

'That's good, because you're not going to get it.'

'Nor do I want you to make love to me.'

'I promise I won't even try. But this is no time to be alone. At the very least, you need someone to hold you through the night.'

She looked into his green-gold eyes and saw, not pity, but tenderness and caring.

If it hadn't been for Zoe...

'Come on,' he coaxed, taking her hand. 'I'll even borrow a pair of pyjamas from Tompkins, if my being naked bothers you.'

She gave a little choke of laughter and admitted, 'It's not so much your being naked...'

'Then what is it? It's a bit too late to be thinking of the proprieties.'

'I was thinking of Zoe,' she admitted in a rush.

'Zoe?' He frowned. 'Why should you be thinking of Zoe?' Then thoughtfully, 'Strange that she should turn up here when I'd just been talking about her.'

'She wants you back.'

He grimaced.

'There's no point in trying to deny it.'

'I'm not trying to deny it,' he said coolly.

'How can you be so...so casual...when it's quite obvious she still loves you.... And if you're hoping to make her jealous, then I won't be a party to it.' She pulled her hand out of his grasp, and made to open the door.

'You seem to have a pretty poor opinion of me,' he said coldly. 'But I can assure you that I'm *not* hoping to make her jealous, and though she may want me back, she doesn't love me, and never has. It was my money she loved.'

Cynically, he added, 'She must have been sick when she heard I'd inherited Josh's estate and was even wealthier.'

'But if he died some time ago, it couldn't have been *that* that...' The words tailed off.

'Brought her back?' he finished for her. 'No. I imagine she thought the time was right. Not only had her lover been posted abroad, but a recent magazine article mentioned that I seemed to be a confirmed bachelor, which might have led her to believe that I still loved her.... And of course enough time had elapsed for me to have cooled off. If you recall, she admitted as much.'

'Yes...'

Looking at her expressive face, he asked, 'But something's still bothering you?'

'She's very beautiful....' Then huskily, 'Do you still love her?'

'No, I don't still love her.' He held open the door. 'If you don't believe me, then perhaps you had better go. On the other hand, if you want to stay and hear the truth about our breakup…'

'Yes, please,' she said meekly.

Closing the door again, he began without preamble, 'The wedding was only a week away, when one night I left the office early and got back to my flat to find my bride-to-be and her bridesmaid, Bridget, having a heart-to-heart.

'I was just about to open the living-room door when I heard Zoe say, "…Of course I don't *love* him, but Robert's good in bed and he's rolling in money. That's what counts. I hate the thought of having to work for rich bitches all my life.… Nor do I fancy the idea of trying to manage on the salary a junior civil servant earns, otherwise I'd have stayed with Simon…"

'Hearing that came as a devil of a shock. Foolishly, no doubt, I'd believed her when she swore that Simon meant nothing to her, and she loved me.

'Bridget said something like, "But surely giving up your career and marrying someone just for their money is taking a big risk?"'

'To which Zoe answered, "Simon will be waiting in the wings to spice things up a bit, so to speak. And If I find I'm bored to tears, I can always get a divorce.… You know what they say about marrying well and divorcing better? I could end up both free and wealthy.…"'

'At that point, I walked in. Realising I'd overheard, she tried to pretend she'd been joking. Which somehow made matters worse…

'Furiously angry, I told her she had half an hour to pack her things and leave.

'Seeing I was deadly serious, she threatened to kick up a fuss and spread it all over the newspapers that I'd thrown her out.

'I warned her that if she tried it, though I didn't relish the publicity, I'd tell them *why*. On the other hand, if she saw sense and left quietly, she could keep the ring and all the things I'd bought for her, including her wedding present, which happened to be a nice little sports car.

'In the end she decided it would be sensible to take what she could get.'

'I'm sorry,' Eleanor said, and meant it. 'You must have been shattered.'

'For a while I was. Now I can only feel grateful that I discovered the truth in time. In retrospect I can see that our marriage would never have worked, we wanted such different things. And though she has style and beauty, she has no warmth, no depth, no sensitivity.'

'Then you don't still regret the breakup?'

'What makes you ask?'

'When you were talking about what had happened in the last twenty-four hours, you said her coming here was wonderful.'

'I said nothing of the sort. What was wonderful, had absolutely nothing to do with Zoe.'

'It hadn't?'

'No. I was referring to last night.'

A kind of glow spread through her, and without conscious volition, she lifted her face to be kissed.

The moment he touched his lips lightly to hers, it sparked off an electric excitement that flashed through her, turning her whole body to flame.

Though only their mouths were in contact, she was suddenly as aroused and hungry for him as if he'd touched her naked body with his own.

It was not only a burning physical desire, but a powerful yearning to surrender herself completely to this man.

But for some reason he seemed to be holding back.

Even when she put her arms around his neck and her lips parted enticingly, his kiss remained comforting, almost brotherly.

In something like desperation, she pressed her body to his, and felt his slight, but unmistakable withdrawal.

Her arms dropped to her sides, and her skin crawling with shame and self-disgust she stepped back, and said stiffly, 'I'm sorry. I seem to be jumping to conclusions and making a terrible mess of things. If Dave didn't want me, why should you?'

CHAPTER TEN

SHE had turned to run, when a hand on her arm he swung her round and said almost savagely, 'Of course I want you!'

'But I felt you draw away.'

He sighed. 'You said you didn't want me to make love to you, and I promised I wouldn't even try. But I'm only human.'

Seeing her uncertainty, he unfastened the belt of his towelling robe and, pulling it off, tossed it aside. 'Do you still think I don't want you?'

When she lifted her eyes to his face she was blushing rosily.

'What I *don't* want, is for you to wake up in the morning and regret it, like you did last time.'

'I won't and I didn't before. I only said I regretted it then because I felt I'd let Dave down.'

'And I'd like to make it quite clear that if we, as two consenting adults, *do* go to bed together it isn't, certainly on my part, intended as either sympathy or therapy. It will be purely for pleasure… The joy we can bring one another.'

'I'm happy with that,' she said softly.

'In that case, come to bed.' He smiled at her, letting the smile trail behind him like a lure, as he crossed the room and disappeared through the open bedroom door.

She had expected him to sweep her into his arms and take her with him, and just for a second or two she remained where she was, feeling abandoned.

Then becoming aware that this was some kind of test, she followed him through to the bedroom and, standing uncertainly, watched him walk across to the four-poster, throw back the bedclothes, and climb in.

Moving closer to the bed, head bent, she began to unbutton her dress with fingers that shook so much they could scarcely complete their task.

When she found the courage to look up, brilliant eyes fixed on her, he was stretched full length, leaning back against the pillows, his hands clasped behind his head, the bedclothes piled carelessly at his feet.

He put her in mind of some sultan waiting for his concubine and, her nipples growing firm, and her mouth going dry, she looked hastily away.

Very aware of his gaze, she shed her dress, unclipped her bra to free her breasts, then unconsciously graceful, slipped her panties down over her hips, and stepped out of them.

When she was naked, feeling nervous and painfully exposed under his scrutiny, she lifted her chin and looked at him once more.

His little smile was teasing and she realised that what he'd been whistling softly, half under his breath, was *The Striptease*.

She might have been embarrassed if the expression in his eyes hadn't told her everything she needed to know. Though she might not be beautiful, he clearly thought her so, and that was enough to make her *feel* beautiful.

The last of her doubts as to whether she was doing the right thing, fled, and when he slid down the bed and held out his hand, she took it with a feeling of thankfulness, and got in beside him.

He lay smiling up at her through thick gold lashes, and her heart turned over. 'What did you think of my striptease?' she asked with wry self-mockery, as she bent to kiss him.

'Quite delightful and very exciting.'

With a swift movement she was unprepared for, he pulled her down on top of him. One hand on the back of her neck, the other on her bottom, his face buried at the angle between her neck and shoulder, he gave her a love bite.

As, laughing and protesting, she began to wriggle, he rolled, pinning her beneath him, fitting the length of his body to hers.

She felt his arms and his weight, the firmness of his flesh, his heart beating strongly and his blood coursing fast.

In a second they both went up in flames.

At first his lovemaking was urgent, direct, focused… Then it became slower, sweeter, but no less intense.… From there it went on to be teasingly indolent and inventive…

By the time Eleanor slept she was sated with pleasure and contentment, and the feeling of being whole and fulfilled that the joy and laughter they had shared, brought.

She awoke to a room full of sunshine, and a feeling of euphoria that even finding she was alone in the big bed, failed to diminish.

For a little while she lay, reliving all the delight of the previous night then, like a dark cloud rolling in, came complete remembrance.

Her breathing grew shallow and she began to tremble as she waited to feel despair and desolation.

To some extent they came, but overlaying them was a healthy anger, and eclipsing them all, an unexpected sense of freedom.

She felt different, released, relieved of a burden she had never seen as a burden. The indebtedness Dave had managed to make her feel, the need to please him, the fear that she wouldn't be able to hold him, had vanished like morning mist with the sun on it.

There was a world of difference between her feelings for him, she realised now, and her feelings for Robert.…

What she felt for Dave had lingered from her childhood adoration and, when they had met up again, she had needed to love someone to start feeling part of life.

With Dave, his mind and hers had occasionally touched, but their spirits never had. With Robert everything touched.

She caught her breath. Up until now, she had told herself that what she felt for Robert was purely physical, sexual attraction, nothing more.

But of course it was a great deal more. She, who had never really loved, loved him with a sweetness and a complexity she hadn't known herself capable of. She loved everything about him, his clever mind, his kindness and compassion, his lithe, hard-muscled body; she loved just being with him, loved going to bed with him.

They were compatible, they liked the same things: the country side, animals, books, music…

And unlike Dave, he understood her. He made her laugh, he made her feel, not only secure, but as if she was willing to ride on a roller coaster.

With him, she found both warmth and magic…. While he could take her to the stars, he was also her comfort and her anchor.

If only he loved her…

But that was like asking for a miracle….

With a sigh, she glanced at her watch. Nearly half past ten… It was time to get up and face all the problems that had to be faced.

Her clothes had been picked up and placed neatly over a chair, and as soon as she had put them on she slipped along to her room.

Having showered, she pulled on a pair of jeans and a cotton top, and took her hair up in a pony-tail. Then, on an impulse, she went into what had been Dave's bedroom, and opened his wardrobe.

It was empty. There wasn't even a coat-hanger left.

She felt nothing. Not even anger.

As she reached the hall, the housekeeper appeared. 'Ah, there you are, Miss Smith. Mr Robert said you'd probably be sleeping in. Will you be wanting breakfast?'

'No, thank you, Mrs Tompkins.'

'A nice pot of coffee, perhaps?'

'If it's not too much trouble.'

'No trouble at all. Would you like it on the terrace? The weather seems to be holding.'

'That would be lovely, thank you. Is Robert…?'

'He went up to town very early this morning, miss. He said to tell you he'll be back for lunch.'

The housekeeper bustled away.

It was another lovely day, and when Eleanor had drunk her coffee, joined by Paddington, she went for a walk in the walled garden.

As she approached the spot where she had lost her ring, she saw that Jackson, a wheelbarrow by his side and a fork in his hand, was about to start clearing the plants.

He looked up to nod, and say a cheerful, 'Good morning, miss. Isn't it a nice day?'

'Good morning, Jackson. Yes, it's lovely.'

'The master explained about your ring. I'll keep a good eye out for it as I clear the ground.'

'Thank you, but there's no longer any need for you to go to so much trouble.'

'Then you've found it, miss?'

'No, I haven't found it. But I don't really want it back. It was inexpensive, and it no longer has any sentimental value for me.'

'Well, if you're sure, miss?'

'Quite sure, thank you, Jackson.'

When she had walked as far as the pond and back, she returned to the garden and sat down on a stone bench, the dog at her feet.

Throwing sticks for Paddington, she had tried to empty her mind of worries about the future and just enjoy this last walk, which had been in the nature of a farewell.

In the few days she had been at Greyladies, she had grown to love both the house and its surroundings. No, she hadn't *grown* to love it, she had loved it on sight. From the first moment it had been as dear and familiar to her as an old friend.

Now she had to leave it.

Still she would have had to leave after a few weeks anyway, she told herself sternly. But a few weeks, even a few days, would have been precious.

The only way she could have left Greyladies gladly, would have been if Robert had been an estate worker, instead of owning it, and had been leaving too.

If he had been poor and had wanted her, she would have followed him to the ends of the earth, lived in a hut with him, slept on the bare floor with him.

Though knowing Robert, he would soon have turned the hut into a mansion with carpeted floors...

'So this is where you're hiding.' Dressed in smart casuals, he was standing looking down at her, his face quiet, unsmiling.

Having fussed the dog, who had risen to greet him, he took a seat beside her and asked, 'How are you feeling this morning?'

Lifting her chin, she said, 'Fine, thank you. I just have to decide what to do.'

'In what sense?'

'Well as senior partner of a business that no longer exists, I owe our suppliers fifteen hundred pounds, possible more, and—'

'To set your mind at rest on that score, I've dealt with everything that was outstanding.'

'Thank you.... I'm really grateful.... Though that must mean I'm very much in your debt as—'

'It doesn't matter in the slightest.'

'As well as owing you ten thousand,' she finished doggedly.

'You can certainly discount that.'

'Then you've managed to get it back?' she asked hopefully.

'I haven't tried.'

'But you've been to the police?'

'No. If you remember, I mentioned that Mrs Benson had told me a lot in return for certain assurances. One of which, was that I wouldn't involve the police.

'Which means of course that they don't have to run. They can stay where they are. I further promised that if Benson gets a job and makes an effort to go straight, I'd let them keep the money.

'No doubt his wife, who doesn't want to see him back in jail, will try and make sure he stays out of trouble.

'So there won't be too much financial pressure, I've promised that until the baby is born I'll foot the bill for any further treatment Mrs Benson needs.'

'That's very generous,' Eleanor said slowly. 'Though I don't see why you should.'

'Let's just say I can afford to. I'm conscious that I've been very fortunate. Life's treated me kindly compared to some people.'

But she knew that even if he hadn't been fortunate, if he'd had nothing, he would never have taken to crime, or battened on to women in the callous way Dave had done. Robert had kindness and principles, while Dave had none.

'You don't think...?' she began hesitantly.

On her wavelength immediately, he said, 'That Benson will try to take me for a ride? I certainly wouldn't put it past him, so I shall pay any money directly to the clinic.'

A thought struck her, and she queried, 'Can I ask you something…'

'Fire away.'

'Last night when you were telling me about Dave, you said, ''When I first started to check back…'' How long ago is that?'

'Two or three weeks.'

'*Before* you came to us?'

'That's right.'

'But if you already knew about Dave's past, why come to us in the first place? Why give us the job?'

'The job was only an excuse. I wanted to meet you, to see for myself what kind of person you were, and how things stood between you and Benson.…'

As she gaped at him, he went on, 'When I had a pretty shrewd idea, I offered you the job because I needed an excuse to have you stay at Greyladies.

'At that point I didn't want to tell you the truth. I wanted you to come to the manor unprepared and see what, if anything, you remembered.'

'I don't understand,' she said blankly.

He glanced at his watch. 'It's a long, and fairly complicated story, so I think we should have a spot of lunch before I tell you the rest.'

Pulling her to her feet, he tucked her hand through his arm in the companionable way she was getting used to, adding, 'Mrs Tompkins mentioned that you'd had no breakfast, so you must be starving.'

His manner was sober, almost grave, and as they walked back to the house she found herself wondering what on earth it was all about.

During lunch he said little, and it wasn't until their coffee-cups were empty that he rose and led the way up to the library.

When she was seated on the soft leather couch, Robert

took a seat beside her and asked, 'From the first you've felt at home at Greyladies, as if you knew the place?'

'Yes... I presumed it must have been through the magazine feature.'

'Yet the refectory and the old kitchen, which were the highlights of the feature, you found you couldn't recall at all?'

'No, it seemed very odd....'

'It wasn't odd. In fact it added confirmation that your feeling of recognition *wasn't* through magazine pictures.

'You see for several decades that part of the house was badly in need of repair and blocked off, and when you were here previously, it was still blocked off.

'But the hall and the staircase, which were just the same, you recognised. And in my bedroom, you subconsciously knew where the bathroom door *should* have been. You knew because you had actually slept in that room before it was altered.'

Dazedly, she objected, 'I don't see how you could possibly know something like that.'

'Through Josh's diaries. As well as enjoying painting, he also wrote prodigiously, keeping a diary all his life until he could no longer hold a pen.

'A couple of months ago, when I was going through some of his papers, I came across them. They told a poignant love story that had lasted for some forty years, before ending inconclusively.

'Intrigued, and wanting to know what had happened to the people involved, I began to dig...

'But in order to keep things simple, I'd better start at the beginning. When Josh was barely twenty, he met and fell head over heels in love with a seventeen-year-old girl named Jenny Linton...'

As Eleanor's gaze lifted to the portrait above the fireplace, Robert went on, 'Though they never married, and spent most of their lives apart, she was undoubtedly the love of his life.'

'And she loved him?'

'Yes, she loved him. But they met too young, and circumstances caused them to drift apart. For various reasons they each married someone else, and for quite a while lost touch.

'When they were past middle age, fate brought them together again. Grandfather was a widower, but Jenny was still married to Elmer Sheering, an American-born businessman.

'It seems that neither Josh nor Jenny had enjoyed what you might describe as a happy marriage. Sheering had proved to be a cold, mean-spirited man with very strict principles, and Jenny had faced a lot of difficulties.

'But Grandfather wrote in his diary, that despite everything she was still the same old Jenny, full of warmth and courage and the joy of living.

'She and her husband had had just one child, a girl named Sarah, who at fifteen found herself pregnant. The sixteen-year-old father, though from a good family, was a young tearaway who denied all responsibility.

'Sheering made his daughter's life a misery, and when the baby was only a few months old Sarah ran away from home leaving the child behind.

'Furious at being saddled with an illegitimate child, he washed his hands of her. He forbade Jenny to either support her or speak to her again, and decreed that the baby be put into care....

'Jenny defied him on both counts. She gave Sarah as much financial help as she could, and insisted on taking care of her baby granddaughter herself....'

His eyes on Eleanor's stunned face, Robert said, 'Yes... Jenny Sheering was your grandmother, which of course accounts for the likeness in the younger portrait.... Would you like me to stop, so you have time to take it in?'

Her voice scarcely above a whisper, she urged, 'No, I'd like you to go on.'

Speaking quietly, and sounding oddly detached, he obeyed. 'Not used to being crossed, Sheering made his wife's life as difficult as possible, and she had just about had enough when he decided to go back to the States to live.

'This was when she and Grandfather met up again, and found they still loved each other.

'Discovering how rocky the marriage was, Josh asked her to get a divorce and marry him. But Jenny, who had been brought up to believe her marriage vows were sacred, was hesitant.

'When she finally broached the subject, Sheering refused to either consider a divorce or support her and the child if she left.

'On hearing this, Josh said he would be only too happy to have them live at Greyladies, and take care of them both.

'Seeing he was about to lose her, Sheering promised that if she went to the States with him he would work to make things better.

'She agreed, on condition that he accepted his grand-daughter and tried to love the child. He swore to do his best, so long as she severed all contact with Josh.

'Which she did.

'It was more than six years before he heard from her again. Then early one February, out of the blue, she rang to say that she and her granddaughter were in London. They had come for Sarah's wedding, and when they had seen the bride-to-be, could she and her granddaughter come to visit him?

'He was delighted, and suggested sending a car for her. But she said it wasn't necessary. While they were in

England, intending to visit an old friend who was terminally ill, and who lived in Cornwall, she had bought a small second-hand car to run around in.

'It was cheaper than hiring one, and the dealer had agreed to take it off her hands when she went back to the States.

'Needless to say, Josh welcomed them both with open arms and refusing to let them book into an hotel, insisted on them staying at Greyladies.

'When Jenny and he talked privately and he asked how things were with Sheering, she admitted that though he had made an effort to be kind to the child, they hadn't really worked out.

'In fact they had discussed a separation, and the few weeks she was in England were to be a kind of breathing space, time to think.

'She said that when the wedding was over and she had been down to Cornwall to visit her friend, she intended to go back to the States and see what her husband had decided.

'When Josh tried to press *her* to do the deciding, she said she couldn't. Sheering had threatened that if she tried to leave him without it being a joint decision, he would prevent her taking the child, whom everyone regarded as his daughter.

'Josh pointed out that as they were both safely in England, there was no *need* to go back. But Jenny said that she had given her word, and was going to stick by it.

'When the wedding day arrived, to Josh's surprise, Jenny asked if she could leave her granddaughter with him. Looking unhappy, she explained that though Sarah had been pleased to see how the child had grown, her husband-to-be had no idea she had ever had a baby, and she wanted to keep it from him.

'Apparently Jenny had tried to talk her into telling him,

but she refused. She said if he knew, he wouldn't marry her.

'So while Jenny was in London, her granddaughter stayed with Josh. He wrote that they had taken the dogs for a long walk in the snowy park, and then sat in front of a roaring fire toasting crumpets.

'As soon as Jenny got back the following morning she packed in preparation to go down to Cornwall for a couple of days, before travelling home.

'Josh did his utmost to dissuade her from going back to the States, but she was a woman with quiet strength and plenty of moral fibre, and he couldn't budge her.

'She and the child had been at Greyladies for almost three weeks, while Josh had taken what he described as a well-earned, off-peak holiday.

'He mentions that the same day they left for Cornwall, he himself was due to fly to the Far East for several weeks on a business trip.

'They parted reluctantly, with Jenny promising that if Sheering *did* agree to a separation, she would bring the little girl back to England and live at Greyladies.

'But she made Josh swear that if she *didn't* return or get in touch with him, he would make no effort to contact her.

'He wrote then how wonderfully happy they had all been together, and described the little girl as being a beautiful, sunny-natured child, with whom he had felt an instant rapport...'

Reaching in his pocket, Robert produced a small book bound in navy leather and, opening it at a marked place, went on, 'Then in his own words, "Like her grandmother, she possess a certain *feyness*, a will o' the wisp combination of light and flame, that I find enchanting."

'"When she first saw the stained glass in the hall, she remarked that it was like living inside a rainbow. A beautiful thought for a child."

'"Yet she has the down-to-earth qualities of kindness and compassion, warmth and courage, and a kind of tensile strength that I hope will stand her in good stead."

'"In so short a time I've grown to love the child as dearly as I love Jenny, and I believe she loves me too. I can only hope and pray that they both come back to me"...'

Tears trickling down her face unheeded, Eleanor said, 'I wish I could remember both him and my grandmother.'

'Maybe one day you will. You half remembered the house, and all the other memories must be tucked away in your brain somewhere.'

Passing her a folded handkerchief, he added, 'Even if you never remember, at least you know who you are now.'

She dried her face and blew her nose. 'I still don't know where I was born, or how old I am, or what my real name is.'

'You were born in Kent on March sixth, and you weren't quite eight when you were taken into care. Coincidentally, you were christened, Claire Eleanor. So at least you won't have to change your name.'

There was a silence while she thought over what she had just learnt. After a moment, her eyes fixed on his face, she asked, 'Why did no one recognise my photograph when the police put it in the papers?'

'Josh, who would certainly have recognised it, was in Hong Kong, and by the time he got home, the story must have been yesterday's news.

'It's obvious from the entries in his diary that he thought you had returned to the States. For months he waited and hoped, until it became clear that Jenny wasn't going to bring you back.

'But true to his word, he made no attempt to contact her, so he never discovered the truth.'

Frowning, she said, 'But surely when we didn't go home

as planned my...grandfather would have made some enquiries?'

'Apparently he didn't. He must have presumed that Jenny had decided not to go back to him, and washed his hands of the pair of you.'

'Is he still alive?'

'No. When I got the address from your mother and tried to contact him, I discovered that he'd died quite recently. I'm sorry.'

She shook her head. 'There's no need to be.' Then urgently, 'What about my mother? Why didn't *she* recognise my picture?'

Robert's mouth tightened. 'I'd like to be able to tell you that she was away on honeymoon and didn't see it, but I'm afraid I can't. You remember being told that one day while you were asleep, a young woman came who *thought* she might know you...?'

'But she was mistaken...'

'She wasn't brave enough to go through with it, so she *pretended* to be mistaken.'

Eleanor took a deep breath, before saying evenly, 'You mean because her new husband didn't know about me she decided to abandon me for the second time?'

'Yes,' he said grimly.

'How can you be sure about that?'

'Because when I first went to see her, she admitted as much.... Having worked so hard to get it, she didn't want to risk her new status and her wealthy lifestyle.'

Something prickled at the back of Eleanor's neck, as if a cold breath had blown over her nape. Huskily, she said, 'So my mother is...'

'Lady Sarah Allenby... Who unfortunately for you turned out to be as cold and selfish as her father. Though she knew you had nothing and no one, she let you be taken into care with scarcely a qualm.

'Even after all these years she was terrified I'd tell her husband, so I was able to blackmail her into giving me the information I needed to enable my detective to trace you.

'It was when he discovered you were tied up with a man, that he checked on Benson's past.'

'I see...'

Then with a last faint hope, 'But she...my mother... wanted to see me, didn't she?'

'That was the only spark of humanity she showed. When she asked me to arrange a meeting, I thought she might possibly want to tell you herself about the past. But if she did, she chickened out.'

Taking her hand, he said, 'Though I decided you had a right to know the whole truth, I hate to give you all this fresh pain.'

'Oddly enough it doesn't hurt. Knowing about my grandmother and Josh, knowing *they* loved me, is what matters. Somehow it makes the future seem less...bleak.'

But just the thought of the future, of leaving Robert and Greyladies made her eyes fill with tears again.

As she struggled not to let them fall, he muttered, 'Damn Benson!' and took her in his arms.

His mouth muffled against her silky hair, he held her quietly until, ashamed of her weakness, she reluctantly drew away.

Picking up her left hand, he rubbed the ball of his thumb over her bare engagement finger, and asked, 'Why did you tell Jackson your ring was no longer important?'

'Because it isn't.'

'I wish you could say the same about Benson.'

'I can.'

Hearing the breath hiss through his teeth, she went on, 'When I woke up this morning I realised two things. I was angry, rather than broken-hearted, and though I'd cared about him, I'd never really *loved* him.

'Maybe I only thought I did because I *needed* to love someone and feel loved in return. I suppose that's why I closed my eyes and refused to see what he was really like.... Now I can see clearly, I just wonder how I could have been such a fool.'

'So what will you do now?'

'Begin all over again. As soon as I've found a job, I'll start saving and pay you back every penny I owe you, I promise.'

'What kind of job had you in mind?'

'I don't really know. Whatever I can get. Though as I can't afford to keep the flat, it will have to be a live-in one.'

'I could offer you a live-in job.'

'You still want an office?'

'Yes, I do, but that wasn't what I meant. The job I was thinking of is a great deal more personal. I want you to be my wife.

'I fell in love with you the minute I saw you. I love all the things about you that Josh loved, your beauty, your courage, your warmth...'

Both her heart and her breathing seemed to stop. Terribly afraid that the whole thing was unreal, that she was hearing what she *wanted* to hear, she simply stared at him.

Usually so in control, so confident, he looked uncertain, fazed by her silence. Then with a faint, taut smile, he added, 'People who know me say I'm a lot like Josh. You cared for him, so maybe you could come to care for me too?'

Looking into his green-gold eyes she saw the love there, and with a rush of gladness realised that this was real, that he was offering her freely what she would have given her soul for.

When he had called her ''my love'' in front of Zoe, and said he hoped she would make her home at Greyladies, he had *meant* it.

The miracle had happened.

Still her voice wouldn't work.

The light dying out of his eyes, he said quietly, 'Forgive me. I'm an insensitive oaf to talk about love so soon after all of this. You obviously need time—'

Throwing herself into his arms, her face pressed against his throat, stammering, almost incoherent, she assured him, 'I don't…I already love you…'

He held her away a little, ordering huskily, 'Say that again.'

'I love you.… So much it *hurts*… I think I've loved you from—'

But he was kissing her hungrily, his mouth stopping the words. Even when he took her hand and led her through to the bedroom, they still didn't speak.

They made love—silent, smiling, transmitting, receiving, affirming all there was between them. A combination of love and friendship, of companionship and trust and sensual joy that would last a lifetime.

SURRENDER TO THE MILLIONAIRE

by

Margaret Mayo

Margaret Mayo was reading Mills & Boon® romances long before she began to write them. In fact she never had any plans to become a writer. After an idea for a short story popped into her head she was thrilled when it turned into a full-scale novel. Now, over twenty-five years later, she is still happily writing and says she has no intention of stopping.

She lives with her husband Ken in a rural part of Staffordshire, England. She has two children, Adrian, who now lives in America, and Tina. Margaret's hobbies are reading, photography and more recently water-colour painting, which she says has honed her observational skills and is a definite advantage when it comes to writing.

Don't miss Margaret Mayo's exciting new novel, *Bedded at His Convenience*, out in August 2007 from Mills & Boon® Modern™

PROLOGUE

'TARAH's dead? She can't be!' Kristie refused to accept the news. 'Of course I'll come. Straight away.' And, as she hurtled her car down the motorway to London, she hoped and prayed that it wasn't true. It couldn't be true. Not her darling sister. She had such a zest for life. There was no way in this world that it could have been snuffed out at such a young age.

Twenty-five was nothing—it was the beginning of life. Their parents had died, both of them, in an avalanche when they were skiing in Norway. They'd been in their fifties and even then it had been hard to accept. But Tarah, her dearest sister. 'No, *no, no!*'

Her keening voice filled the car and she shook her head. She had to stay calm while she drove, and somehow she managed to convince herself that it was all a mistake, that it wasn't her sister who had died; it was someone else.

At the hospital she couldn't fool herself any longer.

'We did our best,' said the surgeon sorrowfully, 'but it wasn't enough. The only consolation is that her baby is OK.'

But Kristie didn't care about the baby. It was her sister she mourned.

'Do you want to see him?'

She shook her head. Why couldn't the baby have died and not Tarah? Why was life so unfair? Tears poured down her cheeks.

'I think you should.'

'Whatever you say.' Still in shock, Kristie allowed herself to be led away from her sister's bedside to the nursery. Baby Broderick lay fast asleep, a sweet little angel dressed in blue. And he looked so much like Tarah that a fresh flood of tears erupted. When they asked her whether she would be taking the baby she couldn't find it in her heart to refuse. It wasn't his fault that he'd been left motherless—*and fatherless*!

Kristie had sympathised with Tarah when she had rung to tell her that Radford had dumped her. But when, a week or two later, she had told her that she was pregnant but wasn't going to tell him because he'd always said that he didn't like children and didn't want a family, she had been furious.

'You can't do that,' she'd said. 'He's the father; he's responsible. You can't bring the child up on your own, not without financial help. He owes you that, at least.'

But Tarah had been adamant, and now Tarah was dead. And all because of this man. Kristie had never met him and didn't want to meet him, because she knew that if she did she would kill him.

She had adopted Jake and made him her own and although it had been a struggle, trying to make a living as a single parent, she had managed.

CHAPTER ONE

THE house was invisible from the main road. Kristie had passed this spot many times without realising that the property lurked beyond the ivy-covered walls and the dense woodland.

It was an interesting building—low and wide, looking as though it had been added to over the centuries, resulting in an eclectic mixture of styles and brickwork. And inside it was even more interesting. Kristie had expected a showpiece, each room beautifully furnished while looking as though they were never used. But it wasn't like that. Yes, there were some fine pieces of furniture, but there was also an everyday feel about the place. A newspaper left here, a book there, a jacket slung over the back of a chair. All sorts of little things that showed it was a house well lived in.

'Felicity would like a summer wedding, wouldn't you, darling?'

Kristie turned as a stunningly beautiful girl entered the room in a wheelchair. She had glossy dark hair and most attractive grey eyes. Kristie couldn't help staring and her heart went out to her. It was tragic. Why? How? And yet the girl herself smiled cheerfully.

'The beginning of June, on my birthday. I can't think of anything more perfect.'

'Darling, this is Kristie Swift, the lady I told you about.'

'The one who's going to arrange everything for me?' Felicity wheeled her chair up to Kristie and held out her hand. 'You come highly recommended and you've no idea what a relief it will be for my mother to have everything

7

taken off her hands. She flaps, poor dear.' But it was said in the softest of voices and with an impish smile that made her look like a young girl, whereas Kristie knew for a fact that she'd just had her thirtieth birthday.

'Isn't my brother here yet?' Felicity asked as she whirled back towards the window, peering out at the long drive.

'He's on his way,' affirmed her mother. 'He shouldn't be long. Let's have a drink while we're waiting, shall we?' And to Kristie, 'Felicity's father died several years ago and my son always takes charge on occasions such as this. I don't know what I'd do without him.' Mrs Mandervell-Smythe was an exceedingly well-groomed woman with iron-grey hair and skin that was hardly lined.

'You'd have to find yourself another man,' suggested Felicity cheekily. 'There's no shortage of offers.'

'But no one who fills your father's shoes.'

'Nor is there ever likely to be,' Felicity conceded. 'Daddy was a rare breed. But I do wish you'd find someone, Mummy. I hate seeing you so alone. Hurrah, here he is at last.' Excitedly, Felicity turned her chair and sped out of the room.

Mrs Mandervell-Smythe smiled indulgently. 'As you can tell, Felicity loves her brother very much. He lives and works in London so she doesn't see much of him.'

Kristie heard Felicity's enthusiastic greeting and the rumble of a man's voice. When he entered the room behind his sister his eyes alighted on Kristie instantly. It was like being zapped by a laser gun—a stunning blow to her whole body, making her breath catch in her throat and her heart miss a few beats.

Then his attention turned to his mother and while he was greeting her Kristie studied him. He was by far the most aggressively handsome man she had ever seen—very much like his sister, with the same black hair and intense dark grey eyes. The sort of man who stood out in a crowd, not simply because he was tall and good-looking, but because of an innate charisma. It was like a body magnetism from which Kristie couldn't withdraw. It sucked in her breath and rooted her to the spot.

He turned to her now, his mother introducing him. 'This is Kristie Swift, who's hopefully going to organise Felicity's wedding. Kristie, meet my son, Radford.'

'Brave lady,' he said, with a dazzling white smile. 'My sister is well known for changing her mind.'

Kristie wasn't listening. Radford. Radford Mandervell-Smythe. In an instant Kristie's feelings changed. Radford Smythe. Or Radford Smith, as her sister had insisted on calling him. It had to be the same man. Radford was an uncommon name. In fact, she couldn't remember hearing of anyone else of that name. The smile that was trembling on her lips faded. In fact, her whole face froze and she couldn't even bring herself to touch his outstretched hand.

'Is something wrong?' he asked, his gaze narrowing, his eyes penetrating hers.

'Er, no, nothing,' she managed to stammer. This was unbelievable. She had wanted to meet this man, to see for herself what type of a guy he was, to give him a piece of her mind. But now that the moment was here she was numb.

'You've gone very pale,' remarked his mother with some concern. 'Are you not feeling well? Sit down, please. I'll send for some water.'

'I'm all right,' insisted Kristie, pulling herself together. 'I don't know what came over me.' At least there was nothing she could tell this family. Not yet.

'My brother has this effect on all women,' giggled Felicity.

'Flick!' reprimanded her mother.

But Kristie's thoughts were running deep and she didn't hear. Someone brought in a jug of water and she tried to pour herself a glass but her hands were trembling so much that it spilled over on to the tray.

'Allow me,' came Radford's cool voice, and she had to suffer him standing close while he filled the glass. He was a virile, good-looking man with a powerful masculinity that haunted her senses. She could see why her sister had fallen in love with him. It was impossible not to feel the magnetic pull of his sexuality.

'Drink up,' he urged, folding her still trembling hand around the glass and helping her lift it to her mouth.

Kristie wanted to push him away. She wanted to be anywhere except here in this room with this man who had—

'I said drink. What the hell's wrong with you?' he asked harshly.

'Radford!' exclaimed his mother. 'That's no way to talk to—'

'The woman's shot to pieces,' he retorted. 'She's certainly not fit to organise my sister's wedding. Where the hell did you get her from?' His grey eyes were utterly cold and condemning as they looked down at her.

'She comes highly recommended,' announced Felicity. 'Michelle used her when she got married.'

'Hmph!' he snorted. 'All I can say is Michelle has no taste.'

'Leave the poor girl alone,' insisted his mother. 'Come and sit down, Radford. It's probably you who's making her on edge. You can be extremely overpowering, just like your father.'

'I've done nothing, for pity's sake,' he flared.

'Even so, give Kristie some room.'

Kristie began to feel embarrassed and with a huge effort pulled herself together, drinking more of the water before setting the glass back down on the tray. 'I'm sorry. I don't know what came over me.' Which was a lie, but how could she tell Mrs Mandervell-Smythe what a swine her son was?

'Don't worry about it,' said the older woman. 'Are you up to carrying on with the wedding arrangements?'

'She looks to me as though she ought to go home and lie down,' growled Radford, eyeing her suspiciously.

Kristie glared but said nothing.

Felicity giggled again, seeming to find the whole thing highly amusing.

'I'm fine now,' said Kristie quietly, while knowing that with Radford Smythe in the room she would be unable to concentrate on a word that was said. She hated this man with every fibre of her being.

She could hear her sister's voice telling her that she had met the most gorgeous man in the whole world. 'He's unbelievably handsome and incredibly sexy, Kristie. Wait till you meet him. You'll see what I mean.'

Kristie did see. He was all Tarah had raved about. All and more. He was the sort of man who drew you to him whether you wished it or not. He had a magnetism that was incredibly strong and Kristie expected that few women resisted him.

Her sister had a broken marriage behind her and had moved down to London to start a new life. She had sworn off men for ever—until she met Radford Smythe. 'I tease him and call him Smith,' she told Kristie. 'He doesn't like it, not one little bit. He actually has a double-barrelled name but he never uses it. He runs the family publishing business. His father's dead and his mother lives somewhere near Stratford. Small world, isn't it?'

Too small. This house was only a few miles from where Kristie lived. She suddenly realised that Mrs Mandervell-

Smythe was speaking to her and she hadn't heard a word that was said.

After that Kristie was careful to pay attention to their requests, making suggestions of her own, jotting everything down in her notebook ready to feed into her computer later. Some day she promised to buy herself a laptop. With the right program she could fill everything in as her clients spoke and it would save an awful lot of time.

Halfway through proceedings, coffee and biscuits were brought in. Kristie felt her nerves jangle again when Radford passed her the plate and his eyes met hers in a deliberate questioning stare. And then he smiled—the sort of smile that would have melted the heart of most girls. Kristie managed a grimace, unable to bring herself to smile properly, and took a couple of shortbreads.

'You're looking better,' he said softly.

Kristie nodded.

'We'll talk later and you can tell me exactly what made you feel faint.'

'I don't think so,' answered Kristie smartly. 'I have another pressing engagement after this one.'

'Perhaps you're doing too much?'

'And is that any business of yours?' The moment the words were out Kristie wished she hadn't spoken them. She saw his mother look at her sharply and Felicity's quickened interest. But most of all she saw Radford's face go granite hard, his eyes darkening to a sooty black. And when he straightened he towered above her like a menacing angel, nostrils flared, his mouth grim and straight.

Kristie nibbled a biscuit and sipped her coffee, aware that she was now the subject of much curiosity. She would have liked to leave, get away from the detestable Radford Smythe. But there was still a lot to sort out and he was insistent on having a say in every aspect of the arrangements.

Even when they moved out into the garden where the wedding was going to be held he dominated the conversation.

'I think the ceremony itself should take place just here,' Kristie said, standing at a spot on the lawn about twenty yards away from the house, directly in line with the drawing room where three arched floor to ceiling windows opened out on to the garden. 'With a covered walkway—just in case it rains.' They all knew that in an English June there was every chance of rain. 'And here—' she spread her hands and did a twirl '—would be a huge flat dais, with perhaps Greek or Doric columns and a cover of silk, all swathed with ribbons to match the bridesmaids' dresses and flowers, and plenty of greenery.'

She was conscious of Radford's eyes on her all the time and more than a couple of hours passed before they had talked through everything. Kristie felt relief as she finally got to her feet. 'I'll be in touch,' she said, looking directly at Mrs Mandervell-Smythe, avoiding any eye contact whatsoever with her son.

'I'll see you out,' he said, much to her dismay.

Kristie wanted to object but felt it would be impolite to draw further attention to herself. He touched his hand to her elbow as he led her to the door. Was this to stop her running away before he'd had the chance to question her odd behaviour? wondered Kristie. It was a million to one chance that they'd met like this—a million to one chance she could have done without.

Admittedly, she'd wanted to meet this man and give him a piece of her mind, but not like this, not in front of his mother and a prospective client to boot. What she had to say to him was strictly private.

When she reached her car he was still following. She opened the door but he put his hand on it before she could get in. 'Suppose you tell me what that was all about?'

'What?' she asked sharply.

'That little display of hysterics.'

'I'm not used to brothers of the bride putting in their two pennyworth,' she prevaricated. Damn him, why couldn't he keep out of her way? Her memories were bad enough without him adding to them.

'Is that so?' Dark brows rose. 'And it upset you that much? I think not. I think there's more to it.'

'You can think what you like,' she retorted. 'I don't need to answer to you. Will you please let me go? I'm running late for my next appointment.'

'How about lunch?'

'Not on your life!'

'I wasn't inviting you,' he drawled, with a cold glitter in his eyes. 'I meant what are you going to do about lunch? You can't run from one job to another without eating. If that's your general practice it's no wonder you feel ill.'

Kristie groaned inwardly. She was making a thorough fool of herself. Thankfully, he took his hand away from the door and she was able to slide inside and start the engine.

But she was not free of him yet. He lowered his head and looked through the still open doorway. 'Goodbye, Kristie Swift. Maybe the next time we meet you'll be in a better frame of mind.'

Never! And she was about to tell him so when she thought better of it. She smiled weakly instead. 'Goodbye, Mr Mandervell-Smythe.'

It wasn't until she was out of his sight and out of the gates that Kristie was able to breathe a sigh of relief. But even so her hands were trembling so much that she stopped the car and took several deep steadying breaths before she could continue. She used her mobile to cancel her next appointment and then headed straight home. Concentrating on work was out of the question.

Kristie lived in a smart townhouse on the outskirts of Warwick. It had three bedrooms, a fairly large lounge and a kitchen, and she loved it. There was no garden at the front but a long patch of lawn at the back. She made herself a strong cup of coffee and sat at her breakfast bar sipping it, looking out at the grass, which was badly in need of mowing. She would do it in a minute. The physical act of pushing the mower would help rid her mind of the aggression that was steadily building to a crescendo.

She had never imagined for one moment that she would meet Radford Smythe. Tarah had raved about him. 'He's fabulously sexy, the most fantastic man in the whole world,' she had enthused. Kristie had been sceptical because Tarah had said the same about her husband—and look what had happened there.

Tarah had been two years older than Kristie, headstrong and fanatical, throwing herself wholeheartedly into whatever hobby or relationship took her fancy. Kristie had always been the one who rescued her when she ended up hurt or disillusioned. It had been like that all their lives, even at school.

When Tarah met Bryan Broderick, the man she married, she had been head over heels in love for all of six months, until she found out that he had been seeing another woman. Kristie had again been the one who had picked up the pieces. Tarah's decision to move to London and create a new life for herself had been met with dismay from both Kristie and their parents, but nothing they could say had made any difference.

And now she was dead!

And all because of a man named Radford Mandervell-Smythe.

CHAPTER TWO

'WHAT do you think was wrong with Miss Swift?' Radford asked as he walked back into the room.

'I think you overwhelmed her,' giggled Felicity. 'She was fine until you came on the scene. Is that a first, someone swooning at your feet?'

'Don't be ridiculous,' he snorted. 'It had nothing to do with me.'

'I think the poor girl's overworked,' announced his mother. 'She's dreadfully thin and pale.'

Radford nodded. 'I don't think we should give her the job. I think I ought to go and see her and tell her that—'

'No!' insisted Mrs Mandervell-Smythe. 'I'd like to talk to her some more. She was very enthusiastic and certainly full of excellent ideas. It would be a pity to dismiss her before we're absolutely sure she's not up to the job.'

Radford privately doubted the woman could do it. She'd gone completely to pieces when he spoke to her and that was no good for business. He certainly had no intention of keeping out of her way. He'd be here to make sure that every aspect of his sister's wedding went without a hitch.

He knew that was what his mother was paying Kristie Swift for, but he didn't trust her. For some reason she had taken a dislike to him. Unusual, to say the least, because he was more used to fighting women off, but he had to admit that he didn't find her in the least attractive either.

So why, he asked himself a short while later, did the image of her pale but interesting face, framed by striking red hair, keep inserting itself into his mind's eye? For some strange reason he couldn't dismiss her from his mind. She had the most unusual light green eyes, very wide and very beautiful, and he wondered what colour they went when she was being made love to.

He shook his head and dismissed the thought. It was of little consequence; it was something that was never likely to happen.

Kristie gulped her coffee and squeezed the mug so hard between her palms that it was a wonder it didn't shatter. For five years she had carried a massive hostility in her heart for this faceless man. She had tried to bury her feelings, told herself that there was no point in harbouring such malevolent thoughts when she was never likely to meet him. And to a degree she had been successful.

But now her pain and distress flooded back to the surface with a vengeance and she knew that if he was going to attend every discussion it was going to make her situation untenable. Maybe she ought to opt out of this job? It was but a fleeting thought. It wasn't Kristie's way. She met all problems head-on, and that was all he was—a problem. A mighty big one, admittedly, but now that she knew the situation Kristie felt sure she could handle it.

She wouldn't let him see again that he upset her but she would find a way to make very sure that he got his due punishment. Quite how she didn't know, but she was very definite in her mind that he wouldn't get away with what he had done.

Her phone rang but she ignored it. Her head ached, her heart ached; she didn't want to talk to anyone. But then came that deep, gravelly male voice over her answerphone. 'Miss Swift, it's Radford Smythe here.'

As if she couldn't tell!

'I have a message for you from my mother.'

It was as though he was in the same room and it sent an unfortunate shiver down her spine. She couldn't forget those unfathomable dark grey eyes, or that harshly boned face.

'She would like to see you again; there's something she forgot. She'll be at home this evening.'

That was it. The connection was cut. It sounded more like an order than anything else. Kristie's hackles rose and she jumped to her feet. She'd ring the darn man back and tell him it was out of the question. But before she could even get to the phone it rang again. She snatched it up angrily. 'If that's you, Smythe, with yet another request, you can—'

'Kristie?'

'Oh, Paul, I'm sorry.'

'Who did you think I was?'

'It doesn't matter. Someone I met today.'

'Someone you don't like by the sound of things. Shall I come and soothe your ravaged breast?'

Kristie laughed. 'It's not that bad. He simply wound me up the wrong way.'

'It's been ages since I saw you.'

'I have work to do.'

'That's always your excuse,' he grumbled. 'I'm beginning to think your business means more to you than I do.'

'My business puts a roof over my head and food in my mouth, you know that.'

'Which I could do if you'd let me,' he said persuasively.

'Paul,' she groaned, 'don't start that again. We're just friends; let's keep it that way.' She had known Paul for over twelve months now and, although she was very fond of him, she wanted to take things slowly. She wasn't yet ready for a committed relationship.

'I'd nevertheless like to come.'

'I'm busy,' she said softly, regretfully. He had no idea what it was like running a one-man business. When she had set up as a wedding co-ordinator she had thought it would be relatively easy. She hadn't realised all the hard work and often long hours that were involved. But she loved her job and wouldn't change it for the world.

'Soon, then?' he asked.

'Soon,' she promised. 'I'll ring you.'

No sooner had she put down the phone than thoughts of Radford Smythe swept back into her mind. She was swiftly discovering that he was not a man who could be ignored, and it was easy to see why her sister had fallen so madly in love with him.

But she wasn't alone with her thoughts for long. The door burst open and Jake came rushing in. 'Mummy, Mummy, look what I've painted for you.'

Chloe walked in behind him. 'We've had to run all the way home from school. I warned him you might not be in, but—'

'Guess who it is.' Jake hopped from foot to foot in his excitement.

'Your teacher?' she suggested hopefully. The stick figure with the fuzzy orange hair and bright red mouth could have been anyone.

'Course not, it's you.'

'I know, sweetheart. I was teasing.' She picked Jake up and hugged him, twirling him around while he squealed with delight. 'I love it.'

The rest of Kristie's day was spent with her young son. Chloe was her live-in babysitter and normally she kept Jake out of the way until Kristie's work was finished. But today Jake was exactly what she needed to take her mind off Radford Smythe. And she certainly had no intention of going to see his mother, not this evening anyway.

Who did he think he was, issuing orders like that? Her sister had obviously looked at him through blinkered eyes, had seen only that he was devilishly handsome and magnificently sexy, ignored the fact that he lacked basic good manners. Well she wasn't going to ignore it—it only added to her already rock-bottom opinion of him.

Kristie waited until the next morning before phoning Mrs Mandervell-Smythe, only to be told that she wasn't in. But Mr Radford Smythe was in, if he could help.

About to tell whoever it was who had answered the phone that she would like to leave a message, a voice that was becoming all too familiar sounded in her ear.

'Kristie Swift?'

She swallowed hard. 'That's right.' She hadn't even thought that he might still be there. She had believed, in fact she had hoped, that he'd gone back to London. She didn't want anything more to do with this man. Because if she did she would pull no punches in telling him exactly what she thought of him.

'Where were you last night?' he asked brusquely.

'I beg your pardon?' Her hackles were rising already.

'I asked you to come for a further consultation.'

Kristie's chin lifted. 'You didn't ask, you ordered, and I don't take kindly to that sort of language. But, as a matter of fact,' she went on, hearing his hiss of disbelief, 'I had something far more important to do.' Little Jake was the focus of her life, more important than anything or anyone else. 'Except that you didn't wait to hear.'

There was a pause before he answered, a pause when she knew he was trying to control himself. She didn't care. He deserved to be treated badly.

'So when would it be convenient for you to call?' he asked, his voice full of dry sarcasm.

'Perhaps this afternoon, about three-thirty,' she suggested.

'I'll let my mother know.'

'Tell me,' she said, before she could stop herself. 'Is it you or your mother who calls the shots? I really would like to know who I'm dealing with.'

There was a long pause and Kristie began to feel uncomfortable. She ought not to have spoken to him like that. He had been doubtful before whether she was up to doing the job, now he must be sure. She had probably burnt her bridges altogether.

'I'm sorry,' she said quickly. 'That was very rude of me. I'll see your mother at three-thirty.' And she put down the phone.

She breathed out a long, deflating sigh. It was wrong to show her hatred of Radford Smythe at this stage. She couldn't afford to lose this commission. She had never realised before Jake came into her life how much it cost to keep a small child. And moving from her flat into a house with a huge mortgage hadn't helped. Chloe's share of the housekeeping costs helped, reduced in return for her babysitting and sometimes office services, but she still needed to work hard to keep her head above water.

Kristie kept herself busy for the next few hours—she even managed to forget Radford Smythe. But all too soon three-thirty approached and as she drove towards their country estate her heart began to beat unevenly. She didn't want to be faced with this man again, not in the presence of his mother and sister. He sent her all jittery, and it had to be because of the hatred that lived in her soul.

But wishing him away had no effect whatsoever. The twelve-foot high gates swung open as she approached and Radford himself met her at the door. He had clearly been awaiting her arrival. 'Thank you for coming,' he said drily, grey eyes penetrating hers with such intensity that it felt as though he was looking into her soul. Or at the very least trying to read her mind. 'Do come in.'

He wore a white open-necked shirt and dark green casual trousers, and he looked totally relaxed. There was even a tiny smile playing at the corners of his mouth. She felt distinctly uncomfortable. It was those probing eyes that did it. Beautiful eyes admittedly, with long thick lashes, but they saw too much. She had a feeling no secret was safe from this man.

He stood back and allowed her to enter and she hovered in the vast hall while he closed the door and then followed him into the room where she had spoken to his mother the day before. It was empty.

'Unfortunately, my mother's not home yet,' he said, still with that annoying little smile.

He was enjoying this, but she sure as hell wasn't. All good intentions fled. 'And you didn't think to tell me? You've let me waste my time?' Fury flashed in her green eyes and she felt like turning round and storming out.

'I didn't think it was a waste,' he answered, his tone even. 'I wanted to see you again.'

'Why?' she demanded hotly. 'To confirm your opinion that I'm not up to the job?' She stared straight into his face, virtually daring him to agree.

'You didn't exactly instil me with confidence,' he answered, his eyes unblinking on hers. 'Why was that, I wonder?'

Kristie ignored the question. 'What time are you expecting your mother?'

Wide shoulders shrugged expressively.

'So what am I doing here?' And why was she suddenly beginning to feel nervous? She had the strangest feeling that he had designs on her. As if she would ever, *ever*, contemplate going out with this man. He had a lot to learn.

'My sister will be joining us shortly,' he announced. 'You needn't fear, your time won't be entirely wasted. The wedding plans will be discussed. Why don't you sit down?'

Kristie didn't want to sit—she wanted to leave, come back again when his mother was here and he wasn't, but to do so would provoke all sorts of awkward questions. So she perched herself on a chair as far away from him as she could without it looking as though she was deliberately avoiding him.

Radford remained standing, leaning back against the edge of a solid oak table on which stood a vase of roses which spilt their heady perfume into the room, his ankles crossed, his arms folded across a magnificently broad chest and his head tilted to one side. 'Is it men in general you don't like or just me?'

Kristie allowed her eyebrows to arch delicately. 'What makes you think I don't like you?'

'Was it a bad experience?' he asked, ignoring her question.

'You could say that.'

'It doesn't mean all men are the same.'

'No?'

'Perhaps you'd like to talk about it?'

'Not on your life,' she tossed back. There was a whole lot of stuff she wanted to say to this man but not at this moment, not when they were likely to be interrupted. What she had to say was very personal indeed—and it most definitely wouldn't be polite!

It might be interesting, though, to find out exactly what sort of a man he was. Sexy and woman-appealing, without a doubt, but what was he like deep down? Why had he dumped Tarah? Perhaps she could find out how his mind worked? Perhaps he was the love 'em and leave 'em type? Not that she was likely to let herself get into that kind of situation. But perhaps during conversation she could find out how many women there had been in his life, whether he'd been serious about any of them, whether he was married, and if not why not.

'It still leaves the question—why did you go to pieces when you saw me yesterday?'

CHAPTER THREE

KRISTIE SWIFT was the most intriguing female Radford had ever met. Since seeing her yesterday he had been unable to get her out of his mind. She was feisty, she was beautiful, and for some unknown reason she had taken an instant dislike to him—to the extent that she had almost passed out. Perhaps he reminded her of someone who had let her down badly. But if that was the case why couldn't she say so? Why ignore his questions? Even now she prevaricated.

'You think it was because of you that I felt faint?' she asked, widening her lovely green eyes and lifting her chin in a proud gesture which he found truly enchanting.

'It was the impression you gave.'

'Then you're being very conceited. Why would a perfect stranger blow me over like that?'

'You tell me,' he said. 'I know only what I saw. The moment my name was mentioned you lost all your colour.'

'You're imagining things,' she retorted, but Radford knew what he had seen and he wouldn't be happy until he had found out the reason why. But he could wait. There was no rush. He moved closer towards her and sat down. He felt her inching away—nothing discernible, but the feeling was there all the same. And he was annoyed by the action. It wasn't the usual effect he had on the opposite sex. It didn't sit easily on his shoulders.

'Would you like a cup of tea?' he asked. 'Or coffee?' It was difficult to keep an edge from his voice.

'Nothing, thank you,' she answered coolly. 'Does your sister know that I'm here?'

'She knows. How long have you been arranging other people's weddings?' He wanted to know everything there was to know about this girl. What made her tick. Where she lived. Who she lived with. He had already noticed that she didn't wear a wedding ring, but he wanted to know whether there was a man in her life.

'Five years—almost. Why?' she questioned fiercely. 'Does it make a difference? I am fully qualified, I assure you, and I'll be happy to provide the names of previous clients.'

Heavens, she was prickly. Maybe he ought to carry out a few checks. His mother had taken her at face value, but he felt sure she hadn't seen this side of Kristie Swift. His sister's wedding was very important to him. Life had dealt her a raw hand and meeting and falling in love with Daniel Fielding was a wonderful happening. He wanted her wedding day to be perfect, totally hassle-free. But if this uptight woman was going to fly off the handle at every little hurdle then she certainly wasn't the right person for the job.

'I think that might be a good idea,' he said. 'One recommendation by Felicity's friend is hardly a good testimony. I'll drop by your office for the list.'

'I'll post it,' she snapped, 'if it's so important to you. Have you spoken to Michelle yourself?'

'I don't know her,' he snarled, his patience wearing thin. 'She's my sister's friend, not mine.'

'Don't you think that Felicity's the main person in all of this?' demanded Kristie, her eyes flashing furiously. 'Shouldn't she have a say? And if she's happy, then I think you should butt out.'

Lord, had she really said that? Kristie's blood ran hot and fluid through her veins and she wished herself anywhere but here. But before Radford could answer the sound of clapping came from the doorway. 'Well said, Kristie.

It's about time my uppity brother got some of his own treatment.'

The change in Radford was dramatic. His scowl turned to an instant smile and as his sister wheeled her chair towards him he spoke to her tenderly. 'You weren't supposed to hear that, cherub.'

'I think the whole house heard. You two weren't pulling any punches, were you? What's wrong, darling brother of mine, doesn't Miss Swift conform to the way the female sex usually treats you?'

'I merely wanted to check her credentials,' he reproved softly. 'It's the normal way to conduct business.'

'And it's normal for someone to tell you to "butt out"? Wonderful, Kristie.'

Kristie gave an uncomfortable smile and wondered how much of the conversation Felicity had heard. It didn't put her in a good light, that was for sure.

Radford stroked a light hand over his sister's jet-black hair. 'I'm glad you found our little altercation amusing.'

Felicity's infectious laughter rang out. 'It's going to be fun having Kristie around. Don't let him harass you,' she said, switching her attention. 'Michelle couldn't sing your praises highly enough. We don't need testimonials.'

'I think maybe we should get on with the business,' said Kristie. The sooner she was out of this house the better.

But her torture didn't end as swiftly as she would have liked. Mrs Mandervell-Smythe returned an hour later and she was forced to go through everything all over again. It was hard to believe that Radford was the same person. He was full of charm and courtesy, listening to her proposals, nodding, agreeing, only occasionally questioning—like when she mentioned creating individual pieces of jewellery. He must have been like this when her sister first met him. The perfect English gentleman. No hint of his darker side.

It was no wonder Tarah had fallen head over heels in love. But how swiftly his temper was aroused, how easily he condemned.

Kristie was glad when the agreement was finally signed and she could take her leave, but even then Radford insisted on walking her out to her car. 'There's no need,' she told him testily at the door, but still he accompanied her.

'Are you satisfied now that I can do the job properly?' she asked huffily as she unlocked the door. Her old red Ford was definitely the poor relation. His black Mercedes sat one side of it and his mother's Jaguar the other. She expected some comment, but none was forthcoming.

'I guess I'll have to be,' he said shortly. 'One slip up, though, and you'll be out. Is that understood? I won't have Felicity upset. She's suffered enough.'

'Don't worry. Everything will run as smoothly as silk,' she assured him. 'And you don't need to hang around to make sure. You can go back to London with complete peace of mind.'

'I wish,' he said, so quietly that she almost didn't hear. But she didn't retaliate. She slid into her car instead and shot off so quickly that gravel spurted beneath her wheels. She saw Radford's look of distaste through her rear view mirror.

The house was empty when Kristie arrived home. Chloe had taken Jake to a friend's birthday party so she had the luxury of being completely alone. Changing into a pair of old jeans and a T-shirt, she pushed her mower furiously up and down the lawn, muttering to herself all the time, vainly attempting to expurgate Radford from her mind.

She was hot and sweaty and on her way to take a shower when the doorbell rang. Snatching the door open, Kristie was ready to send away whichever salesman was calling with a flea in his ear. They were a nuisance. If it wasn't double-glazing it was guttering, or tree-felling, or any of a number of things that they assured her would improve her property.

Her harsh words stuck in her throat when she saw Radford Smythe. Hell, what was he doing here? Hadn't he said everything there was to be said? Or was it for the list of previous clients? Was he still not convinced that she would do a good job?

'What do you want?' she asked curtly.

'Have I called at a bad time?'

No time would be a good time where this man was concerned. 'I was about to take a shower,' she informed him icily.

'Don't let me stop you. I'll wait.'

With an insolence she found annoying, he slowly looked her up and down, starting with the shabby trainers on her feet, working his way over her slender hips and flat stomach. Tension ran through her, especially when his eyes rested much longer than Kristie was happy with on her breasts, which had unfortunately peaked beneath the too-tight T-shirt. It was one she kept specifically for gardening.

And he carried on his inspection right up to her hair, which she had scraped unbecomingly back in a band to keep it out of the way while she worked. Lastly, his eyes returned to her face.

His was totally devoid of expression. She had no idea what he was thinking—probably something along the lines that she didn't look a fit person to co-ordinate his sister's wedding and he'd made a fatal mistake in letting his mother agree.

You're not waiting here, she answered silently. Not on your life. She could just imagine herself standing naked under the steaming jets while he paced impatiently below.

The very thought sent a surge of unwanted heat over her skin. She didn't trust this man an inch.

In fact, she wouldn't put it past him to follow her upstairs and covertly watch as she showered. Or maybe not even secretly, he could well do it openly. He seemed to her to be the type of guy who did and said exactly what he wanted regardless of protocol or circumstances.

Oh, lord, why was she thinking along these lines? He wasn't interested in her, not one little bit. He didn't even want her to plan his sister's wedding. This was probably why he was here—to say that her services were no longer required.

'I'd rather get whatever it is you want over and done with,' she insisted.

Radford inclined his head. 'May I come in then?'

Reluctantly, Kristie stood back. She hadn't realised quite what a big man he was until he stepped into her hall. His mother's house was so spacious that he hadn't filled the room with his presence—well, not quite. But here—she felt as though he had breathed in every little bit of air and left nothing for her. He dominated the tiny space and she moved quickly into her living room, one corner of which served as her office.

'So why are you here?' she asked when he said nothing, when he simply looked around him with interest. It was a fairly minimalist room in natural colours. She hated clutter, not that it was always possible to avoid when Jake was playing with his toys, but she kept it tidy and was glad of this now.

'I was curious.'

Kristie frowned. 'About what?'

'You.'

'And that gives you the right to intrude on my personal space?' she asked incredulously. 'I don't think so, Mr

Smythe. If you're not here on business then I'd like you to leave.' And that was putting it politely. The nerve of the man. This wasn't protecting his sister's interests, this was satisfying his own curiosity.

And yet, angry as she was, she couldn't dismiss his innate sexuality. It emanated from him like a strong, heady perfume, filling the air around him, making him alarmingly attractive. She swore silently as the thought hit her. Please God, she prayed, don't let me be attracted to this man. Don't let me fall into his trap the same way Tarah did.

Unconsciously, she backed away. Radford frowned. 'I don't bite,' he snarled, 'and I have no intention of leaving. You can either take a shower and I'll wait for our talk, or we can do it right now.'

'Now will suit me fine,' she fired. 'What is it you want to know?'

'A little about yourself.'

Kristie gave a quick frown. 'Why? What's that got to do with anything?'

'I'm curious, that's all.'

'You mean plain nosy,' she snapped.

His lips thinned and a cold gleam entered his eyes. 'Politeness costs nothing.'

Immediately Kristie felt ashamed. This was far from the image she normally portrayed. She'd always made an attempt to be cool and calm and professional—except that professionalism had flown out of the window where this man was concerned, swiftly followed by any pretence of tranquillity.

'Tell me,' he said cuttingly, 'exactly what is it that you've got against me?'

Kristie closed her eyes for a moment. This was not the time to discuss the way he had treated Tarah. Chloe and

Jake would be home any minute. In fact, she ought never to have let him in. It had been an insane decision.

'Don't keep denying it,' he snarled.

'Let's just say that there are some types of men I like and some I don't,' she said, swallowing a tight lump in her throat and daring to look him straight in the eye. It was a big mistake. They were rock hard and bored right into her.

'And I belong to the latter group?'

She nodded.

Nostrils flared. 'And you think it's right to categorise someone before you get to know them?'

'I shouldn't have done that,' she admitted. 'I'm sorry. Now will you go?' Lord, it hurt to apologise but if that was what it took to get rid of him then it was worth it.

'You're not getting away that lightly,' he snorted, still with that steely glint in his eye. 'I want to know what this guy did to make you condemn everyone who reminds you of him.'

'Who said it's a certain guy?' she retorted. 'In any case, it's none of your business.'

'Maybe not,' he agreed, 'but it's certainly had a profound effect. Do you have a current boyfriend?'

Kristie glared. 'I refuse to answer any more of your questions. You and I have a strictly business relationship, nothing more. I can't imagine why you're here and I want you to leave.'

'Is this where you work?' he asked, glancing across at the corner of the room where her desk, filing cabinet and bookshelves sat in a tidy huddle.

'It is.'

'It doesn't look very professional.' A deep, disapproving frown scored his brow. 'Don't you have a room you can use as an office?'

'I don't need one,' she answered tightly. 'This suits me fine.'

'I—'

He was interrupted by the sound of Chloe's key in the lock and the next moment the girl's face appeared round the door. 'I saw the car and guessed you had a visitor. I'll go and bath Jake; he's had the time of his life.' Jake looked into the room too but he hung back instead of rushing in to give Kristie her customary hug and a kiss. He was incredibly shy where strangers were concerned, which was as well under the circumstances, thought Kristie. She didn't want to answer any questions about him.

But Radford's curiosity was aroused. 'You share this house?'

Kristie nodded.

'Who's the owner, you or your—er, friend?' He nodded towards the door.

'Me,' she rasped, wishing he wouldn't ask so many questions. 'Mortgages don't come cheap.'

His eyes narrowed. 'So your business isn't exactly flourishing?' Again his eyes flashed disparagingly towards the corner of the room.

It was exactly what he'd like to hear. Any excuse to discredit her. 'It's doing well, thank you, but I can't afford to sit back on my early laurels. It takes a while to get fully established and build a reputation, as you probably know. I imagine you're in business too, Mr Smythe?'

'I run the family business,' he acknowledged.

So he hadn't had to work his way up like most people. No wonder he was overbearingly pompous—he had the world at his feet and clearly thought he could treat people any way he liked. It was time he went.

She moved towards the door. 'I really must take that shower, Mr Smythe. Let me show you out.'

*   *   *

Radford found it difficult to understand Kristie's attitude—he had never met anyone quite like her. And the more she appeared to hold some grudge against him the more intrigued by her he became, the more determined not to be summarily dismissed.

'I'm not sure that I'm ready to go yet,' he said crisply.

'What more is there to be said?' she questioned, her lovely green eyes flashing their displeasure at him. He had never seen eyes quite so beautiful. They were an extraordinarily pale green with a dark line around the iris which stopped them from being lost against the very white whites. They were wide-spaced and sloe-shaped, with extremely long lashes that, he guessed, would make many a man's heart flutter. If she cared to use them.

Was she hostile to all men, he wondered, or had he been singled out for special treatment? There was no way of knowing. And she hadn't answered his question about whether there was a man in her life. His quick glance around the room had revealed no photographs. In fact, he had never seen a room so devoid of personal possessions. It was such a plain room that he wondered how she found pleasure in it. Kristie herself was the only splash of colour.

At his mother's house earlier she had been dressed in a lime green softly structured suit with a cream blouse. She had looked the epitome of a successful woman, very self-confident, very feminine—and utterly desirable. He hated to admit it but his heart had rumbled within his chest and he had felt an urge to get to know her better. It was why he was here. And what a waste of time it had been.

He had been shocked to see her in jeans, not that he didn't like her in them; he did. They showed off her figure to perfection, faithfully tracing the curves of her hips and bottom. His groin ached simply thinking about what lay underneath. And that T-shirt! Before, he'd only been able to guess at her shape. This revealed all. Her breasts were pert and thrusting, simply asking to be touched.

He gave his head a mental shake, he shouldn't be thinking along these lines, not when she'd made it abundantly clear that she hated the very sight of him. He ought to go, he ought to do as she asked, and yet something still made him want to stay and find out more about this enigmatic girl. She had struck a chord with him that no other woman had.

'I really think that—'

'There's nothing more to be said, Mr Smythe,' she cut in sharply.

'You're a hard woman, Kristie Swift.'

'I need to be.'

'Would you be free to have dinner with me tonight?' The words popped out before he'd even thought about them. But he knew what her answer would be.

'Why?'

She surprised him. He had expected a flat no. 'Does there have to be a reason for a man to ask a beautiful girl out?'

'Yes, when it's you,' she shot back.

He was a fool for hanging around, a fool for coming, even, and his voice was sharp. 'And what is that supposed to mean? Are you suggesting I have an ulterior motive?'

'Actually, yes, I am,' she retorted. 'You want to ply me with questions, and taking me out means there'll be no interruptions and I'll have no escape.'

She was astute, he had to give her that. There was so much he wanted to know about her—especially why she was so hostile towards him, but how was he to do that if she wouldn't co-operate? 'You find it hard to talk to me?'

'I simply see it as none of your business.'

He wanted to take the band out of her hair and let it fall

about her face in a fiery glow. He wanted to touch her, to feel that slender body against his. He wanted to kiss her. Each one of these separate thoughts amazed him. Here was this stroppy woman who had no time for him and yet he wanted her like he had no other. 'I don't take no for an answer easily,' he said.

'You'll be wasting your time.' And as she spoke she opened the front door. 'Goodbye, Mr Smythe.'

'For now,' he said with a faint smile. The urge to kiss her as he squeezed past was so strong that he didn't know how he managed to control himself. She was excitingly sexy, and the scent of her perfume that had intoxicated him earlier still lingered. She was all woman without a doubt— if she would only let go. Getting through to her would be an exercise in extreme patience and tact.

He paused a moment, their bodies but a hair's breadth away, and he looked deeply into her eyes. 'It will be interesting getting to know you, Miss Swift.'

Alarm flickered across her face and he felt the heat of her skin shooting across the space between them. She wanted to move, he knew, but she didn't want to give away the fact that he disturbed her. She stood tall and straight, her chin defiant and her eyes a green blaze.

He would have given anything to know why she was so against him. It was a question he had asked himself numerous times since meeting this delightful creature, but no answer had suggested itself. He couldn't make out whether it was something personal or whether she was dead set against the whole of mankind. What he did know was that it would be infinitely interesting to find out.

It was with intense reluctance that he finally moved. He had expected Kristie to give in first and yell at him to go. He had looked forward to seeing her eyes flash again and her cheeks fill with angry colour, but no, she stood her ground and waited. And now he had no reason to linger. He didn't even feel that he dared give her the lightest of kisses—not if he wanted to build up a relationship.

Kristie slammed the door behind Radford. She couldn't think of one good reason why he had come here, except to find out what sort of a person she really was, whether she was worthy of organising his sister's wedding.

What conclusion had he drawn? She certainly hadn't been very polite and she wondered now whether it had been to her detriment, whether he would advise his mother to find someone else. Damn! She could ill afford to lose business this way. Why hadn't she cast her personal hatred aside and treated him with the professionalism the job deserved?

'Mummy! Mummy!' Jake came bounding downstairs and all thoughts of Radford Smythe fled—until she lay in bed much later that evening.

Nothing then would dismiss him from her mind. He was such an amazingly sexy man that he awoke senses she hadn't felt in a long time, if ever. Senses that she knew were dangerous and should be immediately and permanently dismissed. This was a man she hated with every fibre of her being.

She needed to distance herself from him, but how was she to do that when he insisted on taking part in the wedding arrangements? If only he would leave it to his mother, go back to London and not turn up again until the wedding day. But somehow she had the feeling that he wouldn't do that. He was going to oversee this thing every inch of the way.

He had sensed her antagonism—no, not sensed, he had seen it. She had foolishly allowed her feelings to show, and now he was going to do everything in his power to find out why. Hence the dinner invitation.

Maybe she ought to confront him now and get it over with. On the other hand, it could cost her the job. All she had to do was retain her cool, be polite to him at all times, and do everything else to the best of her ability.

Simple.

CHAPTER FOUR

KRISTIE immersed herself in her work the next morning, deliberately squashing all thoughts of Radford Smythe—until the phone rang and it was his mother.

'Kristie, I need to see you. I've had the most wonderful idea.'

Kristie gave a mental groan. It was usual for there to be lots of interchanges of ideas, lots of alterations to plans, and under normal circumstances she'd have dropped everything and gone over. But not if there was a likelihood of her son being present. She'd had as much of him as she could stomach for the time being. 'I'm very busy, Mrs Mandervell-Smythe. I don't think I could come over right now.'

'I wasn't meaning straight away, dear. Perhaps you could join us for dinner tonight and I'll put my proposal to you then?' And as Kristie hesitated, 'I won't take no for an answer. I think you'll be quite excited by what I have to say.'

How could she refuse? Especially as this was one of the biggest weddings she'd so far been asked to organise. The Mandervell-Smythes were very influential people and no expense was to be spared. It could earn her a tidy sum. Besides, Jake would be in bed by then so she wouldn't miss out on their usual playtime—something that was very important to her.

'What time would you like me to be there?'

'Good girl. Shall we say about seven thirty? I'll send my driver for you.'

Before Kristie could demur the line went dead and she was left wondering what it was that Mrs Mandervell-Smythe was so excited about. But soon work took over and all thoughts of both it and Radford were shut out of her mind.

She loved her work. She loved designing very individual weddings. Each one was a challenge. She needed to get right inside the prospective bride's head to find out what it was she was looking for that would make her wedding a day to remember. Of course she made suggestions of her own, some of which were accepted and some rejected. But Felicity had been full of ideas and opinions herself, knowing exactly what she wanted, and she was able to articulate clearly and precisely. She was a very intelligent young woman and Kristie couldn't help wondering what had put her in a wheelchair.

As soon as Jake was in bed Kristie took a shower and got herself ready. She was hoping that Radford wouldn't be present tonight, whilst knowing that the odds against it were very high. He was taking more interest in his sister's wedding that he would normally have done, Kristie felt sure—and it was her own fault. If she hadn't stupidly given herself away at their first meeting he wouldn't have looked at her twice. She had aroused his curiosity and now was paying for it.

She slipped into a silk dress and jacket in her favourite sky blue—an outfit that she had bought for her cousin's wedding the previous summer, and matching patent high-heeled shoes. She fixed her hair up in a loose tumble of curls and draped long silver earrings in her ears.

'You look fabulous,' breathed Chloe. Her housemate was short and dumpy and always bemoaning the fact that no clothes looked right on her.

'You don't think I've gone over the top?' asked Kristie.

The compliment worried her. She didn't want Radford Smythe thinking that she had dressed up for his benefit.

'You'll knock him dead.' Her friend grinned.

'I'm not going to see Radford, it's his mother,' protested Kristie vehemently.

Chloe shrugged. 'Whatever you say.' But it was clear she didn't believe her. Yesterday, after he'd gone, she'd literally drooled over him. 'What a gorgeous hunk,' she'd said. 'Where did you find him?' And further questions had come thick and fast.

She had been disappointed to find out that Kristie wasn't in the slightest bit interested. 'Just hand him over to me,' she'd said. 'I could do with a real man.'

When the doorbell rang at seven fifteen Chloe eagerly said, 'I'll get it. I want to have another look at Mr Hunk.'

'It won't be him. It will be their chauffeur,' Kristie pointed out. But as it happened it was neither.

'Paul!' she exclaimed as he preceded Chloe into the room. 'What are you doing here?'

'I've had better welcomes,' he complained, but there was a smile on his face. 'I came to ask you out but it looks like I'm too late.'

Paul was tall and lanky with mousy brown hair and hazel eyes and he was the kindest and most genuine man you could ever wish to meet. Jake adored him and he was good with the boy too. Even though he knew Kristie didn't love him in the way he wanted, he still persisted.

'I'm sorry,' she said wistfully.

'Where are you going? Somewhere classy? You look stunning, Kristie.' There was the slightest hint of regret in his voice.

'Dinner at a client's, that's all,' she announced as casually as she could.

The doorbell rang again and Chloe ran eagerly to answer

it. When Kristie heard the deep male voice her heart sank into her shoes. Why Radford? What had happened to the driver?

He stopped dead in his tracks as he walked into the room, looking at Paul with a deep, questioning frown. 'Radford,' spoke Kristie quickly, 'this is Paul Derring, a very dear friend of mine. Paul, meet Radford Smythe. I'm co-ordinating his sister's wedding.'

The two men shook hands, both looking warily at the other. It was Paul who turned away first. 'It's time I went. I'll give you a ring later in the week, Kristie.'

She nodded. 'I'll see you to the door.' She felt Radford's eyes on them both as they left the room, and so it appeared did Paul.

'Am I getting my nose pushed out?' he asked, pausing in the doorway.

'Definitely not,' she asserted. 'I didn't even expect him to come and pick me up. His mother said she was sending her driver.'

'He didn't look pleased to see me. I think he has his eye on you.'

'Nonsense! In any case, he's not my type. Don't worry about him, Paul.' As she spoke she linked her arms around his neck and kissed him with much more meaning than usual. She felt sorry for him because he had turned up to take her out and here she was being picked up by another man.

Taken by surprise, Paul hesitated a moment before returning her kiss with a passion that was rare for him also. Not that he had never wanted to kiss Kate in this way—she was aware of that—but he had always respected her feelings.

When Paul finally left she closed the door and turned around—and discovered Radford watching her, a frown dragging his brows together, his lips unsmiling. 'You amaze me, Kristie Swift. I'd never have guessed you liked the sort of man you can wrap around your little finger. I thought you had more spirit than that. There'll be no excitement in your life with a man like Paul Derring.'

'Who said I want excitement?' she protested swiftly and furiously. She was embarrassed that he had seen her kiss Paul, especially as it had been so out of character, an act of defiance almost. And yet, in a way, perhaps it was a good thing. If Radford thought she and Paul were a permanent item it would keep him off her back. There would be no more dinner invitations, no more wanting to get to know her better.

'You certainly need more than he can offer,' he commented tersely.

'You don't know him,' Kristie tossed back, her eyes flashing green fire.

Thick, well-shaped brows rose. 'I'm a pretty shrewd judge of character.'

'Without even speaking to him?'

'Yes,' he answered confidently. 'If I were him and another guy came into the room who was going to take my girl out to dinner I most definitely wouldn't have walked away and left him. The man's a wimp.'

'How dare you?' Kiristie's fragile hold on her temper was slipping. 'For one thing, it's not you taking me out to dinner, and Paul knew that.' But then an awful thought hit her—one that made her go sick to the bottom of her stomach. She glared accusingly. 'If this is some con-trick, if you think you're going to—'

His smile held no hint of pleasure. 'We *are* dining at my mother's house. Not that I wouldn't have preferred to take you out myself but—'

'Some hope of that,' she snapped, charging past him. But

Radford had other ideas. His arms came out and she was caught in a band of steel. 'Let me show you what it's like to be kissed by a real man.' His voice which had been hard and uncompromising, deepened to a smoky growl.

The feel of that strong-boned body against hers sent an unwanted message to Kristie's brain. This man was dangerous. Not only that but he was filling her senses. It was something she could well do without. Even now he was taking control of her body, her mind and everything else sensual.

When his mouth came down on hers it sent a further assault shuddering through her. One arm remained around the small of her back while his other hand cupped her chin in a grip so hard she wanted to cry out.

And all this happened in the space of a few seconds.

His aftershave was subtle and sensual, teasing her nostrils, adding to the chaos inside her. Every inch of her body responded, while at the same time she knew that it was imperative she escape.

But in the end she didn't have to put up a fight. She was suddenly as free as the air around her—free in the physical sense, but not from the feelings which ran rampant inside her. Feelings this man had managed to arouse in the merest atom of time.

It was deeply worrying and she could see why her sister had been so besotted by him. Her voice was harsh when she spoke. 'That was an appalling thing to do. What would your mother think if she knew you'd assaulted me?'

'Assaulted?' Hot, indignant eyes blazed into hers. 'You call one brief kiss an assault? And actually it lasted a lot less time than the one you gave your boyfriend. Nor can you deny that you found it pleasurable.'

He was right, damn him—the effect of the kiss still lingered, her body felt sizzlingly alive, something it had never done when Paul kissed her. Her eyes sparked and she wiped the back of her hand across her mouth in a deliberately insulting gesture. 'Don't ever do that again.'

'You don't mean that, Kristie. You're angry because you responded to me against your will.' His mouth twitched at the corners and he looked annoyingly relaxed as he leaned back against the doorjamb, his thumbs hooked into his trouser pockets.

'Responded?' she huffed. 'To you? You have to be joking. You're the last man on earth I'd respond to.' Her sister was dead because of this man. She hated him with every breath that she drew. And what she ought to have done was turn that job down the second she found out who she was dealing with.

'Why?'

The direct question caught her by surprise, but not the hard glitter in his eyes. She had expected that. He was a man who didn't take kindly to being spurned. 'Because you think you're God's gift,' she snapped. 'You turn women's heads as inevitably as flowers to the sun, but not this one, I assure you. I have better taste.'

His breath whistled through his teeth and Kristie waited for the onslaught that never came. She could actually see him controlling his temper. 'I think we should go,' he said stiffly.

Kristie knew the time was fast approaching to confront him, yet still she felt a need to know him better. Though how, when all she ever wanted to do was put space between them, she didn't know. This evening was going to be a huge ordeal. It would crucify her being civil to him, but for his mother's and sister's sake she had to do it.

Before they left she popped into the kitchen where a smiling Chloe was lurking out of the way.

'He kissed you,' she breathed, wide eyed as Kristie reapplied her lipstick.

'Paul?'

'No, Mr Hunk. I think he fancies you, and he's a much better catch.'

'Not in my opinion,' declared Kristie strongly, but she didn't want to talk about him. 'You will ring me if Jake wakes and wants me, won't you? I hate leaving him like this, it's—'

'Just go,' ordered Chloe. 'Everything will be all right. Go and enjoy yourself.'

As if she could. And if Chloe knew the whole story she wouldn't be saying this.

The black Mercedes was spacious and sumptuous but as she sank into the soft leather seat Kristie wished it would swallow her up. Radford's sexuality filled the space, drawing her into his web like a spider did a fly. He was a dangerous, threatening male and she needed to be on her guard at all times. It would be so easy to fall for him. That one brief kiss had taught her that. But her brain was sending out warning signals which she'd do well to heed.

'I don't bite,' he snarled as she huddled against the door.

Kristie's eyes flashed. 'I never for one moment thought you did.'

'Then why shrink away from me? My kiss got you rattled, did it? You're afraid I might try it again. Don't worry. You're perfectly safe; I like my women willing.'

His women! Confirming her opinion that he enjoyed playing the field. Why was it that men with money and power thought they could have any girl they wished? Was it a game they played, dumping them when they got tired of them and going on to the next gullible female? It made her mad just thinking about it.

She deigned not to answer him, keeping her eyes on the road ahead and her hands folded tightly in her lap.

'I hope you're not going to keep this up all night,' he rasped. 'My mother will wonder what on earth she's letting herself in for. More than likely she'll cancel the contract. Which, in my opinion, won't be a bad thing. I've had a feeling about you right from the start.'

Kristie's head turned sharply in his direction. 'If you kept your nose out it would be all right. I'm quite capable of liaising with your mother and Felicity. There's no need for you to even be here.'

'My mother thinks there is. Since my father died she finds it difficult to cope. She never had to make decisions; he made them all for her.'

'And you've stepped into his shoes? Is that for her own good? I don't think so. What would happen if there was a catastrophe while you were abroad, let's say? She'd have to cope then. You're doing her no favours.'

'And you're an expert on this, are you?' he charged angrily. 'You're one of the breed of women who think they can do anything a man can do?'

'I know I can,' she retorted.

'Hmph!' he snorted, and then remained in disapproving silence for the rest of the journey.

Radford couldn't understand why Kristie hated him so. He had thought it might be men in general—until she kissed Paul Derring. What she saw in this other man he had no idea. Paul wasn't a man; he was a mouse, meekly skulking away the moment he arrived. It was something he certainly wouldn't have done, he'd have wanted to know exactly what interest this man had in his girlfriend.

Perhaps Paul liked dominant females. Perhaps he liked to be led rather than do the leading. And perhaps this was what Kristie favoured as well. It could be the reason why she was so against him. For once she had met a man who preferred to take charge, and she didn't like it.

He smiled grimly to himself. Kristie Swift was going to prove a challenge. She might not know it yet, but he was determined to win her over. It didn't sit well on his shoulders to be spurned and he had probably made matters worse by kissing her.

But what a kiss. It had been a spur of the moment thing but it had sent his testosterone levels soaring. She had tasted wickedly sweet and her body had been softly feminine and desirable against him, sending a plethora of sensations to his every extremity. He had wanted more; he had wanted to deepen the kiss, he had wanted to touch and stroke and make her his in every way possible.

Considering he had thought her an unbalanced woman to start with, his change of feelings was quite startling. He could hardly believe them himself. Even sitting here, Kristie shying as far away from him as possible, he wanted to reach out and place his hand over hers, assure her that he didn't bite, that it would be all right for her to relax and get to know him properly. Either that or shake her! He had never met anyone so infuriating and for once he was unsure how to deal with a situation.

She looked totally gorgeous in that sky blue suit and if she would only relax it would be a very pleasant evening. He wondered how she would react to the proposal his mother was about to make.

CHAPTER FIVE

'So what do you think?'

Kristie looked at Mrs Mandervell-Smythe in stunned silence and it was several seconds before she spoke. 'I don't know. You've taken me by surprise. It's very generous of you, but—'

'Radford told me that you work in a corner of your living room. That's no good, my dear, especially as you have a woman and child living with you. How on earth do you cope? It's the perfect solution. Do say yes.'

Mrs Mandervell-Smythe had no idea how impossible the situation was. How could she work in this house with Radford present? The use of a room as an office was a very charitable gesture and it would certainly help matters; it was often difficult to concentrate with Jake running around, even though Chloe did her best to keep him out of the way. But...

'Come, let me show you,' said the older woman decisively.

Kristie paused to glance at Radford as she left the room behind his mother. He had dropped into an armchair, totally relaxed, listening with interest to their conversation. There was an enigmatic smile on his lips now—the sort of smile that told her this was more his doing than his mother's, and she glared at him accusingly.

'Run along,' he said. 'You don't want my mother thinking you're ungrateful, do you?'

'This is your idea, isn't it?' she hissed softly. 'And I

don't find it in the least amusing. I think you have a cheek, trying to interfere in my life.'

'How can you work with some damn child around all the time? I merely have your best interests at heart,' he returned, still with that infuriating smile.

'Which I can do without,' she shot back, and to her relief he didn't join her as she hurried to catch up with his mother. They walked through a series of corridors until they reached a room which Kristie judged to be at the west end of the building, well away from their living quarters.

'This was my husband's study,' explained Mrs Mandervell-Smythe as she pushed open the door. 'It's never used these days. Radford has his own office here, of course. In fact, he has his own suite of rooms, but mostly he works from London. Amazingly, this time he's in no hurry to get back. I expect it's because of Felicity's wedding; there's so much to think about and he knows I couldn't do it without him. Nor you, of course, my dear. It's such a relief to have all the work taken off my shoulders.'

Kristie smiled faintly. There was no relief on her part. His mother might be pleased that Radford was staying but she definitely wasn't.

'So what do you think?' asked the older woman as Kristie gazed around the oak-panelled room. 'Could you work here?'

It was a large room with a huge desk and endless shelves. Near one of the two windows which looked out over the garden at the back of the house were two deep leather armchairs. It would be a dream to work here compared to the cramped space she had at home. There was only one drawback.

'It's very generous of you Mrs Mandervell-Smythe—'

'Please, call me Peggy, everyone does.'

Kristie smiled weakly. 'Peggy, then.' Somehow it felt wrong calling Radford's mother by her first name, but she didn't want to argue. 'I don't really feel I can take you up on your offer. It's—'

'Nonsense. You'd be doing me a favour, as a matter of fact. Otherwise we'd be on the phone to each other all of the time. Felicity's a devil for changing her mind, as I think Radford warned you. It simply makes sense.'

Peggy was right and if she was honest with herself it was the offer of a lifetime. Free use of an office! How lucky could she get? But not if Radford was going to be on her back every hour of the day; it would lose all its pleasure. 'Whose idea was it, yours or Radford's?' she asked.

'Mine,' said Peggy instantly. 'As soon as he told me about your working conditions I knew Edward's study would be perfect for you. It's criminal that it never gets used. Please say yes. It won't cost you a penny. You can use this door—' indicating one of the French windows '—and come and go as you please. There's ample parking space round the back here.'

'How about the main gates?'

'I'll give you a remote. There is absolutely no reason why you shouldn't take up my offer. I thought you'd jump at the chance. Why are you hesitating?'

'Perhaps she thinks we'd interfere?'

Kristie turned at the sound of Radford's deep, gravelly voice. Why was *he* butting in? Her green eyes flashed hostility, but before she could say anything his mother spoke.

'Of course we wouldn't; you'd have total privacy, Kristie. You talk to her, Radford. Make her see sense.'

Kristie knew his mother was pressurising her because it helped to have her on the spot, but after the wedding, what then? After the wedding Radford wouldn't be here, she told herself. Nor would he remain here for the whole of the run up to the wedding. It was twelve months away. So why not take advantage of such a liberal offer?

'She knows it makes sense,' he said. 'I think it's me who's the stumbling block.'

His mother frowned. 'What are you talking about?'

'For some reason Kristie Swift has taken a dislike to me.'

Kristie could have spat in Radford's eye. What the hell did he have to say that for? Her gripe with him was private, nothing to do with his parent.

'Nonsense!' his mother said. 'Why would she do that?'

'You'd best ask her.'

'Your son is not why I am hesitating,' Kristie told her firmly. 'In fact—' her mind was suddenly made up '—I'd like to take you up on your offer. It will be a great help. I shall work normal office hours and you'll hardly know I'm here.'

Peggy smiled happily and put her hands together as though praying. 'I'm so pleased, and I'm quite sure you won't regret it. No one will interfere, I can assure you of that. This office will be your private domain. There's a lock on both doors, I'll give you the keys.'

Kristie felt Radford eyeing her but she ignored him, ignored also the skittering of her senses. 'I'll pay for phone calls, of course, and electricity,' she said firmly.

'No, you won't,' insisted the older woman. 'You're doing me the favour by putting the room to some use. I won't hear another word said about it. Move in as soon as you like. Radford, go and find the keys.'

The air cleared the moment he left, but Kristie didn't miss the look he gave her. It was triumph. He had deliberately goaded her into saying yes and she had stupidly fallen for it. And somehow she had the feeling that he wouldn't leave her alone, no matter what his mother said.

She made up her mind there and then that the doors would remain firmly locked.

By the time they got back to the main part of the house Felicity's husband-to-be had arrived and Kristie's fear that she might find herself alone with Radford was quickly dispelled.

Daniel Fielding was perfect for Felicity. Not particularly good looking, but thoughtful and caring and kind and intelligent. And they were both deeply in love. It was there for everyone to see.

Kristie spent some time talking to him but felt Radford's eyes on her, even though he was chatting away to his mother and sister. It was unnerving having him watch her like this; it sent a funny feeling down her spine, and she couldn't help wondering whether his mother noticed his interest in her.

When dinner was announced Radford came across and took her elbow and led her into the dining room. She couldn't ignore the tingles that his touch created and was delighted when she discovered that she was not to be seated next to him. It wasn't long, though, before she discovered that sitting opposite him was just as bad.

'Tell me, Kristie,' said Radford, once their first course had been served, 'what made you decide to become a wedding co-ordinator? You must get so many headaches it can hardly be worthwhile. Have you ever been married yourself? Is that how you realised how much work is involved and that you could save other people a lot of trouble?'

His question aroused everyone's interest but it was to him that she looked. Although he guessed that none of the others could see it, he could tell that she resented him asking such personal questions.

'Actually, no, I've never been married.'

So it wasn't her husband who'd hurt her. It was some other man to whom she'd been attached, someone who was a lot like himself, apparently. He was glad she'd agreed to his mother's offer because now he could work on her. There was an awful lot he wanted to know about Miss Kristie Swift.

'I became a wedding co-ordinator because—well, because I like organising. I'd done various design and management courses over the years and this appealed to me. It's something I enjoy and something I do well.'

'I wonder whether you'll think the same when my darling sister's finished with you.'

'Radford!' hurled Felicity. 'Don't be insulting.'

He grinned. 'You know what you're like, cherub. You don't know your own mind from one minute to the next.'

'Don't believe him,' said Felicity to Kristie. 'He's trying to wind us both up. He's not approved of you from the word go and I don't know why. I think you're perfect for the job and I'm so glad you've agreed to use Daddy's office. I'll be able to come and talk to you and—'

'Darling.' It was Peggy's turn to speak. 'Kristie won't want us interrupting her. We'll still need to go through the usual channels. In fact, Kristie, I shall have a separate telephone line installed. Radford, you'll see to it for me, won't you?'

'Anything you say, Mother.' It was a wry comment and not lost on Kristie. He saw the flicker in her eye, could almost read her mind. There was not much he didn't notice about her. She was thoroughly uncomfortable sitting here with his family and she was wishing herself at home, though how she found any peace there he didn't know. He had thought she would jump at the chance of an office here; was somewhat surprised when it took her so long to make up her mind.

He wasn't stupid enough not to realise that he was the big deciding factor, although she needn't have worried; he wouldn't be here for much longer. Much as he wanted to stay and get to know her better, there were other pressing issues to deal with. His PA had phoned him only that morning with a whole list of queries that needed his personal attention.

Kristie was uncomfortable now beneath his gaze, trying hard to concentrate on eating her seafood medley. There was a pink tinge to her cheeks and an angry flash of green in her eyes. He was pleased his mother had sat her opposite him.

Peggy had despaired of him ever finding the right woman and if she knew exactly which way his thoughts ran she'd do her utmost to throw them together. It would be an all-out blatant attack, one that Kristie would be sure to notice, and one that had frightened off other girls before her.

He sensed Kristie's relief when the meal was finally over. She had toyed with her food, hardly eating a thing, looking at him from beneath her long lashes whenever she had thought he wasn't watching her. She had joined in the conversation, answering easily and interestingly, but when she had been forced to speak to him the shutters had come down.

No one else had seemed to notice, so perhaps he was being too sensitive. Though he doubted it. This woman hated him and he intended to find out why—hopefully when he took her home tonight. Meanwhile, he would take pleasure in looking at her beautiful face and body.

He'd never been out with a redhead before. Not that her hair was exactly red—nearer a light auburn. But the more he saw of her the more he wanted her. There was no denying it. She alerted every male hormone inside him, sent his testosterone levels sky high and his need of her burnt like a furnace. He allowed his foot to touch hers beneath the table and was rewarded by a further blaze of green and another heated flush, revealing that she wasn't exactly immune to him either.

It brought a smile to his lips which in turn sent yet another green flash in his direction. He found it amazing that he enjoyed it when she was angry with him. His whole body ached with a sudden desperate need to bed her. Whether she saw it in his eyes or whether it was her own desperate need to escape, he didn't know, but she suddenly stood up. 'I really ought to be going, Mrs Mandervell— Peggy. I have no wish to outstay my welcome. It's very kind of you to let me use your husband's office. I'll move in after the weekend, if that's all right?'

Peggy beamed. 'It's more than all right. Radford, did you find those keys?'

He'd been hoping his mother wouldn't remember—it would have given him an excuse to see Kristie in her new workplace. Now he fished them out of his pocket and dangled them in front of her nose. 'One set of keys.' And he knew full well that she would keep her door firmly locked. Not against anyone else, just him. It brought a grim expression to his face. What the hell was he doing feeling an interest in this woman? He'd go back to London tomorrow and forget her.

When he stood up too Kristie said quickly, 'Don't put yourself out; I'll call a taxi.'

'No, you won't,' insisted his mother. 'Radford will take you.'

'My mother's given her driver the night off,' Radford explained, his lips compressed at her horrified expression. There was going to be no fun in driving her. All he was going to do was get totally frustrated. Damn the woman. What had he done to upset her, for God's sake?

He determined there and then to drive her straight home and say nothing on the journey. But it didn't work out like that. The very nearness of her heightened and alerted every one of his senses; the scent of her body assailed his nostrils like an aphrodisiac. The thought of dropping her off and walking away was abhorrent.

Kristie didn't shrink against the door this time, so maybe, just maybe, there was faint hope. He wished he knew what dark thoughts ran through her mind, what it was that she held against him. He didn't even know whether it was personal or men in general.

She had said men of his type—but what type was that? As far as he was concerned he was no different from other men. He was successful, yes. He ran a profitable business, but so too did plenty of others. Did she have it in for all of them? She'd seemed to like Daniel Fielding who, in his opinion, wasn't much of a man—even though his beloved sister adored him. He had no great ambitions, he was content to muddle along in his job as a property surveyor. And from what little he'd seen of Paul he was not very much different.

Oddly, Kristie was full of ambition herself. She was doing well with her wedding design company. He could see for himself how dedicated she was and, although he'd said he wanted to check out her credentials, deep down he admired her guts and courage. She would go far.

'Why did you want to leave early?' he asked as he pulled out of the driveway. 'Not that I'm complaining, but I felt you cut the evening short.'

'Did I?' she asked with a frown. 'I hope your mother didn't think that. But it is ten-thirty.'

'And that's your curfew, is it?' he couldn't help asking.

'Not at all,' she answered decisively. 'I was up at five this morning; I'm rather tired.'

He raised a brow as he looked at her. 'I thought you might have been running away from me?' There was an almost full moon slanting into the car, giving her face an icy beauty as she shot him a glance.

'Don't flatter yourself,' she snapped.

'Why? You've been giving a very good impression of disliking me. Though, I have to admit, there have been occasions when your guard has slipped and I've glimpsed beneath the surface a woman of passion.'

He sensed rather than saw her dismay and as he expected she denied it. 'The world would have to end before I felt passionate about you,' she retorted.

'You're denying that when my foot touched yours beneath the table it didn't trigger a response? And don't forget I was watching you closely.' So closely that he had seen a dull flush of desire before it was replaced with blazing fury.

'So what?' she asked with a shrug.

'It's a step in the right direction.'

There was an instant hiss of breath and a flash of those dramatic green eyes. 'Don't flatter yourself. I'm not going to take one single step in your direction.'

He allowed himself a faint smile. 'You'd stand no chance, pretty lady, if I really wanted to assert myself.' Which he did, very much so, despite the fact that he'd told her he liked his women willing. But Kristie Swift was different; she was a challenge. Simply looking at her aroused him to such a degree that he knew he wouldn't be content until he had bedded her. And it wasn't simply that. She was interesting in other ways. She was well-educated, intelligent, charming, funny—yes, funny. He had seen her making Daniel and Felicity laugh, and it had peeved him that he couldn't share. She would make a good friend.

Who was he kidding? It was more than friendship he wanted. He wanted her body. Even now, when she was openly rejecting him, his hot male blood surged through veins and arteries with a force that left him breathless.

'I think you're overestimating yourself, Mr Smythe,' she tossed back. 'You can fling anything you like at me and I'll resist it.'

She was feisty, he'd give her that, but if anything it increased his hunger. 'Is that a challenge?'

Frosty eyes glared. 'Actually, no. I expect you to behave like a gentleman.'

'You think I can keep away from someone as excitingly sexy as yourself?' She was asking the impossible.

'Is that how you see me?' she shot back. 'A sex object? Why am I not surprised? You were clearly brought up with a silver spoon in your mouth. Whatever you asked for you were given. And it's my guess it's the same with the opposite sex. You give a smile and lift a finger and the object of your attention comes running. Well, tough luck in my case because this girl's not interested.'

Strong words! He needed to convince her that she was wrong, that he wasn't like that, that he'd worked his way to the top on his own merits. But he knew that she'd flatly refuse to believe him if he told her now. Getting to know her, letting her find out about him, needed to be a gradual process. The trouble was he knew he wouldn't be very big on patience where Kristie Swift was concerned. He was too hungry for her.

'I see you don't deny it,' she tossed scathingly.

'Would you believe me if I did?'

'Of course not.'

'So there's no point. What I think we should do is get to know each other slowly. In that way you'll find out for yourself that I'm not the ogre you seem to think.' He changed down the gears as they approached a set of traffic lights, glancing at her questioningly as he stopped.

'I actually want nothing further to do with you,' she declared. 'I'll be glad when you go back to London.'

Her flat statement not only disappointed him, it angered him. Her attitude towards him was unwarranted. 'How the hell can you talk like that when you don't know me?'

'I don't want to know you,' she riposted.

His breath whistled through his teeth. 'Well, bad luck, because you're going to see an awful lot of me while you're working for my mother.' Now, why had he said that when it was his intention to go back to London? Indeed, he must go. But he would be back, he knew that. He wasn't going to let it end here.

'In that case,' she retorted, 'I won't take up your mother's offer. I saw it as somewhere peaceful I could work, not a hell-hole to be tormented by you. And I'll let you tell her the reason why.'

Radford's lips were grim as he shot away from the traffic lights. He was handling this whole thing badly, which was unlike him. He was renowned for his tact and diplomacy. But not, it appeared, where this young woman was concerned. She rubbed him up the wrong way at every turn.

'There's no need for you to upset my mother,' he said quietly.

'So you'll keep out of my way?'

He couldn't promise that. He wanted to see more of her, a lot more. 'I'm returning to London tomorrow.'

Her relief was palpable and he had no intention of ruining things by admitting that he would be returning. Let her think that he'd gone for a long time.

When they reached Kristie's house he killed the engine and got out of the car.

'You don't have to see me in,' she said hastily.

'Oh, but I do, it's the gentlemanly thing.' He waited for a backlash; was surprised when there was none.

She simply inserted her key fiercely into the lock and opened the door, turning only briefly to say, 'Thank you for the lift.' And then it was shut in his face.

CHAPTER SIX

KRISTIE drove to her new office on Monday morning filled with more than a little trepidation. She had been uneasy the whole weekend, wondering whether she was making a huge mistake, and once or twice had even lifted the phone, prepared to call the whole thing off.

But offers like this came once in a lifetime and she would be a fool to turn it down. Radford was returning to London—so why was she worrying? Perhaps because she didn't believe him.

She pressed her remote control as she approached the immense iron gates. They glided slowly open and she drove her car as near as she could to the long study windows. The idea was that if she could sneak in this way, instead of going through the house, then there was less chance of Radford, if he was still here, discovering her presence.

It was a total shock to see a whole host of new equipment—computer, laser printer, scanner, copier—everything she could possibly need, even a laptop. Stationery, pens, pencils, a drawing board. It was unbelievable, and she felt distinctly uncomfortable. How could they spend all this money on her on top of not wanting any rent? It would tie her to them for ever more. She couldn't do it.

She was on the verge of leaving when a tap came on the door. 'Kristie, it's Peggy.'

With a wry grimace she turned the key.

'What do you think?' asked the older woman, a smile a mile wide on her face. 'I asked Radford to install everything he thought you'd need, but if he's forgotten anything then—'

'Peggy, I can't. It's too much,' protested Kristie.

'Nonsense! It's giving me so much pleasure. Don't spoil it.'

'But it must have cost an awful lot of money.'

'So what? I can afford it. I have little to spend my money on these days. I don't go on holiday any more, I don't enjoy it without Edward, and I have wardrobes full of clothes. It makes me feel good to do this for you. I know you might find this strange, Kristie, but I feel an affinity with you. I feel as though we could be good friends.'

Kristie liked Peggy too; she was a warm and caring woman and although there was a huge age gap it didn't feel like it. But as for being friends, with Radford on the horizon, it was not a good prospect. What would Peggy say, she wondered, if she found out how he had treated her sister, how he had summarily ended their affair when he'd tired of her? Whose side would she take? It was a delicate situation and she ought to have thought this through before accepting her offer.

'It's kind of you to say that, Peggy,' she said sincerely, 'since we hardly know each other. You're being far too kind.'

'I took to you the instant I met you. You're the sort of girl I'd like Radford to marry. Not that I think he ever will get married. He's thirty eight, for goodness' sake, and not a sign of a wife on the horizon. He's happy enough though, running the business. He likes London, he loves the hustle and bustle of a big city. His apartment overlooks the Thames, so he has some breathing space. I couldn't see him ever settling down here.'

Kristie's relief was enormous. 'Did he live here as a child?'

'Oh, yes, this house has been in my husband's family for generations. He loved the open spaces then. He was a proper outdoor boy. Before Felicity's accident they were inseparable.'

'So what happened to your daughter?' It was a question Kristie had longed to ask.

Peggy's face grew sad for a moment. 'She fell off her horse. A proper daredevil she was. She tried to take a hedge far too high. He reared, she fell off, landed on her back and broke her spine. She was only eleven at the time. But she's brave, she never lets it get her down.'

'I can see that,' said Kristie. 'She's remarkably cheerful. I admire her deeply.'

'And now she's found herself a wonderful man who'll look after her for the rest of her life.'

'He's one in a million,' agreed Kristie, 'and I'm honoured to be arranging their wedding.'

'So you don't feel too badly of me for equipping your office? I do want you to be settled here.'

'You're more than generous, Peggy, but I would still feel better if you'd let me pay some rent.'

'You don't want to feel a charity case, is that it?' asked the other woman with an understanding smile. 'Very well, we'll sort something out. Now, tell me, is there anything else that you need? Molly will bring you morning coffee and afternoon tea, and I'd really appreciate it if you'd take lunch with me.'

But Kristie shook her head. 'Thank you, but I'm either out or too busy for lunch. I usually grab a sandwich on the run. Has Radford gone back to London?'

Peggy's attention was successfully diverted. 'Yes, he went last night, much to my surprise. As soon as he got back he packed his bags and left. Said he had some urgent business first thing this morning. I don't suppose I'll see him again for ages.'

Relief washed over Kristie. Now she could get on with her work without having to worry that she might be disturbed by the one man in the world who challenged her senses against her will. He was someone she had never wished to meet. If the event happened, then she had vowed to give him a piece of her mind he would never forget. So why hadn't she? Why had she allowed herself to be attracted to him? Was this how it had happened with Tarah? Had her sister been drawn to him against her will as well?

When Paul found out that she had moved office he wasn't pleased. 'I distrusted that guy right from the moment I met him. It was his idea, wasn't it? He's after you, Kristie, can't you see that?'

He had called to see her that same evening and Kristie had been full of enthusiasm about her new office. 'You're wrong,' she told him now. 'It was Radford's mother who suggested it. He's not there any more. He's gone back to London.'

Paul looked only slightly mollified. 'I still think it's the wrong thing to do. I thought you were happy working from home?'

'I was but Peggy was very insistent, and it makes sense. Jake often interrupts me at all the wrong times. I shall get my work done a lot more quickly.'

'Can you afford it, though? You always said working from home made financial sense.'

She didn't want to admit that she'd been offered it for nothing, even though Peggy was now going to come up with a figure, which she suspected would be nominal anyway, so she shrugged. 'My business is doing OK. It's time I moved on.'

'Does that mean it will be a nine to five job now and you'll have more time for me?' he asked hopefully.

'I guess so,' she admitted. And she knew Jake would love having Paul around more.

In fact, Paul visited her every evening that week, coming early so that he could play with Jake, and then either taking her out for a meal or eating in with her. If it hadn't been for thoughts of Radford lurking in the back of her mind, Kristie would have relaxed and enjoyed herself. She'd always felt comfortable in Paul's company; they never argued, they simply rubbed along easily together.

It was on the second Monday in her new office that Kristie's peace was disturbed. Peggy had taken to visiting her for a few minutes each morning and safe in the knowledge that Radford was in London, she'd got into the habit of leaving the door unlocked. But this morning the tap was louder than normal, and she didn't even have time to call out before the door was pushed roughly open.

She knew before she even saw him who it was. His mother always waited to be invited, but not this man. He strode confidently into the room, a black polo shirt and black trousers making him seem more threatening than normal. 'What are you doing here?' she asked coldly.

He smiled, a grim smile that set her teeth on edge. 'Polite as usual I see.'

'You're supposed to be in London.'

'My mother needed me.'

'Why, what's wrong?' Peggy had been all right when she left on Friday.

'She's not ill, don't worry. A few discussions about the wedding. I warned you Flick would change her mind.'

'And she needed to discuss them with you, not me?' asked Kristie sharply.

'She wanted to talk them over *before* she spoke to you. Have you had a good weekend?'

'I'm sure my private life's very low on your list of priorities,' she tossed scathingly. 'Why are you here? To tell me about the changes, or to torment me?'

'Is that what I do?' His lips quirked, brows rose. 'Why is that, I wonder?'

Kristie heaved an impatient sigh. 'Will you tell me why you're here and then go—please.' If this was going to happen on a regular basis then she really had made a big mistake. Last week had been heaven, this week looked like being a nightmare.

'I merely popped in to ask whether you'd let me take you out to dinner this evening?'

'You're not going back to London?'

'In good time,' he answered with a devilish smile. 'What's your answer?'

'I think you know,' she told him shortly.

He crossed the room and sank down into one of the leather armchairs, looking for all the world as though he'd come to stay. 'I've spent this last week thinking about you,' he told her. 'Wondering why you hate me so much. Oh, I know what you've said but it doesn't ring true. So—here I am and here I intend to stay.'

Kristie's heart clocked along at a disturbing rate. She would have preferred to wait until after the wedding before there was any altercation between them. She didn't want to upset his mother. But could she wait? Not if he was going to pester her like this, that was a fact. He would goad her and goad her until she blurted it out.

But not, she thought suddenly, if she pretended to have a change of heart. Not if she apparently warmed towards him. Could she do that? It was a case of having to if she didn't want to upset Peggy. They had become very close this past week. Peggy had confided all sorts of things in her, and she couldn't bear the thought of doing anything to spoil her pleasure in Felicity's wedding.

'It looks like I have no choice,' she said as evenly as she could.

His smile was triumphant. 'I'll prove to you that I'm not the big bad wolf you think I am.'

'We'll see,' she said quietly. 'Now, if you wouldn't mind, I do have a lot of work to get through.'

'What time are you likely to finish here?' he asked, pushing himself to his feet and coming to stand directly in front of her.

Kristie could smell the woody scent of his aftershave and it sent a prickle of awareness through her senses. This was going to be the most dangerous thing she had ever done. 'Usually around five, but I shall naturally need to go home and get changed.'

'I'll pick you up at your house, then,' he said. 'Shall we say about seven-thirty?'

She nodded.

'Good. I look forward to it.'

But she didn't. She was falling well and truly into his trap. It would be difficult, if not impossible, not to respond to his overt sexuality—and that was the last thing she wanted. Hopefully, though, he wouldn't be here very often. She could cope with the odd few days now and then.

Concentration was impossible and she was glad when she received a phone call that necessitated her going to see one of her other clients. It was six-thirty before she finally got home and it was a mad rush then to bathe Jake and get him ready for bed. She wouldn't have missed Jake's bath time for the world. Sometimes she felt guilty for leaving him with Chloe, and she always tried to make up for it with plenty of hugs and kisses and reassurances of love.

He was asleep by the time Radford came and she was able to greet him calmly and walk out to his car without showing the turmoil that knotted her stomach. All she had to do was have a good time and ignore all the other signs.

But that was easier said than done. It started in the car— just the feel of him next to her was enough. He managed somehow to haunt her senses without even looking at her, without saying a word. It was a strange sensation. She'd never met a man before who aroused her simply by being there.

And in the restaurant, a secluded, cosy little place in the country—she'd not even known that it existed even though it was only a few miles from her home—the sensations continued. Radford didn't say a word out of place. He was the perfect gentleman and yet, sitting opposite him, being forced to look at him, to breathe in the very essence of him, she became so stimulated that she half-expected him to see it, to comment on it.

Of course he couldn't know how she was feeling deep down inside. No, not deep down—everywhere, even the surface of her skin sizzled. She couldn't understand how she could react like this to a man she had hated for the last five years. It didn't make sense. How could she look at him and get an immediate sexual response? It made nonsense of all the harsh thoughts she had harboured against him.

During the meal they talked mainly about his sister's wedding; it was a safe topic and she was happy to discuss it. 'Your mother told me how Felicity came to be in a wheelchair,' she said softly.

Radford pursed his lips and nodded slowly, his eyes shadowing. 'I feel partly to blame,' he said, putting down his knife and fork. 'I was with her at the time and should have tried to stop her. She was so headstrong; a mind of her own, even at that age. The memory of that accident, when she lay there so pale and lifeless, will remain with me for ever.'

This was a side of Radford that Kristie hadn't seen. A side that made him more human and vulnerable. A very different image from the one she had always carried in her mind. Not that it made her think any differently about him, but she could see now why he was always so attentive to his sister's needs. It was his way of trying to make up.

'How did she take it when she learned that she would never walk again?'

Radford winced. 'Very badly. She was angry with everyone for a long time. Temper tantrums became the norm. My mother was at her wits' end.'

'I don't think I'd be happy either,' agreed Kristie. In fact she couldn't think of anything worse.

'But gradually she accepted the inevitable and became her usual cheery, sunny self. I'm so glad she met Daniel. He's perfect for her.' Radford picked up his cutlery and resumed his meal.

They had both ordered fish as their main course, Radford the trout and Kristie poached salmon with a herb crumb topping, which she found truly delicious. 'I've never organised a wedding for anyone in a wheelchair before. It's certainly opened my eyes.'

'From what I hear you're doing a very good job,' he said, his grey eyes warm and kind. 'I take back what I said in the beginning about you not being up to it.'

'Apology accepted,' she said with a demure smile. Feelings were still churning inside her but they had settled down somewhat and to her amazement she found that she was enjoying herself. She was actually beginning to relax. Something she had never expected to do in Radford's company.

Perhaps it was because he was being the perfect gentleman. No advances, no cross words either, simply good conversation. The only hiccup was when he said, 'Tell me about yourself. Do you realise I know nothing about you.'

She tried to turn it into a joke. 'A woman of mystery, that's me.'

He sat back in his seat, a smile playing on his lips as he looked at her. 'It's up to me to guess, is that what you're saying?'

'Not at all. My relationship with your family is purely professional. My private—life is just that, private.' It would be so easy to give too much away and the time still wasn't right.

He cocked his head to one side and looked at her long and hard. 'I was hoping that tonight you might let your hair down and enjoy yourself.'

'I am,' she admitted. 'Very much so, actually.'

'And it surprises you?'

'Well, yes.'

'So you're beginning to realise that I'm not the ogre you think I am?' And all the time his smile was very much in evidence. Not a voracious smile, a warm friendly one that made her feel good inside. In fact her whole body was glowing with pleasure, something she had never expected where this man was concerned.

She picked up her wine glass and took a sip, and for some reason she couldn't take her eyes away from his. That one sip became two, and then another, and before she knew it she had finished the whole glass.

All evening Radford had been attentive to her every need and he did not fail her now. Rather than let the wine waiter do his duty he broke their eye contact to refill it himself, but the action brought his hand dangerously close to hers where she had left it holding the glass.

Kristie half-expected him to touch her, but he didn't. The

smile remained though, and it was not until their plates were taken away and dessert menus placed in front of them that their attention was diverted from each other. They both chose the raspberry pavlova.

'We have a lot more in common than you think,' quipped Radford. 'Let me see, you like your coffee black with just a little sugar?'

She nodded.

'So do I. How about tea? Do you like tea?'

'Not much.'

'Nor me. We're two of a kind, wouldn't you say?'

'I wouldn't go that far,' she said, but she couldn't help smiling.

All in all it was a fun evening, no hint of tension, simply two people having a good time. Even when she caught Radford looking at her with a curious smile, the sort of smile that told her he knew about the emotions churning her stomach, it didn't worry her. So long as he didn't mention them then all would be well.

On the return journey, though, in the close confines of his car, she couldn't ignore them any longer. He'd got through to her whether she wanted him to or not and she was glad when they got home. It was time now to free herself of his presence.

He accompanied her to her front door and this time she didn't feel that she could slam it in his face. 'Would you like to come in for another coffee?' she asked reluctantly, hoping against hope that he would refuse. He'd had one glass of wine and two cups of coffee in the restaurant.

'How about your ten-thirty curfew?' he asked with a straight face.

'I think I could stretch it,' she said.

'Then I'd be delighted to accept your offer.'

But the moment she opened the door Jake came racing
along the hall, tears streaming down his little face.
'Mummy, Mummy,' he called. 'I've been waiting for you.'
Kristie heard Radford's surprised intake of breath.

CHAPTER SEVEN

'JAKE, darling, what's wrong?' Kristie bent down to fold him in her arms, brushing his tears away with a gentle finger.

'My tummy hurts.'

'Where's Chloe? Has she given you anything for it?'

He shook his head and at that moment Chloe came into the hallway. 'He's not long woken, poor little mite. All he wanted was his mummy.'

'I think I'd better go.' Radford's hard voice broke into their conversation. 'I'll see you tomorrow, Kristie.'

She didn't even look round as he left. All Kristie was interested in was her son's well-being.

Jake was Kristie's son! Radford scowled as he returned to his car. Her son! How had that happened? Stupid! He knew how it had happened. But why hadn't she told him? Why had she let him believe that he belonged to Chloe? Or had she? Had he simply assumed?

And who the devil was the father? Surely not Paul? No, he'd have moved in if that was the case. Some other man she'd ensnared as surely as she was ensnaring him.

Damn! Just when he'd thought he'd found the perfect woman. He pulled his thoughts up short. Perfect? Kristie? When she hadn't hidden her dislike of him? What was he thinking? Yes, they'd had an enjoyable evening—more than enjoyable, in fact. It had taken every ounce of his willpower not to make a move on her. But to call her perfect? Not by a long chalk.

One thing was clear, though. Whoever it was who had done this to her was the one who had made her wary of men. More than wary, in fact—downright hostile towards them. Only Paul seemed to be in favour. And even he hadn't managed to work his way into her home. This woman had a real problem. He might as well forget her.

He wished now that he hadn't let his mother persuade Kristie to make her office with them. The less he saw of her the better. London, here I come, he decided. And nothing except an emergency will bring me back to Warwickshire.

But it didn't work out. The following morning his mother had an appointment with her doctor for her annual check, and Felicity wanted him to help with something to do with her wedding.

'Isn't that what you're employing that damn woman for?' he barked.

'My, my, who's upset you?' she asked with a big grin. 'Didn't your evening go as planned?'

His frown was sharp. 'What do you know about it?'

'There's not much goes on in this house that I don't know about,' she tossed back. 'Want to tell me?'

'There's nothing to tell,' he snarled. 'What is it you wanted to discuss?'

It was mid morning before they finished and by then he was so aware of Kristie in the house that he knew he had to go and see her. He'd observed her car pull up on the drive, seen her get out wearing a smart ivory trouser suit and matching, ridiculously high-heeled shoes. He'd watched the sway of her hips as she walked to the French windows. His testosterone had pumped—violently. Lord, that woman was a menace. She might be a deceptive little witch, but she certainly had what it took to arouse every one of his base instincts.

He rapped sharply on her door and turned the handle. Complete resistance. He cursed silently beneath his breath. He'd wanted to walk in, not give her the chance to refuse to see him, though why he thought she might do that he wasn't sure. They'd had a very pleasant time last night, he'd done or said nothing to upset her, so she had no reason to lock him out. Except that she probably knew he'd want to know why she hadn't told him about her son. And she clearly didn't want to talk.

'Open the door, Kristie,' he said loudly.

No response.

'Dammit, open the door.'

'I'm busy,' came the faint reply. She had a beautiful melodious voice which brushed across his nerve-endings and caused the hairs on his body to stand to attention. He'd noticed from the beginning how lovely her voice was, how well she spoke. There was nothing harsh about her at all— even when she was angry.

Radford shook his head trying to banish these thoughts. They were wrong. He wanted nothing to do with this— gorgeous creature. These last words slipped unbidden into his mind and he tried to dash them away. She was deceitful, a liar, she hated him. How could she be gorgeous? Turn around and run, he told himself firmly. But his hand lifted seemingly of its own volition and knocked on the door again.

He heard the sound of movement and then the key turned and the door swung wide. Kristie had taken off the jacket to her suit revealing a silky sleeveless top, also in ivory, which faithfully followed the line of her curves. His eyes were inevitably drawn to her breasts, high and pert and beautiful. He couldn't help himself. Desire throbbed painfully through him, making him angry with both himself and her.

'Why did you lock me out?' he snarled.

'You think that's what I did? Why would I do that?' she asked, her finely shaped eyebrows rising delicately.

'You tell me.'

'I think you have a complex.'

Radford snorted savagely. 'Why didn't you tell me the boy was yours?' Lord, he hadn't meant to blurt it out like that. It was none of his business. What was she doing to him?

Kristie closed the door and returning to her desk sat down. Very quietly she said, 'I wasn't aware that I had to tell you anything.'

'We sat last night and talked, or at least I talked. You refused even then to tell me anything about yourself. What's the big secret?'

'There is none,' she answered calmly. 'I'm a very private person. I don't discuss my affairs with all and sundry.'

'And that's who I am, Mr All and Sundry?' he barked, really beginning to lose his temper now, especially as she was being so reasonable, when what he wanted was a blazing row. He needed to clear the air. 'I thought I was beginning to mean a little more to you than that.'

'Then you're kidding yourself,' she answered. 'I have a business arrangement with your mother, and that's as close as you and I are going to get.'

'How old's the boy?'

'You mean Jake?' she asked, her calmness beginning to desert her. There was a tartness to her voice now.

'Yes, I mean Jake.'

'Five.'

'And who's Chloe?' he demanded.

'His babysitter, his nanny, my home help, whatever you like to call her.'

'Where's the child's father?'

She paused a moment, eyeing him coldly, appearing to consider whether to tell him. Her mind made up, she lifted her chin determinedly. 'It's no business of yours.'

Of course it wasn't, but, hell, he wanted to know. 'He's the one who did the hatchet job on you?'

'Exactly,' she retorted, her cheeks flushing now. 'He's a swine of the highest order.'

'And well out of your life?'

There was a slight hesitation. 'I'd like him to be.'

Radford frowned. 'He's still hanging around?'

'I met him recently.'

'I hope you told him where to get off.' If he ever bumped into the guy who'd given her such a complex he'd take great delight in dealing with him himself.

'He doesn't take no for an answer easily.'

'Perhaps you need police protection?' He couldn't bear the thought of her being intimidated. 'Can I help?'

She smiled then, a slow, sad smile. 'I don't think it will come to that. And I can handle myself, thank you very much.'

It was with reluctance that he let the matter drop. 'How's your son now? Is his tummy better?'

'He's fine,' answered Kristie. 'He'd overindulged on jelly and ice cream. Thank you for asking, but I'm sure you're not really interested.'

He didn't like children, Tarah had told her that. Her sister had not had an inkling that he was going to end their relationship and had reached the conclusion that it was because she'd talked about marriage and family. So why was he asking about Jake now?

'Dammit, Kristie. How can you say that?' he demanded, striding over to her desk.

'Easily,' she replied, calmly looking up at him, hoping

he couldn't see her inner turmoil. 'You don't strike me as a man who likes children.' Not only because Tarah had told her but because he'd called Jake a 'damn child' the first time he'd ever seen him. 'How can you work with some damn child around all the time?' he'd asked.

'And how have I given that impression?' he rasped harshly. He splayed his hands on the desk and towered menacingly above her. Careful, Kristie warned, you're going to give yourself away. The idea had dawned on her last night that she could get her revenge on Radford for causing the death of her sister, even though indirectly, by keeping secret the fact that Jake was his son. How cruel was that? The very thought delighted her. It wasn't normally in her nature to behave like this but Radford Mandervell-Smythe had done one very bad thing, and for that she could never forgive him.

'Never mind about how,' she retorted.

He shook his head and pushed away from her. 'You're a very strange woman to understand. You're more complex than I first thought.'

'And that troubles you, does it?' she scorned. She wanted him to be troubled, deeply troubled, like she'd been in the days after her sister's death. It had been the biggest upheaval of her life. Losing her beloved Tarah and being landed with a new baby had almost threatened her sanity.

She'd toyed with the idea of finding Radford and dumping the child on his doorstep—only the fact that she knew Tarah wouldn't like it had stopped her. But in truth Jake was his responsibility, and in some small measure using this office rent-free—because his mother had still not come up with any figure—was what she deserved. Except, of course, that it was his mother footing the bill and not Radford. Although, she argued with herself, as it was still a family business he was indirectly paying.

'I'd like to get to know you better.' He looked away as he spoke as though he was already regretting the words.

'I don't think that would be a very good idea,' she retorted. 'We have nothing in common.' Except a dear little boy named Jake.

A horrifying thought struck her. If Radford ever did find out that Jake was his then he would do his utmost to take him from her, even though she had officially adopted him. Another very good reason why she must never tell him. She had grown to love Jake as though he was her own and couldn't bear the thought of him being taken away from her.

'You intrigue me,' he said.

'And that's a good enough reason why I should see more of you?' she questioned coldly. 'I don't think so. In fact, I'd like it if you went now and never came back.'

'You didn't enjoy yourself last night?'

Kristie couldn't lie. 'Actually, yes I did, much to my surprise.'

'But you wouldn't care to repeat it?'

'I see no point.'

His breath hissed out through his teeth. 'Actually I was going back to London today, but I think I might hang around for a few days. I enjoy a challenge.'

Kristie was horrified. 'What do you mean, a challenge?' She knew very well what he meant but she needed to hear it put into words.

'I want to prove to you,' he announced loftily, 'that all men are not the same.'

'And you think you could do that?' she demanded with a toss of her head and a flash of her electric green eyes.

An odd little smile came to his lips—a confident smile that only served to infuriate her further. 'I'd like to give it a try.'

'You'd be wasting your time,' she proclaimed strongly.

'But you're not saying that I cannot?'

What would be the point? Radford was the sort of guy who could railroad anybody into anything. If he was really determined she wouldn't have a leg to stand on. 'Would that stop you?'

His smile now was genuine. 'You're getting to know me.'

Worse luck! This was a man she had never wanted to meet and she had the awful feeling that she was going to dig herself into a hole far deeper than she was prepared to go. Where are your guts, girl? she asked herself. This isn't what you want, so say so, for goodness' sake.

She couldn't. There was one tiny part of her that was attracted to this man. And that tiny part was taking over. It wanted to see more of him. It wanted to enjoy the buzz of excitement she felt when he was near. It wanted to taste his kisses. It wanted to reach out and touch him, to feel that hard, finely honed body against hers.

The very thought sent her mouth dry and she touched her tongue to her lips and saw a flash in Radford's eyes and the way he drew in a swift breath. She prayed he hadn't read her mind or it would all be over. Any protests would be in vain.

'We'll have lunch together,' he announced.

His audacity shouldn't have surprised her but it did. He really did think that he could snap his fingers and she would jump. Probably most girls did, but not this one. Oh, no. She looked at her watch. 'That's impossible. I have an appointment at two.' Liar! She'd planned to spend all day here.

'Then we'll have an early lunch.'

Kristie shook her head vehemently. 'I don't have time for proper lunches. I have sandwiches in my bag.'

'Then I'll have sandwiches too and join you.'

He made it sound so simple and yet simple their relationship could never be. But there was no stopping him, she knew that, and so she shrugged. 'If that's what you want, but I'm warning you, it will be a short lunch. I'm very busy.'

Not until he had gone could she breathe easy again and she found it hellishly difficult to concentrate. It seemed like only minutes before he was back—with a bottle of wine, two glasses, a plate of sandwiches and a bowl of salad. 'We'll share,' he announced confidently.

'You do realise I'm driving afterwards?' flashed Kristie. 'I can't possibly drink wine.'

'It's non alcoholic,' he told her with a smile. 'A fruity drink, that's all. But it looks like the real thing. Shall we take it out on the lawn?'

Kristie knew she was lost. There was no point in demurring. The lawn overlooked the swimming pool which she had looked at several times with great longing but had never dared ask whether she could use it

He unrolled a blanket and she sat down and opened her lunch box but didn't feel like eating. Radford poured the wine and she sipped that instead. It was surprisingly refreshing, beautifully chilled and slightly sparkling. It was peaceful here and as she looked around she spotted a hoist at the far end. 'Does your sister use this pool for therapeutic purposes?' she asked.

Radford nodded. 'Most days—except in the winter, of course. I did want to have one put in the house but my mother wouldn't let me.'

'Will Felicity still live here when she's married?' She was happy with these safe topics. Not happy with the way her body was behaving, but he was not to know that.

'Yes. We have everything here for her convenience. A

suite of rooms has been prepared for them so they'll have their independence. She's so excited.'

'It's going to be a beautiful wedding.'

'I have only your word for that.'

'Believe me, I won't let you down. It will be a day to remember.' That was what she called her business—A Day to Remember. And at every single wedding she had organised the brides had said afterwards that it definitely had been a memorable day. She tried to make each one unique and Felicity's was going to be the grandest of them all.

'Do you think you'll ever get married yourself? Or will your hatred of men last a lifetime?'

Kristie had been looking at the sunlight glinting on the water. Now she turned and met Radford's enquiring eyes. 'I don't hate all men,' she told him sharply. His eyes were narrowed against the sun, silvery and penetrating, and tiny shivers of excitement began to dance through her veins.

'Oh, I forgot, there's Paul, isn't there?' he drawled. 'Tell me, does Paul set you on fire the way I do?'

The audacity of the man! He'd said it so calmly, as though it was a perfectly ordinary question. How could he know? Surely she hadn't given herself away? 'In your dreams,' she said with a faint laugh, hoping to make a joke of it.

'You can't deny it. I've seen that give-away pulse in your throat. I've actually felt the heat of your skin. I bet it's hot now.'

He leaned forward and touched her arm, letting his fingers slide right up to her shoulder and then slowly across to her throat, where his thumb rested on the pulse in question. And there was precious little she could do about it.

She didn't say a word. She couldn't; she was totally hypnotised by what he was doing. At the same time she steeled herself not to respond because, goodness, she wanted to.

She wanted to lay her hand over his, she wanted to touch him too, feel the heat of *his* body. Oh, lord! This was all wrong. This was insanity. This wasn't in the plan of things at all.

She dashed his arm away angrily. 'What the hell are you playing at?'

He grinned, a wicked, white, predatory smile. 'You're beautiful when you're angry. Those delicate green eyes of yours darken and flash fire and your face becomes animated. It makes me want to kiss you.' Even as he spoke he leaned towards her and hooked a hand behind her head so that there was no escape, then his mouth came down on hers.

CHAPTER EIGHT

KRISTIE knew that she would look back on this moment and ask herself why she hadn't jerked away from Radford, but for some reason she remained motionless. She accepted his kiss. It was a fatal thing to do, it gave entirely the wrong impression. She began to struggle, but not before she had felt the full impact of a kiss so dangerous that the memory would be with her for all time.

It was an assault on her senses. Tingles ran from the tips of her toes and fingers and congregated in her stomach. Blood pumped through her veins at an alarming speed. It rushed through her head and she could hear the hammer throb of her heart and pulses. The intoxicating maleness of him filled her nostrils and she could taste the sweetness of the wine on his lips.

'That wasn't so bad, was it?' he asked, letting her go when she had thought he would persist. 'In fact, I gained the distinct impression that you found it pleasurable. It was your conscience that made you put a stop to it. I oughtn't to be kissing this man, you told yourself, it goes against my principles.'

He was so right, but she wasn't going to admit that. She picked up her wine glass and tossed back the remains. 'You're far wide of the mark.'

'Then why didn't you stop me from the beginning?' he asked. 'Come on, admit it, you were as curious as I. And reality was greater than the dream, wouldn't you say?'

Kristie tossed her head, her eyes flashing angrily. 'Since

I've never dreamt about kissing you I cannot answer that question.'

'What a little liar you are,' he said with a knowing smile. 'But I'll forgive you—for the moment. Eat your sandwiches.'

How could she eat when her body was on fire? 'I'm not hungry,' she said and glanced at her watch. 'I really should be going.'

'Running away won't solve anything.'

'I'm not running away.'

'So why do you want to leave so suddenly? We've been here less than ten minutes.'

'I think you know why,' she snapped. 'I didn't come out here to be mauled by a beast like you.'

Her harsh words, said in the heat of the moment and unforgivably rude, had a dramatic effect on him. His smile faded, nostrils flared, and she had the feeling that if she'd been a man he would have punched her.

'Dammit woman, no one speaks to me like that. I would never *maul* someone, as you so crudely put it. You're scared of your own feelings; that's the trouble. They're making a mockery of your *pretension* of hating men. It's gone on so long that you haven't even realised that your values have changed.' He got up then and glared down at her. 'Do you know what? I pity you. You're going to lead an awfully lonely life.'

Kristie scrambled to her feet. 'You know nothing,' she declared heatedly.

'I know you're one very mixed up lady.'

Maybe she was. And he was the one who had done it. She grabbed her sandwich box and with a further heated glare in his direction headed back to her office. She spent an hour there fuming. It was the last straw when she went out to her car and found it wouldn't start.

She lifted the bonnet and looked in vain beneath it. She didn't know anything about engines but maybe, just maybe, something might jump out at her. A loose lead, perhaps? Anything, please, she prayed. I need to get away from here.

She heard Radford's footsteps crunching on the gravel. 'Having trouble?' And she groaned inwardly, even though she knew that she needed his help. He slid behind the wheel and turned the key. The engine gave a grunt and a groan but that was all. Her car was fifteen years old and had only recently begun to give her trouble. But why now of all times?

'Mmm,' he said, coming to stand beside her. 'It sounds as though it's your starter motor. I'll call someone out and meantime I think I'd better run you to your destination.'

'I'm going home,' she declared stiffly. 'My appointment's been cancelled. But I don't wish to put you to any trouble. I'll call a taxi.' She fished her mobile out of her bag but Radford would hear none of it.

'Nonsense. I have nothing planned for this afternoon. It will be my pleasure.'

Grim pleasure by the look of it. He still wore a tight expression and he was careful to keep his distance from her as they returned to the house while he telephoned the garage. 'They'll collect it later today and return it tomorrow,' he told her. 'Shall we go?'

Such prompt service, thought Kristie, wasn't what she usually got. She always had to wait several days when she had any problems. But then, Radford was a man who got things done. One only had to look at him to see his overriding arrogance.

The kiss still loomed over them like a black cloud and as she sat silently beside him Kristie was conscious that their relationship had deteriorated. Not that there had been much of one in the beginning but it was even worse now.

And it was her fault. She shouldn't have called him a beast. Perhaps she ought to apologise? But by the time she had made the decision they were home and the moment was lost.

Chloe and Jake returned at the same time and Jake ran excitedly towards her. 'I didn't know it was you in that car,' he said. 'Whose is it?' His blue eyes widened with wonder at the big black limousine.

'It belongs to Mr Smythe. I work in his mother's house now.'

Radford got out of the car and smiled at Jake, going down on his haunches in front of him. 'Do you like it? Would you like a ride in it?'

'Oh, yes, please,' exclaimed Jake excitedly, forgetting his shyness when faced with this beautiful big car.

'You'll have to ask your mummy first.'

'Mummy, Mummy, can I?' he asked, hopping from one foot to the other, his eyes bright with excitement.

How could she say no in view of such enthusiasm? But, as she glanced from one face to the other, Kristie wasn't really thinking about her answer—she was looking for any signs of resemblance. And she couldn't think how she hadn't noticed before that their eyes, although one pair was blue and the other grey, were the same shape, even their eyebrows were the same. Not that Radford would notice, of course. He hadn't a clue that this was his son. She smiled grimly. Revenge was sweet.

'Can I, Mummy? Please say yes.'

'You can come with us,' said Radford, seeing her hesitation, guessing she was nervous about letting him out of her sight. 'Chloe too, if you like. But this young man—' he ruffled Jake's hair as he spoke '—is going to sit in the front and watch the controls for me. Isn't that right, son?'

Kristie knew it was a figure of speech, but hearing him

say 'son' sent a cold shiver down her spine. Already, though, she could see Jake's lip beginning to drop and knew she couldn't disappoint him. She raked up a huge smile. 'Of course.'

Radford grinned conspiratorially at Jake, as much as to say that he had known they would win. Effortlessly, he lifted the boy into the passenger seat, not leaving him until he had patiently fastened his seat-belt.

Kristie was stunned. These weren't the actions of a man who disliked children. But she had no time to dwell on it because Chloe was nudging her and whispering, 'What's going on with you and Mr Hunk?'

'Nothing,' hissed Kristie. 'Shut up. He'll hear you.'

'Tell me about it later.'

'There's nothing to tell,' insisted Kristie.

'Come on, you two,' Radford called out. 'This little boy is impatient to be off.'

They quickly slid into the back set, Chloe behind Jake and Kristie behind Radford, and the first thing she encountered were his eyes through the rear view mirror. She looked away but not before she had felt their full impact. She might have been mistaken but there seemed to be a challenge in those grey eyes and it made her faintly uneasy. Was he trying to tell her something, trying to prove that he did like children, perhaps? Or maybe he had put the act on for her benefit. Kristie didn't know what to think. All she knew was that she wanted to be out of this car as soon as possible.

Jake, on the other hand, couldn't sit still and his eyes were everywhere. 'What's this for? What's that? How does this work?' The questions came thick and fast and Radford patiently answered every one. But when Radford suggested they stop at McDonald's Kristie put her foot down.

'I don't encourage Jake to eat junk food,' she said

tightly. In fact, she was amazed that Radford would want to set foot in one of those places. High class restaurants were more his style.

'Now and then won't hurt him.'

'Maybe not, but the answer's still no.' She was glad when they returned home and relieved when Radford didn't get out of the car. She'd had the horrible feeling that he might invite himself into her house. 'What time shall I pick you up in the morning?' he asked.

'You don't have to do that,' she returned tightly. 'I'll get a lift off Chloe.'

'What's happened to your car?' asked the other girl as Kristie looked at her in anticipation.

Kristie grimaced. 'The starter motor's gone. Mr Smythe's getting it fixed for me.'

'Not something else!' exclaimed Chloe. 'You really ought to get yourself another one.'

It wasn't high on her list of priorities at the moment, although admittedly she had been thinking of it. But so long as her old Ford ran she didn't feel justified in spending money on another.

'And I can't give you a lift tomorrow because I have a dentist appointment.'

'Of course,' said Kristie. 'I'd forgotten.'

'So,' said Radford with a satisfied quirk to his lips, 'it looks as though my services will be needed after all. Shall we say eight forty-five?'

Kristie nodded silently and unhappily. She was spending far more time with this man than was good for her soul. There was a definite spark between them and if she wasn't careful it would ignite. But she must never forget what had happened to her sister. He didn't want a serious relationship with anyone or he would have been married long before now. He simply enjoyed playing the field. And she was his next target.

As soon as they were in the house Chloe slid her a meaningful glance. 'So what's going on between you two?'

'Who? Me and Mr Smythe? Absolutely nothing.'

'It's not what it looks like from my side of the fence.'

'You're imagining things, Chloe,' she declared shortly. 'He's not my type.'

'But he fancies you. I can tell from the way he looks at you.'

Kristie snorted indelicately. 'Radford knows how I feel about him.'

'So you have talked about feelings?' asked the other girl with a delighted smile. 'Or perhaps you've even—indulged?' she added with a wicked glint in her eyes.

Kristie couldn't stop the warmth that flooded her cheeks.

'So I'm right, he *has* kissed you. Tell me about it. What was it like? I bet he's the world's best kisser. He looks—'

'Shut up, Chloe!' cried Kristie. 'Go and get Jake his tea. I'm going to take a shower.'

Chloe waltzed into the kitchen singing about washing a man out of her hair and Kristie ran upstairs and slammed her bedroom door. The annoying thing was that Chloe was right.

After she'd showered and changed into a cool cotton pantsuit Kristie sat down with Jake while he had his tea. But even here the topic didn't change. All Jake could talk about was Mr Smythe and his car and when was he going to see him again? It was not until her son was in bed and fast asleep that Kristie began to relax.

The worst part was there would be more of the same tomorrow. It truly had been a fatal mistake moving her office.

When Paul phoned later he was the very antidote she

needed. There were no complications in their relationship and when he asked her to go out with him the following evening she willingly agreed. And the best thing was that if Radford tried to coerce her into dating him then she would have the perfect excuse.

It annoyed her that thoughts of Radford kept coming into her mind when she was doing her hardest to forget him. She flicked through the TV channels until she found a film that looked promising, but even then one of the characters looked faintly like Radford and she switched it off in disgust and went to bed.

Amazingly, she dropped straight off and slept dreamlessly, not waking until Jake jumped on her at seven-thirty the next morning. The three of them usually ate breakfast in the kitchen and today was no different. She totally ignored the few odd comments Chloe threw in about Radford, and when her son asked when he was going to see him again she shut him up as well.

'Mr Smythe's a very busy man, Jake. He only brought me home because my car wouldn't start.'

'But I like him. He said he'd take me out in his car again.'

Kristie frowned. She hadn't heard Radford say that. 'We'll have to see, won't we,' she said, silently vowing that it wouldn't happen if she had anything to do with it. She didn't want Radford anywhere near Jake.

Thankfully, when Radford came to pick her up Chloe and Jake had already left. Kristie was waiting and when she saw his car she hurried out of the house.

The very sight of Kristie walking towards him sent Radford's blood racing. Ever since yesterday, ever since he'd kissed her, he had been unable to get her out of his mind. She was beginning to grow on him far more than he had ever anticipated, despite the fact that she had accused him of mauling her. He'd been annoyed at the time but he knew that it had been a knee-jerk reaction. She was more angry with herself for allowing the kiss than with him for instigating it.

'Amazing, a woman who's ready on time,' he quipped, her beauty exciting him beyond measure. 'Good morning, Kristie. And it is a good morning, isn't it? The sun's shining, the birds are singing, and I have you in the car beside me. What more could a man ask for?'

Kristie totally ignored his comments, merely returning his greeting without any warmth.

Ouch, he thought. The kiss obviously still rankled. But he refused to be subdued. 'And how's the little man today?'

'Jake's fine,' she murmured.

'And yourself?'

'I'm all right too.'

'He enjoyed the ride. We'll have to do it again. Maybe we could take him to the seaside some time? I'm sure he'd enjoy that.'

If the flash of fire from Kristie's eyes had been real he'd have gone up in flames. This woman was full of fury, without a doubt. But he didn't see why it should be constantly projected at him. What had he done, for pity's sake? Maybe he resembled the guy who had hurt her. If that were so it could account for the way she'd reacted when they first met. But goodness, did she need to carry it on? He would never harm her the way this man had. Surely she could see that?

'I don't think that's a very good idea, Mr Smythe,' she told him icily.

He lifted his shoulders in what he hoped was an insouciant shrug, though in point of fact he was hurt by her rejection. 'It was just an idea. You needn't get on your high horse.'

Her stunning green eyes flashed again. 'I don't plan to have any kind of relationship with you.'

'And taking your son to the seaside constitutes a relationship, is that what you're saying?' His temper too began to rise.

'If I want Jake to see the sea then I'll take him myself.'

He gripped the wheel and willed himself not to say anything he would later regret. 'You're cutting off your nose to spite your face, you do know that? Why should your son miss out simply because of some misguided grudge you have against me?'

Kristie closed her eyes and he knew she was biting back a harsh response.

'But you needn't worry any further,' he went on. 'I'll consider the matter closed. I had a phone call from the garage. They're having trouble locating the spare for your car. It might be tomorrow before it's ready.'

He sensed her disappointment, guessed that half of it was directed at him. She didn't want to subject herself to any more lifts, she didn't want to sit in his car with him. Lord, it was painful having her think like this, and it made him all the more determined to prove that he was nothing like this man who had hurt her so much.

He very much needed a gently gently approach and he wasn't sure that he was up to it.

'We have a spare car languishing in one of the garages,' he told her now. 'You may use it if you like.' It would mean he wouldn't get to chauffeur her around but it wasn't doing him any good anyway, and she would probably think more of him for the offer.

'Whose is it?' she asked with a faint frown.

She was wearing a different perfume this morning, a little

more exotic than her usual one, more sophisticated. He wondered if subconsciously she was trying to tell him something. Perhaps that she was not a lady to be messed with? Whatever, he liked it and he found himself breathing more deeply so that he could imprint it in his memory.

'The car belongs to my mother. She bought a new one and kept that one for emergencies. I think I'd call this an emergency, wouldn't you? It's taxed and insured and thoroughly roadworthy. I'll sort the keys out and make sure it's ready for you.'

'I seem to be causing your family a lot of trouble,' she retorted. 'I should never have taken up your mother's offer in the first place.'

'But it's not my mother, is it? It's me. I remind you of Jake's father and you're determined to punish me for it. Isn't that so?' He glanced across at her and saw the look of guilt before she managed to hide it.

'If you know that why do you insist on making a nuisance of yourself?' she demanded heatedly.

'Because I am not Jake's father.' Heavens she was making this difficult. 'I am an entirely different man, and I take offence at being categorised.'

Kristie's eyes were pure ice as she looked at him. 'I have no wish to pursue this conversation.'

'Because you're losing, is that it?' They arrived at the gates to his family home and he turned towards her as he waited for them to open. 'You're doing yourself no favours, Kristie. Why don't you let yourself get to know me? You'll soon see that I'm nothing like—'

'You are *exactly* like him,' she retorted furiously. 'I'm going to tell your mother that having an office here is not working out.'

'And what reason will you give her?' he asked, his own

voice icily cold now. She was blowing this thing up out of all proportion.

Kristie gave a slow shrug. 'I'm not sure yet.'

'But not that it's because I remind you of someone you don't like? You know what she'd do if you said that, don't you? She'd tell me to go back to London. But I wouldn't. I'm determined to make you like me. One way or another, Kristie, you and I are going to become lovers.'

CHAPTER NINE

RADFORD'S threat made every one of Kristie's muscles bunch in protest. The thought of them becoming lovers both horrified and excited her at the same time. If she hadn't let him kiss her she would never have felt like this. She would have been totally sickened by the thought of him touching and kissing her. But that brief coming together of their lips had somehow whetted her appetite. It was a dreadful feeling and one that she knew she needed to banish to the deepest recesses of her mind.

But how? If he disappeared, if he returned to London and did the job he was supposed to be doing, then all would be well. He wasn't going to do that, though. He was going to stay here and torment her.

'You've gone very still,' he said to her now. 'The idea doesn't appeal, I take it?'

'Of course it doesn't appeal,' she riposted. 'And you know it. So why force yourself on me?'

'Oh, I won't force myself,' he said with the wickedest of smiles. 'I'll make very sure that you're ready for me.' The gates to his family home opened and he drove the car slowly through. 'In fact, I think part of the pleasure will be in persuading you that I'm not at all like your arch enemy.'

He was like a wolf ready for the kill with his lips bared back against his teeth and Kristie felt like spitting out the truth there and then, but there would be no joy in doing so. It would put an end to her plot and he would stake a claim in Jake, which was the last thing she wanted. So she returned his smile, even though it was lifeless and held no meaning.

'Very funny. It will take you a lifetime to do that, and I'm sure you wouldn't want to waste your energy on something so futile.'

'I don't happen to think it's futile. I happen to think that it would be relatively easy to get you to change your mind.'

Kristie sniffed and straightened her spine. 'Then you don't know the first thing about me.' As he slowed the car in front of her office she opened the door and jumped out. Without waiting to hear what his response would be, she took a short cut across the lawn—and almost pitched on her nose when her high heel sank into the grass.

She hissed out an expletive and tugged herself free, but not before she heard Radford's chuckle. And when she glanced back over her shoulder he was following her. 'What are you doing?' she rasped.

'I thought I'd enter the house this way.'

'Oh, no, you don't. This office is out of bounds. It's mine for as long as I work here.'

'I thought you were going to tell my mother you didn't want it any more?'

Kristie clenched her fists and didn't know what stopped her raining them against his chest. 'Maybe I will do just that. I've had enough of you.'

At that moment Felicity's wheelchair came trundling round the corner. 'Is this a stand-up fight? Can anyone watch?' She was grinning from ear to ear and appeared to be hugely enjoying herself. 'It looks like you've met your match, darling brother of mine.'

Kristie hid her embarrassment. 'I'd be obliged if you'd tell him to keep away from me,' she snapped.

'I don't think it will do any good.' His sister laughed.

'When Radford makes up his mind about something nothing stops him. He's finding you a challenge, Kristie.'

Kristie shook her head and turned her back on the two of them, opening the door with a shaking hand and making her way inside.

'I wanted to speak with you,' called out Felicity.

As there was no wheelchair access through this particular French window, Kristie was forced to come outside again. 'I'm sorry. I didn't realise.'

'I'll go and see how Mother is,' said Radford. 'She felt a migraine coming on. I'll see you later, Kristie. Hopefully we can do lunch again. Perhaps even a swim beforehand.'

It wasn't until he was out of sight that Kristie managed to relax enough to smile naturally at his sister.

'He can be very trying,' suggested Felicity.

Kristie didn't want to say too much because he was her beloved brother after all. 'I'm not sure that—'

'He wants a relationship and you don't. That's it, isn't it?' Felicity's lovely grey eyes looked directly at Kristie. 'And he's being his usual bullying self. I guessed you were the reason he didn't go back to London straight away. He homed in on you the moment he saw you. Which is unusual for him. He usually takes his time. He likes to get to know a girl from a distance before he makes his move.'

Kristie didn't believe that. Tarah had given her the impression that it had been love at first sight when the two of them had met. He hadn't watched her from a distance, that was for sure.

'You obviously have something the other girls haven't had.'

'So how many have there been?' Kristie said with a frown.

Felicity's fine brows lifted. 'Who knows what he gets up to in London?'

'Has he brought any of them here?'

'To meet my mother?' Felicity laughed. 'Not likely, though they do phone him. But his type is not my mother's type—except for you, of course,' she added with a sly grin.

'What do you mean?' Kristie said jerkily. Surely they hadn't been discussing her as potential wife material? How humiliating. Everything was getting worse.

'Don't worry. My mother hasn't said a thing. It's simply that I know her, and I've seen the way she looks at you and Radford when you're together. I wouldn't be surprised if it wasn't why she offered you an office here.'

Kristie's heart began to beat uncomfortably fast. It looked as though she really had walked into this one. And there was no way out without upsetting Peggy, which she didn't want to do, not at this stage anyway.

'I don't want anything to do with your brother,' she said quietly now, 'and I don't want to talk about him any more.'

'That's a pity. I'd like you as my sister-in-law. It's all right,' she added quickly, seeing Kristie's shocked face. 'I'm on your side. I could put a word in for you if you like. He shouldn't make a nuisance of himself if you don't—'

'I can manage my own affairs,' said Kristie quickly. 'What was it you wanted to see me about?'

Felicity grimaced. 'I've changed my mind about the design of the earrings for the bridesmaids. You haven't commissioned them yet?'

And so the subject of Radford was safely pushed to one side and Kristie spent her morning quietly without any further interruptions. Except in her mind, of course. How could she work here and not have him pop into her thoughts at all too frequent intervals? Even thinking about him sent her hormone levels rising. Thank goodness she was seeing Paul tonight, everything would be normal again. She could completely forget Radford and concentrate on this man who had been a major part of her life for the last twelve months.

There were no ups and downs with Paul; he was a solid, calming influence. Even if she had business worries he made her see that there was a way out. Nothing was ever as bad as she imagined when Paul was around. She was looking forward to their dinner date very much.

A phone call took her away before lunch, much to her relief. Peggy's car had been got ready and the keys brought to her. It was bigger and newer than her own car but very easy to drive and she spent the afternoon discussing details for another glitzy wedding. She was going to have her work cut out these coming months and would need every little bit of help Chloe could give her.

She had already thought about networking her two computers so that she could work in either place, and she felt that this was now becoming a necessity. In fact it might be better to move back so that Chloe could work with her when Jake was at school. On the other hand, she wouldn't have all her lovely new equipment which really was a boon.

She was home before Jake finished school and she took the opportunity to have a long soak in a fragrant bath. It was heaven. And before Paul came to pick her up she was able to spend a couple of precious hours with her darling son.

'What have you been doing at school today, darling?' she asked as she cuddled him after his bath. He felt soft and sweet and warm and she loved him so very much.

To her amazement tears came to his eyes. 'My friends made Father's Day cards. I couldn't because I don't have a daddy. Joshua said I must have one because everyone has a daddy. So who is mine? Is it Paul?'

Kristie's throat closed and her eyes grew moist too. 'No, darling, it isn't Paul.' It looked as though the time was fast approaching when she would need to tell him the truth about his birthright. She had always thought he would be much older before he began asking questions, more able to understand. And she hadn't really prepared herself.

'But I want a daddy.'

'I know you do, sweetheart.' Kristie held him even tighter. 'We'll have to see what we can do about it, won't we?'

And for the moment that seemed to appease him.

He was in bed before Paul arrived, giving Kristie the time she needed to compose herself. It had upset her, hearing Jake ask about his daddy.

'I adore you in that colour,' said Paul, looking admiringly at her lilac dress and jacket. 'I'm looking forward to tonight. I've booked us a table at The Manor. Is that all right?'

'Perfect.' He was always solicitous of her needs, often consulting her before he made a choice. Unlike Radford, who took complete control and expected everyone else to fall in with his plans. And why had he sprung into mind? This was supposed to be a Radford-free evening. She wanted to enjoy herself; she wanted to relax and have fun.

The Manor was a place they'd used many times before. As the name suggested, it was an old manor house, once in a state of decay but now restored to its former splendour. It was on the outskirts of Stratford-upon-Avon, with its lawns running down to the banks of the river.

Even though it was mid-summer it wasn't warm enough to sit outside but they had a window seat with splendid views of the water and the swans. 'I've been looking forward to this,' said Kristie once they were settled at their table.

'Me too,' he agreed. 'How long's it been since we last had dinner out?'

Kristie couldn't remember. 'Time flies. And I've picked up another client today. I'm going to be so busy it's unbelievable.'

'Is it working out, this new office lark?'

'It's good,' Kristie assured him.

'It seems a bit stupid to me, all this to-ing and fro-ing when you were quite comfortable at home.'

'Not at all. There's such a lot of useful equipment.' She didn't tell him that it had been bought especially for her. 'It makes life a lot easier. How about your work? Are you still as busy as ever?' She felt sure that his next question would be about Radford and she wanted to forestall him.

Paul talked right through their first course. 'People constantly amaze me,' he said. 'Some of them are oblivious that their lives are in danger. Faulty wiring is one of the culprits. But enough about me. Tell me about this new job you've picked up.'

They chatted animatedly right through the meal. It was like old times before Radford came on the scene, thought Kristie. She felt comfortable with Paul. Nothing ever disturbed her when they were together. It was an easy, uncomplicated relationship.

'Do you see much of Radford?' he asked casually as they waited for their coffee.

'He pops home occasionally,' she admitted. 'But he's mostly in London.' She prayed forgiveness for the little white lie, and she wished with all her heart that Paul hadn't brought his name into the conversation. She hadn't felt this relaxed in a long time.

'And when he's home does he offer to take you out?'

'Paul,' she pleaded, 'let's not discuss Radford tonight. I'm really enjoying myself. I don't want anything to spoil it.'

'And Radford would spoil it?'

'Yes,' she declared emphatically.

'There's nothing going on between you?'

'Most definitely not.'

He smiled then. 'I'm glad because—well, because I—' All of a sudden he seemed unsure of himself. And then he fished a small leather box out of his pocket and, opening it he took out a diamond ring. 'Because, Kristie—will you marry me?'

CHAPTER TEN

RADFORD had been looking forward to a swim with Kristie and was bitterly disappointed when he discovered that she'd disappeared without telling him. He'd eaten a very lonely lunch because his mother and Felicity had gone out, and then spent all afternoon waiting for Kristie to return.

When she didn't he began to wonder whether she was staying away because of him. Was he wasting his time? Ought he to go back to London and forget her? But how could he banish her from his thoughts when she filled them every waking hour? She was the most intriguing woman he'd ever met—so much so that he lay awake at night imagining her in bed beside him.

He even dreamt about her—the most fantastic dreams where their lovemaking transported him to the edge and beyond. He always awoke feeling blissfully happy, only to sink into depression when he realised that it had all been a dream and was unlikely to ever come true.

Not that he was going to give up trying, but his hopes weren't high. Kristie Swift was an aggressively determined woman who, once her mind was made up, didn't change it. And she had certainly made up her mind about him. Right from the word go. He would never forget the look she had given him when they had first met. Shock, horror, distaste. And for what reason? Because he looked like another man. What did he have to do to convince her that he was nothing like that person? Why wouldn't she give him a chance to prove it?

He waited until he guessed she had put Jake to bed and

then he rang her, but it was Chloe who answered and disappointment welled. He had looked forward to hearing Kristie's lovely melodious voice, had even felt a stirring of his hormones as he dialled the number. 'It's Radford.'

'Hello.' Her voice was slightly breathless and he smiled to himself. He hadn't failed to notice that she seemed smitten by him.

'How are you?' he asked.

'I'm—fine.' She clearly hadn't expected that question.

'And how's Jake?'

'He's fast asleep.'

'In that case, do you think I could have a word with his mother, please?'

'I'm sorry,' Chloe said huskily. 'She's not here.'

He frowned. 'She's not still working, surely?'

There was a slight hesitation, then, 'She's gone out to dinner with Paul.'

Damn! The very thought of her spending time with the other man sent streaks of jealousy through his brain. 'I see. Thank you. Tell her I've called, will you?' He didn't realise how clipped his tones were.

'Is there a message?' asked Chloe.

'No, nothing. I'll see her tomorrow.' And he slammed down the phone. He shouldn't have left it so late in the day. He recalled the way she'd kissed Paul, a full on kiss with her body pressed close to his. And now she'd gone out with him for some intimate dinner for two. How often did this happen? Was he being a fool?

There had definitely been a faint response that time he had kissed her—and if she loved Paul there wouldn't have been, would there? He asked himself the question but wasn't sure of the answer.

In his mind's eye he saw the two of them enjoying a candlelit dinner in some secluded place. He saw her responding to Paul. He saw her touching his hand, stroking, caressing. He saw them lean towards each other and kiss. He saw the love in her eyes.

And he felt bitterness rise in his throat. Tomorrow, he determined, he would begin an all out attack. He couldn't risk losing her.

As soon as he saw her arrive for work the following morning he went along to her office and knocked on the door. He didn't even attempt to open it because he knew he would find it locked. It always was.

When she let him in he found himself studying her face intently to see whether she'd spent a night of passion.

'Is something wrong?' she asked sharply. 'Is my mascara smudged?'

'Not at all.' She certainly didn't look like a woman who'd been well and truly made love to, so perhaps there was hope after all. If she was his woman she'd go around with a smile on her face all the time; he'd make sure of that. There wouldn't be a moment when she wasn't thinking about him and the excitement of their lovemaking.

'Chloe told me you phoned last night,' she said irritably. 'Why?'

'I wanted to take you out.'

A delicate eyebrow lifted and she shook her head and laughed, a light trickle of sound that feathered along his nerves. 'You don't give up, I'll hand you that, but you don't really think I'd have agreed?'

He knew deep in his heart that she wouldn't, but he wasn't going to admit it. Never before had he wanted a woman as desperately as he did Kristie now. Simply standing here looking at her made his heart rain hammer blows within his chest, and every male hormone he possessed ran rampant through his body.

'How are we ever going to resolve our differences if you won't spend time with me?' he asked.

Her eyes flashed scathingly. 'Hasn't it occurred to you that I don't want to be friends? That I don't want to sort things out?'

'Hmph!' he snorted. 'You're sticking your head in the sand instead of facing your problems head on. I won't go along with it. I want to prove to you that I'm not out to cause harm. Why don't you tell me what your bad experience was?'

Alarm filled her eyes and she looked at him in horror and he almost wished he hadn't said anything.

'I was wrong to ask. You don't have to tell me,' he said quickly. 'It clearly still hurts very much; but put yourself in my shoes. How do you think I feel when I see fear and hatred in your eyes every time you look at me?'

Kristie shrugged. 'You know the answer to that, don't you? Go back to London. I don't know why you're hanging around anyway.'

She really knew how to turn the knife. Why the hell was he bothering? Why didn't he do as she said?

Because he loved her!

The thought hit him like a punch in the stomach. How had that happened? How could he love such a woman? The answer was clear. Love happened whether you wanted it to or not. It took nothing into account. And he had fallen hook, line and sinker for Kristie Swift. The only female he had ever met who hated his guts from the word go. Challenge wasn't the word for it. It went deeper than that. He was desperate to change her mind. And nothing or no one was going to stop him.

'I shall stay for as long as I like,' he told her, his eyes firm and steady on hers. 'Faint heart never won fair lady, isn't that what they say?'

'Maybe, but faint or strong it makes no difference. You'll be wasting your time. Paul's asked me to marry him.'

Another body blow! And this one was entirely unexpected. He took a deep breath and fought the anger that came over him. She couldn't marry this man—he wouldn't let her. He would fight every inch of the way, dirty if he had to.

His eyes blazed with a passion she had not yet seen, but one that would be very much to the fore in the future. 'Until I see his wedding ring on your finger I shall see you as fair game.'

'You can't do that,' she retorted with very real fury in her eyes.

'Can't I? Believe me, I can and I will.' His nostrils flared as he fought for control. Getting angry with her wasn't the answer. It was no way to win her over. He had thought he would do it gradually, but that wasn't going to work now. It had to be action all the way.

It had been an error of judgement, letting Radford think she was going to marry Paul. She had thought it would get him off her back; instead she had made the situation worse. In truth, she hadn't yet given Paul his answer. It was one great big dilemma. Jake needed a father and he loved Paul. But she didn't love Paul. Would marrying him be the biggest mistake of her life?

The most disturbing thought of all was that if Radford hadn't come on the scene then she might have said yes. She might have married him for Jake's sake, and that wouldn't have been fair on Paul.

Radford was the last man in the whole country she wanted anything to do with and yet that one brief kiss had shown her how easy it would be to fall for his undisputed charm. Even now, standing here glaring at him, she couldn't fail to be aware of the strong electrical impulses that were shooting between them.

It was as though he had knocked a switch and turned the booster on. And when he took a meaningful step towards her she lost all power in her arms and legs. Even her throat locked tight and she was unable to speak. Her eyes were the only thing that moved. She stared at him in increasing fear because she knew that he was about to kiss her and she would be unable to stop him.

His smile was slow and sexy and his eyes as dark as a midnight sky. She castigated herself because she was doing nothing. Her heart became a thumping mass when he got so close that she could smell the intoxicating maleness of him and feel the heat of a body that was aching for love.

Kristie closed her eyes because she didn't want to see any more; she didn't want to feel any more. This was a nightmare happening while she was awake; something over which she had no control. His lips, when they touched hers, were warm and firm and light. She could have broken free any second she wanted, but she didn't. When his arms came around her they too were gentle. The bonds were of her own making.

As he urged her against his body she could feel an echoing rapid thud in his chest; it was almost as though their two hearts were drumming as one. His gentle persuasion soon had her melting in his arms and when he deepened the kiss, when he gained access to her mouth with his tongue, she could no more have rejected him than she could have dived to the bottom of the deepest ocean.

Paul, and her promise to give him his answer soon, was the last thing on her mind. As Radford's kisses became more urgent and demanding Kristie found herself kissing him back. She couldn't stop herself. Something incredibly powerful was happening inside her. So powerful that it took precedence over everything else. Sensations such as she had never experienced before tore through her body like an express train, sending a red-hot fever through her limbs and an urgent moistness between her legs.

Alarmingly, Radford seemed to know exactly how she felt. He began murmuring words of encouragement as knowing fingers touched first one and then the other tightly peaked breast, the silky top she wore and the gossamer bra providing little resistance. And when she didn't stop him, when she groaned her approval, wriggling her hips ecstatically against his, he lowered his head and sucked her nipples through the fine material.

The sensations he aroused were incredible; she was fast reaching fever pitch—and every one of them zoned in to one area of her body. Never in a million years would Paul have managed to stir her to this extent. If she married him she would be stuck in an unexciting union. Life would follow a mundane pattern. They would perhaps make love once a week, but other than that they would simply be friends. If Radford was doing nothing else, he was opening her eyes in this direction.

When Kristie reached out and touched Radford's manhood—was it need that drove her or curiosity?—she realised that she was in danger of spinning out of control. It had happened almost without her being aware of it. Radford had the power to make her do things that she didn't want to do. She could see why Tarah had enthused over him.

As she thought of her sister Kristie suddenly realised that she was letting The Enemy make love to her and she froze. Before she knew it she would be letting him have his evil way. She could even get pregnant. Another bastard child to bring into the world. Because she knew without a shadow of doubt that Radford would hot-tail it back to London if ever that happened. Not that she would want him to marry her. No, thank you. Not on those terms. Not ever.

With a brilliant flash of her green eyes she worked her hands up between them and pushed hard on his chest. 'What the hell are you doing? Get away from me. I don't want this. Don't touch me again, ever.'

To give him his due, he stepped back but he frowned in confusion. 'Kristie, I wasn't—'

'Wasn't what?' she snapped. 'Trying to take advantage? Of course you were. It's what you've been after ever since we met. And don't try to deny it.' Lord, she felt awful, she'd been in danger of spinning out of control. This man who thought he was God's gift had almost got her eating out of his hand. How he'd managed it she wasn't sure. But somehow she had taken leave of her senses. She'd actually touched him! The very thought made a fresh rage of heat tear through her body.

She shook her head wildly, red hair flying, green eyes sparking. 'Get out of here.'

'You don't mean that.' In contrast, he was calm and controlled, leaning back on the edge of her desk as though they were having a perfectly normal conversation. His very calmness served to enrage her further.

'Don't I?' she spat. 'The truth is I never want to see you again.'

'You're angry because you let your heart rule your head for once. It's something you've schooled yourself against for so long that now it's happening it's scaring you. Tell me I'm wrong.'

'You're wrong.' But she was lying, and he knew it. She was scared by the depth of emotions he had managed to arouse. She was attracted to him far more than was good for her. It was this she was fighting now, and she was so scared that she wanted to run away. She really had pinned herself into a corner here in this beautiful house. Nothing was going according to plan.

'I'll go,' he growled softly. 'But don't think you've seen the last of me.' His eyes never left hers as he moved towards the door, stirring her senses still further but increasing her anger at the same time. And then he smiled, a wicked, primeval smile. 'This is only the beginning, lover.'

Lover? What an exciting thought. How she would love to share her bed with him. But it was impossible. Whatever was happening to her body and mind she had to put his treatment of Tarah first. She needed to make very sure that nothing like that happened to her. In fact, she wouldn't let him into her office. If she rejected him often enough he would get the message and go back to London. Or was that wishful thinking? She hadn't failed to discover that Radford Smythe was one very determined man, and unfortunately he had his sights set on her.

Why she remained in her office for the rest of the day Kristie didn't know. It was impossible to concentrate on work, even though she did her very best. Images of Radford kept forming in her mind's eye.

Radford the hated enemy!

Radford the perfect lover!

The heat rushed to her skin every time she thought along these lines, but she couldn't stop herself.

Paul had kissed her last night. A long, lingering kiss which she'd found very pleasant. Not exciting, not exhilarating, just pleasant. Nevertheless, she had almost convinced herself that she was in love with him and that marrying him would be the answer to everything.

It had troubled her, Jake asking about his daddy. Marrying Paul would put an end to such fears. Even the fact that Jake had asked her if Paul was his daddy should have told her something. Paul was the only male in his life and they got on well—like father and son, in fact. Why not cement the relationship?

But then Radford's kiss would rise like a phoenix from the ashes. It would fly in her face, tormenting her, telling her that she would never be happy with Paul, that he would never make her feel truly woman, senseless with desire, hungry for everything that he had to offer.

No, that couldn't be true. Radford was her enemy—he was the man who had caused Tarah's death. She hated him from the bottom of her heart. She did. *She did!* But it was getting harder to convince herself of the fact.

From the corner of her eye she saw Radford strolling across the lawn towards the swimming pool. She moved closer to the window. All he wore was a pair of brief black swimming trunks with a towel flung over one shoulder. And what a gorgeous body he had. She couldn't take her eyes off him.

His legs were long and muscular, his back broad and well muscled, his waist and hips narrow, skin firm and tanned. Just watching him sent a flurry of sensation to the very heart of her. He walked with the lithe grace of a feral animal, and all of a sudden he turned his head and gave a brief wave. Surely he hadn't seen her watching him?

But clearly he had. He must have sensed it, and Kristie drew back with a jerk, the blood rushing to her cheeks. There was no way on this earth that she wanted Radford to think that she was interested in him. Because she wasn't. Not in the slightest.

Or so she tried to convince herself. In truth, he had insinuated himself not only into her mind but her heart as well and he was there to stay for all eternity. It was frightening. Because of what had happened to her sister she ought to have more sense, and yet still she couldn't help herself.

It was time to make a dash for it. To pack up and leave while he was in the pool and could do nothing about it. Or was that the coward's way out? She decided it was, and so for the next hour she forced herself to get on with her work and not think about him. To a certain degree she was successful.

When she finally ventured out to her borrowed car Radford was nowhere in sight, and as she drove round the house she saw that his car was not on the drive at the front either. It was as though a weight had lifted from her shoulders and she sang to herself on the journey home.

Her good mood didn't last long. When she arrived, the first thing she saw was Radford's sleek black car parked outside her house. Everything inside her burst into angry life and she banged the door open and marched inside.

There was no one about. Then she heard the sound of Jake's laughter coming from the garden. A glance through the kitchen window revealed a breathless Jake chasing after a football which Radford dribbled around the lawn. Jake was pulling and tugging at Jake's legs and Chloe was watching and clapping her hands.

Kristie stormed outside. 'What's going on?' she demanded, arms akimbo, eyes flashing furiously at Radford.

'We're having a game of football.'

'I can see that, but what are you doing here?'

'Waiting for you.'

'Why?' She couldn't say too much in front of Jake, but she sure as hell would have a lot to say to him when they were alone. Meanwhile, Jake came running towards her, laughing as she gathered him in her arms.

'Come and play with us,' he begged. 'We're having lots of fun.'

Kristie didn't want to play football with Radford; she didn't want him here, full stop. He was taking a liberty turning up like this in her absence—not that Jake or Chloe seemed to mind; they were having a ball.

Chloe couldn't take her eyes off Radford and now she looked from him to Kristie, giving a helpless shrug as Kristie glared.

'I don't want to play, darling,' she said to Jake. 'I've had a busy day and I'm going to take a shower.' As he ran off to get his ball she turned to Radford with a grim expression. 'I shall expect you to be gone when I come down.'

He spread his hands. 'Why? When the sole purpose of my visit was to see you.'

'Whatever you have to say can wait until tomorrow,' she told him coldly. 'In fact, I can't see why you couldn't have spoken to me earlier. There was no need for this.'

'It's not exactly words I'm after,' he growled in a voice too low for the others to hear.

Kristie felt as though an elastic band had been twanged inside her, reverberating through her veins at a tremendous rate, but, curse it, this wasn't what she wanted. She wanted to put a million miles between them—for ever! Either that or she wanted to hurt him as he had hurt her sister. Keeping from him the fact that Jake was his son didn't seem to be enough any more. What he didn't know didn't bother him. And she wanted him to feel pain.

'I can't believe you said that, right here in front of my son,' she hissed through closed teeth. 'What sort of a crazed maniac are you?'

A flash of anger narrowed his eyes. 'I'm neither crazy nor a maniac. I'm simply a man with very human desires.'

And at this moment he desired her! 'And you think that making advances to me in front of Jake is the right thing to do?' She kept her voice down but her whole face was a mask of displeasure and out of the corner of her eye she could see Chloe watching them. Once Radford had gone she would be subjected to the third degree and Chloe would never be able to understand why she was spurning Radford's advances.

It wasn't her intention, though, to tell Chloe the truth. What Radford had done to Tarah was far too close to her heart to share it with Jake's babysitter. Because that was really all she was. She wasn't her close friend and confidante; she was her paid employee. There were times when it didn't feel like that, times when they huddled together in girlie conversation and had a good laugh. But some things were private, and this was one of them.

'Advances?' he asked harshly. 'I wasn't aware that's what I'm doing.'

'Suggestions, then,' she grated. 'You had no right coming here and you know it.'

'Jake was pleased to see me.'

Kristie closed her eyes for a couple of seconds, praying that this was all a bad dream and when she opened them again he would be gone. But no such luck. He was there right in front of her, larger than life. A gorgeously handsome man with compelling dark eyes who, under other circumstances, she would have fallen instantly in love with. 'Jake is pleased to see anyone who'll play with him,' she retorted.

'Or who has a smart car that he'd love another ride in. In fact, I've promised him one. I said we'd all go to McDonald's for tea.'

'You've what?' Kristie's voice rose shrilly, causing both Jake and Chloe to look at her curiously. She lowered her voice again angrily. 'You had no right.' Lord, the man was taking over.

'Well, I'm sorry, but the deed's done. Promises can't be broken, especially to a child. Chloe said you had no plans for tonight.'

'Chloe doesn't know everything,' she retorted. 'Paul will probably call round.' Which was an outright lie because Paul was going to visit his parents in Cheltenham. He'd wanted her to go with him, perhaps hoping that she might give him her decision and they could tell his mother and father that they were engaged, but Kristie had declined to go. She wanted more time to think; she didn't want to be rushed into things.

'You're not wearing his ring yet,' Radford pointed out, looking deliberately at her bare finger. 'So in my eyes it makes you fair game.'

'You'd steal another man's girlfriend?'

'Only if I thought they weren't right together.'

Kristie threw him a scathing glance. 'And what sort of an excuse is that? A pretty poor one, if you ask me.'

'So you're going to let Jake down?'

This was emotional blackmail and Kristie's heart sank like a lead weight into the pit of her stomach. 'You know I wouldn't do that.'

His smile was triumphant. 'Run along and get your shower, then. I'll be waiting.' And his words held more than a hint of promise.

Radford had never been in a McDonald's before and didn't expect to like it very much. But needs must, he had thought. He wanted Jake on his side. With the boy's enthusiasm and the woman he loved sitting opposite him where he could watch every expression on her lovely face, every movement of those incredible green eyes, he enjoyed himself as much as if he'd been dining in a five-star hotel. Perhaps more, because Jake's enthusiasm was infectious and he was see- ing things through a young person's eyes for the very first time.

He'd never bothered much with children, had never really wanted any of his own—probably because his cousin's two children were holy terrors. But if he had a son as well-behaved and as polite as Jake, then perhaps it wouldn't be so bad after all. He found himself watching Kristie's son even more intently.

He could see a faint resemblance, but only very faint; he obviously took after his father. Simply thinking about the man who had hurt Kristie so much tightened every muscle in his body. She didn't deserve that. He wanted to care for her; he wanted to reassure her that not all men were the same. It was an underhand trick, trying to do it through her son, but if it worked then it would be worth it.

Although Kristie laughed and appeared to be having a good time, he was aware that she resented every second of his presence. She tried not to talk to him if she could help it, but Jake drew them both into his conversation, as did Chloe. Chloe was a funny little thing but she had told him confidentially while they were waiting for Kristie to come home that she wished Kristie could find herself a good man. And he had read into it that she meant he could be the one. Not Paul. He wondered if she knew that Paul had proposed to Kristie?

Kristie hadn't actually told him whether she had said yes or no. She'd given the impression of agreeing, but he had a sneaky feeling it wasn't true. Otherwise she'd surely be wearing his ring?

When they got back to Kristie's house he didn't give her the chance to say thank you very much and goodbye. He hoisted Jake up on to his shoulders when they got out of the car and marched to the door.

'Can we play football again?' asked Jake, loving his lofty perch.

Kristie answered for him. 'I don't think so. It's time for bed.'

Jake pulled a face.

Radford said, 'Just five minutes, then you must do as Mummy says.'

Kristie glared. Even that was too much. But Radford smiled and proceeded into the house when she opened the door, stooping so as not to bang Jake's head, carrying him right through into the garden, where the boy raced around like a mad thing.

Five minutes passed in no time but it wasn't in Radford's mind to leave when Jake was called in. Oh, no, he intended to spend the evening with Kristie. He followed her into the house. The way she had reacted to him that morning had told him a great deal about this young lady's feelings.

He had been pleasantly surprised when she had responded. In fact, pleasant didn't begin to describe it. He'd been ebullient because it had proved she wasn't immune to him. She might verbally attack him but her body told another story; it had no way of keeping up her defences. And tonight he meant to press home his advantage. Chloe had already told him that it was her night off, so there would be no one to interrupt them. And he certainly hadn't believed Kristie when she had said that Paul might pop round; it had been an excuse for his benefit.

'I'll bath Jake while you talk to Radford,' Chloe said pleasantly, winking to Radford behind Kristie's back.

He waited for the expected refusal and was pleasantly surprised when none came, but he soon found that it didn't mean she was agreeable to him staying. She simply wanted Jake out of earshot.

'What do you mean, walking into my house like this?' she demanded as soon as they were alone.

'Aren't you pleased to see me?'

'No, I am not,' she countered furiously.

'Methinks the lady doth protest too much.'

'With just cause,' she snapped.

He lifted a sceptical brow. 'If you're not interested in me, tell me, why were you watching me through your office window this afternoon? Tell me you weren't excited seeing my naked body. I know I would have been if I'd seen yours. We really must take a swim together some time.'

'Over my dead body,' she riposted, as he had known she would. 'And I wasn't watching you—I happened to glance out of the window, that's all.'

'I see.'

'No, you don't. You don't see anything,' she flared, angry because he was smiling. And he had good cause to smile. The greater her denial, the more likely it was that he'd hit on the truth. Especially as her cheeks had gone a delicate shade of pink.

'I see more than you think,' he said. 'May I congratulate you on the way you've brought up your son. He does you credit.'

To his amazement, she flushed further. 'I do my best.'

'More than that, considering you run your own business as well.'

'It troubles me sometimes that I have to leave him,' she admitted.

'But you have a treasure in Chloe and, as far as I can see, Jake hasn't suffered by your absences.'

'Perhaps. But he didn't suffer at all when I worked from home,' she reproached him.

His eyes narrowed. 'Are you blaming me or my mother? You didn't have to accept her offer.'

'No, I didn't,' she answered sharply. 'And there are times when I wish I hadn't.'

'Yes, I know. But on the whole I imagine it's working out very well?'

'I love all the new equipment,' she admitted. 'It's a great help. I presume you had a hand in that?'

He inclined his head. 'I tried to think of everything, but if there's—'

She stopped him quickly. 'No! Your family's already been more than generous.'

'It's because my mother likes you. You'd really upset her if you left. You do know that?'

'Of course. But it wouldn't upset me if you left now. You're outstaying your welcome.'

'I'm sorry you feel like that.' It had taken her longer than he expected. He had thought he must be making progress. 'But the whole point of me coming was to spend time with you,' he argued. There was no way on this earth that he was going to leave.

'Why? In any case, as I've told you, Paul will be here later.'

'Then I'll stay till he comes,' he said, calling her bluff.

He watched the battle she had with herself, a battle she lost. A whole host of conflicting emotions crossed her face—everything from anger and resentment to final acceptance of the inevitable.

'You're wasting your time,' she said in a dull, flat voice.

'I don't think so, but if I am, then that's my worry, not yours. Ah, here's Jake all clean and ready for bed. Have you come for a goodnight kiss, young man?'

Jake grinned and ran across to him, clambering on to his lap as though he had always known him.

Radford hugged the boy and was surprised by the depth of feeling that welled up inside him. This was a totally new experience. 'You have a good night's sleep, Jake.'

'Will you come and read to me?'

He glanced across at Kristie and caught her appalled

look. 'Perhaps another time,' he said, letting the boy slide to the floor, watching him as he ran across to his mother.

'Will *you* read me a story, Mummy?'

'Of course, sweetheart.' She stood up and took his hand. 'Say ni-night to Mr Smythe.'

'Ni-night,' said Jake obediently, 'and thank you for taking me out.'

'You're welcome, son.'

The room was silent after they'd left. Chloe was still upstairs, probably getting herself ready to go out, and he was alone with his thoughts. If he ruined things tonight then he could kiss goodbye to any sort of a relationship with Kristie. It was, he felt, a make or break time.

CHAPTER ELEVEN

RADFORD could faintly hear Kristie as she read to her son. As always her voice made his skin prickle; it was truly beautiful. Without stopping to think what he was doing, he crept up the stairs following the musical sound. He paused in the doorway to Jake's room and held his breath at the vision of Kristie sitting on a chair at the side of the bed.

A sunbeam stole through a slit in the curtains and highlighted her hair. She looked Madonna-like in her beauty and the sight of Jake's rapt little face as he watched her, his eyes gradually closing, would remain with him for ever. It was the perfect mother and child picture. Full of love. His heart ached suddenly for a child of his own who would look at him like that.

With a lump in his throat he turned and padded softly back down the stairs, and when Kristie returned he was sitting in the same seat as before, his eyes closed. He opened them when she spoke his name.

'I thought you were asleep,' she said, still in that same lovely voice. He wanted her to read a story to him. It was silly, he knew, but he wanted her to sit beside him and recite something, anything, just so that he could listen to her. It wouldn't send him to sleep, though, like it did Jake. It would excite and arouse.

'Would you like a drink?' she asked. 'A coffee perhaps, or some beer?'

Beer! Paul's beer undoubtedly. 'No, thank you.' He wasn't a beer person; he preferred Scotch. But not when he was driving. 'I'd love a coffee. Shall I make it?' And, without waiting for her answer, he jumped to his feet. 'Come and show me where everything is.'

The white kitchen was sleek and uncluttered and he couldn't help but admire her very orderly life. Not that he could work in a mess himself; he couldn't, but he remembered how shocked he had been when he had first seen Kristie's minimalist living room. But, having sat there for the best part of half an hour, he was surprised how much it had begun to grow on him.

'I only have instant, I'm afraid,' she said.

'That's all right; I'm an instant fan. Living alone has taught me to do things the easy way. Now my mother; she wouldn't thank you for instant coffee. It has to be the very finest of beans, which she grinds herself. Or, to be correct, whoever's making the coffee grinds them. I've heard Cook complain more than once when she's been particularly busy and my mother's demanded coffee. It's the same with her tea. No tea bags for her, oh, no. Loose tea made the old-fashioned way. My mother has standards to keep, you know.'

Kristie laughed, as he had intended she should, and he filled the kettle while she reached out mugs and spoons and the coffee and sugar jars. It was a cosy, domesticated scene and he wondered if she felt the same, or whether she was still wishing he would do a disappearing act.

He turned to face her while waiting for the kettle to boil. 'Is it really so bad, having me in your house?' he asked, deliberately keeping his voice seductively low.

Kristie avoided looking at him. 'I suppose not,' she murmured, though not very convincingly.

'So long as I toe the line? Is that what you're thinking?'

She nodded.

'I can't promise that, Kristie. You know how I feel about

you and, if you're honest, you're not entirely immune to me either.'

She closed her eyes and a shudder ran through her. 'That's the whole trouble,' she said, more to herself than to him.

He hid a smile. Her defences were cracking. 'And it wouldn't be playing the game if you were unfaithful to Paul? Or is it because you still class me the same as that monster who screwed you up and you're afraid that if you let yourself even so much as like me you'll get more of the same treatment?'

Dammit, he shouldn't have said that. He shouldn't have said anything that would spoil the harmony of the moment. He didn't want her thinking harsh thoughts, only good ones. But, as it happened, he had no idea what she was thinking because she didn't answer him. 'The kettle's boiling,' she said instead, and he gave her some breathing space while he filled the mugs.

When he turned around she had gone outside, so he took the coffee to her and they sat on a wooden bench. It had been a hot midsummer's day and was still pleasantly warm. Her garden was long and neatly lawned with a few shrubs around the edges. There was a swing and a slide for Jake, and the heavy fragrance of a honeysuckle growing against the house wall filled the air around them.

For a while they sat in silence, each busy with their own thoughts, but sitting so close without touching her was the hardest thing he had ever done. He was so conscious of her that it hurt and he drank his coffee scalding hot in an attempt to give himself something to do.

He desperately wanted to put his hand on her leg, or round her shoulders, and draw her close. Any sort of contact would be welcome. This was sheer purgatory. 'How long have you lived here?' he asked at last. God, what a stupid question. Did he really want to know? He should have said, I want to kiss you, I want to make love to you; I want you to love me too.

How would she have taken that? he wondered. With fright probably. She'd have got up and put as much space between them as possible.

'About five years,' she said quietly. 'I moved here after Jake was born. I lived in a flat before then. It was no place to bring up a child.'

This was the most she had ever disclosed about herself and he was surprised, but before he could say anything else Chloe came out to find them, a heavy, totally unsuitable perfume surrounding her. She was dressed up to the nines and grinning widely. 'I'm off then, Kristie. I'll see you in the morning. Bye, Radford. Have fun.'

'What did she mean, have fun?' asked Kristie sharply when she had gone. 'What were you two talking about before I came home?'

'Nothing.' Which was the truth, but for some reason Kristie didn't look as though she believed him. Not that he minded; he found it quite amusing. 'What could we talk about with Jake ever present? I quite like the suggestion, though.' He took her empty mug and placed it on the ground beside his own and then half turned towards her, reaching out to stroke a stray strand of hair from her cheek.

Her skin was soft and velvety and he allowed his fingers to linger for a moment longer than was necessary. She didn't move, only the slightly faster rise and fall of her breasts revealing her vulnerability. With greater daring he slid his hand beneath her chin and compelled her to face him. Her awesome green eyes were wide and troubled as if she knew she oughtn't to let him do this but for some reason she had no control.

He traced the pad of his thumb over her lips, feeling how

they trembled, feeling her breath warm on his palm. 'You're beautiful, Kristie, quite the most beautiful woman I've ever met.'

She edged back and her voice was husky. 'And there have been plenty?'

Did that bother her, the thought that he'd been out with other girls? He felt secret elation because it could mean only one thing. 'I've met plenty, yes, but there are not many that I've been serious about.'

'And you've never married?'

'I guess I haven't met the right girl.'

'Do you enjoy playing the field?'

'I don't play the field,' he told her sharply. Where had she got this impression?

'You mean you don't take a girl out, let her think you're serious about her, and then drop her when things start to get heavy?'

'Good lord, no. I would never do such a thing.'

'I'm not so sure,' she muttered.

Anger got the better of him. 'I don't know why you're so keen on making me out a blackguard,' he snorted. 'I can assure you that I'm nothing of the sort.' And if this conversation carried on the way it was going he would get precisely nowhere. Throwing caution to the winds, he took her face between his palms and kissed her. And even though she struggled he did not let her go.

The kiss thundered through his head, triggering responses in every corner of his body. His blood rushed out of control and his heart hammered non-stop. And even though there was no response from Kristie, even though she still fought him, he was determined to win. He knew that deep down inside she was feeling the same trembling emotions, but whereas he was giving them free rein Kristie was holding everything in check.

But she couldn't do it for ever.

Lord, she tasted beautiful—sweet and feminine and utterly sexy. His hormone levels rose by several hundred percent and he couldn't contain a groan of desire. Still with his mouth pressed to hers, he slid an arm around her back and urged her to her feet so that he could hold her against him and feel the full impact of her sensational body.

It was almost his undoing. Only by sheer strength of will did he hold back. It was like being a teenager all over again. But twice as wonderful.

When Kristie's lips eventually parted on a sigh, allowing him to deepen the kiss, he knew he was on the verge of winning. And when her sigh was followed by a moan of sheer pleasure he felt triumphant.

She returned his kisses now with a hunger that amazed him. It was as though all her pent-up feelings had been released. Her tongue searched his mouth, tasting him as he had tasted her, her eyes closed, her hands roaming over his back, nails clutching. This was more than he'd expected and he took every possible advantage.

'Kristie—' he groaned against her mouth '—what are you doing to me?'

No answer, more moans, more kissing, more touching. He felt her breasts heaving against him and he knew that he had to touch them. Without either of them seeming to know what they were doing, he led her indoors. And there their lovemaking began in earnest.

All he had to do was run a finger over her sensationally pert nipples for her to jerk with pleasure. It pleased him that they were so sensitive and responsive, and in no time at all he had lifted off her silk top and flicked aside her lacy bra. His groin tightened and ached intolerably at the sight of all her beauty.

He stroked in wonder, gently at first but then hunger

getting the better of him. He cupped each breast and tweaked her nipples between finger and thumb, and her wild enjoyment only added to his own almost out of control desire. He laid her down on the couch and kneeling beside her he took each of her nipples in turn into his mouth. She squirmed and writhed and cried out, holding his head tightly as if wanting to keep him there for all time.

Allowing one hand to wander free, he touched and stroked, pushing her skirt aside in order to trace his fingers along the inside of her thighs. Higher and higher he went, each inch of the way expecting to be slapped back, but Kristie was beyond stopping him. She was thrashing about now, actually lifting herself so that he could find the moist, hot, heart of her. It was doing murderous things to him.

And he wanted more, but not here where Jake could wander down and find them. In her bedroom, with the door closed and no fear of being disturbed. 'Let's go to bed,' he whispered hoarsely, and she made no demur as he lifted her into his arms.

In fact she clung to him as he carried her upstairs, kissing him so fiercely and wildly that he almost fell. He felt as though he'd drunk a half bottle of whisky. Drunk on a woman's love! What a spectacular thought.

He hesitated at the top of the stairs. He saw Jake's door slightly ajar but which of the other three led to Kristie's room? She waved towards one of them and turned the handle as he nudged it open. Once inside he set her on her feet. A brief glance at the room showed that it was a little more personal than downstairs. A photograph on each of the bedside tables, a painting of an alleyway in some far off land on one of the walls, and a vase of silk flowers on the dressing table. But it was the bed that interested him most—a bed draped in cream satin. He couldn't wait to get her there.

It was with indecent haste that they undressed each other. She was so eager that it was hard to believe that she was the same person who had fended him off for so long. It made him wonder whether she had been like this with Jake's father. What a lucky man he had been, and what a fool for letting her down so badly.

Undoing the buttons on his shirt, Kristie kissed every inch of skin as it was exposed, doing to his nipples what he had done to her. It was an electrifying experience. And when she unbuckled his belt and slid down the zip on his trousers it took every ounce of his willpower not to throw her on the bed there and then and take what he wanted so badly.

He'd already kicked off his shoes and socks, and now all that remained were his briefs. Both of them stood for a few seconds facing each other, conscious that all that stood between them now were two tiny items of clothing. The last hurdle. Was she ready for it?

He thought so, but decided to lay her on the bed first. She was so gorgeously beautiful and sexy, the epitome of the perfect woman, that he wanted to feast his eyes on her for a few full minutes before they became one. Kristie, though, had other ideas. She was, amazingly, far more impatient and she grabbed at his navy briefs and began tugging them down.

'Two can play at that game,' he said with a grin and, tipping her on to the bed, he yanked off her panties and flung them into the air. They landed on one of the photos and, fearful it might get knocked over, he gently retrieved them, looking at the picture casually as he did so.

His heart slammed to a halt.

What the hell?

'Tarah!'

CHAPTER TWELVE

KRISTIE had forgotten in the heat of the moment about her sister's photograph. Now, with Radford gasping out Tarah's name, every little bit of desire fled. It brought back reality with a bang. What had she been thinking? She sat up and bunched her knees to her chin, watching the emotions that raced across his face.

He couldn't believe what he was seeing. He sat up and stared at the photo for a long frozen minute, and then slowly turned dark questioning eyes in her direction.

'Recognise her, do you?' she asked icily.

'What is—Tarah's—photograph doing—here?' he asked slowly and jerkily.

'Why, do you know her?' Kristie didn't want to admit at this stage that she knew all about the way he had treated her sister. She would save that pleasure for later.

'I—I used to go out with her.' And his eyes were drawn again to the picture in the plain silver frame.

Tarah was posed against a palm tree in some idyllic island paradise, pouting prettily for the camera. She had been so beautiful, with such a zest for life, that Kristie had to fight a lump in her throat. Life was so unfair. Be careful, she warned, don't give anything away yet. Radford still needs to suffer. 'Really? What happened between you?'

He slowly withdrew from the bed, standing a few feet away to look down at her. There was utter sadness on his face. 'We drifted apart. I guess it was never meant to be.'

Drifted apart? That was an understatement considering he was the one who had ended their relationship.

'But you haven't answered my question,' he said. 'Why have you got Tarah's photograph at your bedside?' And then he seemed to see her clearly for the very first time. He looked from her to the photograph and back again, shock and uncertainty in his eyes. 'You aren't—she's not—your sister?'

'She was.'

Radford frowned harshly. 'What do you mean, was?'

There was a long painful silence in the room before Kristie finally managed to choke out, 'She's dead.' And how she held back the tears she didn't know.

'She can't be.' The words were forced from a stiff throat. 'I haven't seen her for years, but—she can't be dead.'

'I can assure you she is,' snapped Kristie, glaring at him now. 'And I really don't wish to talk about it. Will you go?'

'But how—when—?'

'I've told you, it's too painful to talk about. Just leave me alone.'

He stepped into his trousers and pulled on his shirt. 'I don't understand.' Shoes and socks followed. 'You have to tell me, Kristie. I can't go away and—'

'Not now,' she insisted.

'Tomorrow, then. I'll come and see you in your office tomorrow.'

She supposed she owed him some sort of an explanation and tomorrow she wouldn't be feeling quite so emotional. Having virtually invited him into her bed hadn't helped. She felt stupid now. How could she have let herself get so carried away?

Because she couldn't help it, that was why. Because she was far too attracted to him for her own peace of mind.

Silently, he left the room, but Kristie didn't move until she heard his car start up and move away. She listened until she could no longer hear it and only then did she get up off the bed and drag her clothes back on.

In one way it was a relief he had found out. At the same time she wasn't yet ready to tell him about Jake. He hadn't suffered enough. Actually he hadn't suffered at all. And why should he be distressed about Tarah when he had lost all feelings for her? He would feel upset, yes, because he had once been close to her, but it wouldn't devastate him.

Kristie wasn't looking forward to their conversation the next day and when Chloe came home the first thing the girl saw was her unhappy face.

'What's happened?' she wanted to know. 'Didn't it go well with Radford?'

'What do you mean, go well? Did you two cook something up behind my back?' Have fun, Chloe had said, but Radford had denied knowing what she meant. Clearly, though, something had been said.

'Of course not,' insisted her house-mate. 'But I've seen the way he looks at you. And why did he turn up here if he didn't want to spend time with you? He's fallen for you, Kristie, in a big way.'

'You're talking rubbish,' Kristie defended. 'He wants an affair, I think, but he's not serious about me. He's never serious about any girl. And besides, I have Paul. He's asked me to marry him.'

'What?' The other girl's eyes were wide. 'You never said. When? Have you accepted? Gosh, this is exciting. I never thought he was serious about you, nor you him. I told Radford that—' She stopped short, her face flushing.

'You told Radford what—exactly?' asked Kristie. So she hadn't been wrong. And knowing that Chloe thought Radford the sexiest man on two legs, it wasn't difficult to guess what had been said.

'I mentioned that I thought Paul wasn't right for you, that's all.'

'And what gave you the right to say that?' asked Kristie crossly. 'You know nothing about my relationship with him. Paul's one of the kindest, most considerate men you could ever meet.'

'So why's it taken him this long to ask you to marry him?' questioned Chloe.

'Because he's not the sort to jump in with both feet.'

Chloe shook her head in disbelief. 'Or was it because you gave him the impression that you weren't in the market for marriage? But now that Radford's come on the scene he thought that he'd better make a move before he lost you altogether?'

Kristie hadn't realised how perceptive Chloe was, but she still intended to protect Paul. 'It's nothing of the sort. And I'm not happy with you discussing me behind my back.'

Chloe had the grace to look ashamed. 'So what did you say to Paul? Did you accept?'

'Not exactly. I'm thinking about it.'

'Which means,' said Chloe, 'that you don't really love him. Otherwise you'd have said yes straight away.'

'Jake needs a father.'

'And you think that marrying Paul is the answer? Don't do it, Kristie.'

'I would never marry Radford, if that's what you're thinking. Even if he asked me—which he never will.' It was the first time she'd had such a conversation with Chloe and she was not sure that it was wise. Chloe wasn't renowned for keeping her mouth shut. 'I think I'll go to bed,' she said now. 'Goodnight, Chloe. Oh, by the way, did you have a good night? I forgot to ask.'

'No, I didn't, as a matter of fact,' replied the other girl. 'My date didn't turn up. I went to the cinema on my own.'

'I'm sorry,' said Kristie.

Chloe shrugged her ample shoulders. 'It's the story of my life.'

Kristie couldn't sleep. Only a few hours ago she and Radford had lain here hot in the throes of passion. And if he hadn't seen her sister's photograph he would still be here. And they would have made love. And she would have enjoyed it—tremendously. She would have been drawn into his web of sex and excitement and she would have remained there until he decided he'd had enough of her.

She went cold at the very thought. What a merciful release she'd had. And all night long she endured the same recurring thoughts.

When morning came she was tempted to avoid him by working from home, except that she knew perfectly well that if she didn't turn up Radford would come looking for her. And it would be harder to get rid of him.

She'd been at her desk for about an hour before he paid her a visit; an hour in which she'd been unable to concentrate, flitting from one job to another, answering calls, making others, but wishing herself anywhere but here. She didn't want to talk about Tarah. She'd cried all her tears and put her heartache away and she didn't want to resurrect any of it.

'Good morning, Kristie. I've brought us some coffee and biscuits.'

Kristie let out a deep sigh. This had all the makings of a long visit and she wasn't up to it. She'd had all night to prepare herself and yet she still wasn't ready for this conversation.

'You didn't have to,' she said.

'But I wanted to.' He took the tray over to the two armchairs and indicated that he would like her to join him. 'You look tired. Didn't you sleep well?'

'Not really,' she admitted.

'I guess it was my fault for raking up the past. But you can't blame me. It was such a shock discovering that you're Tarah's sister. And then to be told that she's no longer alive. I find it hard to take in.'

'Not as much as I do,' she retorted, settling into her chair and deliberately staring out of the window rather than at him. His very presence sent her senses skittering and she knew that if she looked into his eyes she would be lost.

'Kristie, you don't have to bear this thing alone. It's sometimes best to talk.'

'You don't understand, do you?' She turned her head sharply and shot him a resentful glare, ignoring the way her pulses leapt. 'I don't want to talk. It's not something that happened recently. I've done all my grieving.'

'I still can't believe it,' he said, shaking his head. 'Tarah was always full of life. She had such great plans. How did it happen? When? I wasn't going to jump in with these questions straight away, but I can't help it. I've thought of nothing else all night long.'

He sounded as though he cared but she knew he didn't. His only concern was because Tarah was her sister and the shock of the discovery was ruining his plans to seduce her.

'And you think I haven't?' she snapped.

'I know you have,' he said quietly.

'If you knew that you'd do the decent thing and keep away.'

'I need to know what happened.'

'It was almost six years ago.' Her voice was so soft he had to lean forward to hear.

'That long?' he asked with a frown.

Kristie nodded. 'There was nothing the doctors could do for her.'

'Cancer?'

'No.'

'A road accident?'

'No, just a normal, routine operation.' If a Caesarean could be called normal. 'A woman's thing. Unfortunately complications set in. She never recovered.' She knew that by saying 'a woman's thing' she would stop him from asking any further questions.

He shook his head slowly, sitting right back in his chair, his fingers strumming the arms. 'It's unbelievable.'

'That's what I thought.'

'Do you have any other brothers or sisters? Tarah never talked about her family. I know she'd had an unhappy marriage, but that's as much as she told me.'

'There's no one else,' she said huskily.

'Parents?'

'Dead.'

He looked as though he didn't know where to put himself. 'So you're alone in the world?'

'I have Jake. He's my world.'

'I'd like to be a part of it too.' It was Radford's turn to speak quietly.

Kristie felt her heart give a leap, but she pretended not to hear and he didn't repeat it. Instead he passed her mug of coffee and offered the plate of biscuits. They were homemade and looked delicious but Kristie wasn't hungry even though she'd had no breakfast.

She sipped her drink and wished he would go. Of course he didn't. He sat there deep in thought, eating biscuit after biscuit until the plate was empty. He looked surprised to see them all gone.

'I have work to do,' said Kristie, getting to her feet.

'Can I take you out tonight?' he asked, rising too.

'I'm seeing Paul.'

'Tomorrow, then?'

'Isn't it time you went back to London?' she asked sharply. 'How can you afford to take so much time off?'

'I'm in touch every day. And at the moment I have something far more important to do.'

'Felicity's wedding is months away,' she retorted.

'I wasn't talking about Flick. Or my mother.'

Kristie's eyes flashed a brilliant green. 'If it's me, then you're wasting your time.' Despite her feelings, or even because of them, she was determined to keep her hatred well fuelled.

'Because of Paul?' he asked drily. 'I don't consider him a threat. In fact, I don't think you'll ever marry him.'

'Then you don't know me very well at all,' she riposted. Tonight she would accept Paul's proposal, and tomorrow she would wear his ring. And see what Radford had to say then.

CHAPTER THIRTEEN

RADFORD had been very fond of Tarah and he found it hard to accept that she was no longer alive. He had never met a girl so vivacious and full of fun and there had been times when he'd been close to asking her to marry him. He felt deeply saddened by the discovery and wished he had known at the time. No matter that they had parted on bad terms, he would have still paid his respects.

It was ironic that he'd now met her sister and had fallen deeply in love with her—a very different love from that he'd felt for Tarah. He couldn't help wondering what would have happened if Tarah was alive and he was still going out with her, and he then met Kristie. Maybe he would even have married Tarah. What sort of complications would have arisen then? He didn't dare think about it.

Kristie was the woman he had been waiting for all his life. A cliché, yes, but it was true. He'd fancied himself in love more than once, but always there had been a modicum of doubt at the back of his mind, something that stopped him from taking the final plunge. But with Kristie it was different. He wanted to spend the rest of his life with her. She had touched on the right nerve; she had taken his heart and made it her own. He was bound irrevocably to her.

The problem now was persuading her to feel the same about him. He had been boasting when he had said Paul wasn't a threat, but the way she had said, 'Then you don't know me very well at all' troubled him deeply. It sounded as though she had definitely made up her mind to marry him. And if that was the case he needed to do something about it quickly.

'I think I know you better than you realise,' he said. 'If you're going to marry Paul simply to spite me then it will be the biggest mistake of your life. And I would urge you not to do it.'

Her eyes flashed in that beautiful way that sent his testosterone levels rising. 'So that you think you'd stand a better chance?'

'Not at all. And I really mean that. Whether our relationship develops or not, I don't want you doing something that you'll later regret.' He did wonder whether Kristie knew who he was, whether she knew that he'd been dating her sister. But even so he couldn't see that as a reason for her disliking him. The culprit here was definitely Jake's father.

She still looked at him suspiciously. 'Why?'

'Because I care for you. Whether you believe that or not I don't know.'

'I don't,' she answered sharply.

He winced. It seemed there was nothing he could say or do that would change her mind about him. But he would never give up. It was time he left her now, though. Kristie was already moving back to her desk.

'Maybe I'll see you later?' he asked as he reached the door.

'Maybe,' she agreed, but not with much enthusiasm.

'And I really am sorry about Tarah. You have my deepest sympathy.'

She didn't look at him again, her eyes were already on the papers in front of her. He closed the door quietly.

'Come in, Paul.' Kristie had invited Paul to supper and her nerves were a bit jittery.

She had thought long and hard about whether to accept

his proposal, and yet really there had been nothing to think about. She couldn't marry him; it was as simple as that.

'I can't keep you in suspense,' she said, as soon as they had walked through to her living room and sat down with a drink. 'I was going to wait until later in the evening but it wouldn't be fair.'

He looked into her sad green eyes. 'I think I know what you're going to say.'

'I'm sorry, Paul.' She gave a wistful smile. 'It wouldn't work. I love you dearly as a friend and I've tried to feel something more for you, you've no idea how much I've tried, but I simply can't. I know Jake adores you, but marrying you for Jake's sake is not the answer. And keeping you hanging on isn't the answer either. I should never have done it.'

He looked crushed and she wanted to hug him, but it would be too dangerous. She might say the wrong thing out of pity. 'It's Radford, isn't it?' he asked quietly, his fingers clenching around his glass. 'You've fallen for him?'

Kristie nodded and looked down at an invisible spot on the carpet. 'I didn't want to. I can't even think how it happened because—'

'Never mind how it happened,' he cut in. 'I think I knew the first time I saw him that he was a rival, no matter how much you denied it. He has far more going for him than I have.'

'It isn't his money,' declared Kristie. 'And in truth I'm annoyed with myself for feeling anything. I've fought it ever since I met him.'

'Why? Because of me?'

Kristie gave a weak smile and nodded. It wouldn't hurt to let Paul think that.

'Actually, I think I already knew what your answer

would be,' he admitted. 'I hoped you'd agree to marry me, of course I did, but deep down inside I knew I was clutching at straws. You've always been totally honest with me.'

'I'm sorry,' she whispered, putting her hand over his.

He put his over the top of it and they were quiet for a moment. 'This is the end, isn't it?' he asked.

Kristie nodded.

He took a long swallow of his beer. 'I guess I need to get on with my life, find myself another girl, and try to forget you. Not that I ever will—forget you, I mean. You're a sweet, kind girl, Kristie. Whether you marry Radford or whether you marry someone else, he'll be the luckiest man alive.' He was silent for a moment before saying, 'Do you mind if I don't stay for supper?'

The lump in Kristie's throat was hard to swallow and she shook her head. 'I truly am sorry, Paul.'

'Me, too,' he admitted with a nod. 'I'll see myself out.'

Kristie felt truly awful after he'd gone, and she threw their supper into the bin because she couldn't face eating. This was the worst thing she'd ever had to do but she'd made the right decision, of that she was sure. It would have been so unfair on Paul to keep him hanging on any longer. In one way she had Radford to thank for bringing it to a head.

Her sleep was disturbed that night and it was something of a relief when she discovered the next day that Radford had been called back to London. Hopefully he would stay there for a long time.

'He was reluctant to go,' Felicity told Kristie when she arrived at the office next. 'Would it have something to do with you? He looked sort of sad.'

'Who knows?' said Kristie with a shrug.

'Have you told him there's absolutely no hope?'

'Constantly.'

'So it's nothing new?'

'Maybe he finally got the message,' she suggested, while knowing that nothing was further from the truth. He'd turn up again, if only to find out whether she was marrying Paul.

'My mother wants to know whether you'd like to join us for dinner tonight.'

Kristie frowned. 'Is it a special occasion?'

'No, she simply thought it would be nice for us to meet socially instead of always talking business.'

She couldn't help wondering if there was any significance in her asking while Radford was absent. Did Peggy want to quiz her about him? Felicity had said that she'd seen her mother watching them when they were together. She'd said she thought it was why she had offered her the use of an office and that she'd never cared for his previous choice of girlfriends.

The whole thing sounded ominous, yet what excuse had she? Chloe would be at home so there was nothing to worry about where Jake was concerned. So reluctantly she accepted. 'Tell her I'd love to. I can be here about eight. I have to bathe Jake and put him to bed first.'

'Yes,' Felicity said with interest. 'Radford told us about your son and the mistake he'd made thinking he belonged to your lodger.'

'Not my lodger,' Kristie corrected, 'my general factotum. She does anything and everything. I wouldn't be without her.'

'So, if it's not a rude question, where's the boy's father?' asked Felicity. Then she saw the murderous expression that crossed Kristie's face and added quickly, 'I'm sorry. I shouldn't have asked that. It's none of my business. I'll tell my mother you've accepted.' And with that she wheeled away.

Kristie spent the rest of the day wondering whether she'd

done the right thing in accepting Peggy's invitation. But what was done was done; she couldn't change it. And knowing that Radford would be absent helped; it helped her get through the day too. She was able to concentrate more fully on the work in hand. This was how it should be, how it had been before she met him.

It seemed a different world that she lived in now. A world where her senses were being taken over by a man she desperately wanted to despise. They were scary feelings and always she banished them, but they had a way of wriggling themselves back to the surface. Perhaps the whole truth of the matter was that she was afraid to let herself get too closely involved in case he rejected her the same way as he had Tarah. He was such an easy man to like, to love. To *what*? How had love come into the equation?

Kristie shook her head, buried the thought, and got on with her work. And every time it threatened to raise its head again she battered it back down. She didn't even want to think along those lines. Of course she didn't love him.

It was almost time for her to go when she had a phone call from Radford. She'd picked it up and answered cheerfully, 'A Day to Remember, Kristie Swift speaking.'

'Hello, Kristie Swift,' he said, and much to her annoyance the sound of his voice set her pulses racing. She'd convinced herself that it was nothing like love that she felt—it was a physical thing, some sort of chemical reaction over which she had no control. And she was determined to fight it. She put the tips of her fingers to the pulse at the base of her throat and felt it leaping. Damn him! How could he do this to her?

'You sound happy today,' he said. 'Would that be because you've finally agreed to marry the man you don't love, or because you've rejected him and it's a great load off your mind?'

Kristie closed her eyes, picturing him gloating, and a swift feeling of anger came over her. 'It's none of your business,' she snapped.

'Oh, I think it's very much my business. You could not possibly respond to me the way you do if you were in love with another man. Therefore you don't love him. Therefore you've told him so. I hope. Am I right?'

'I don't have to answer. If that's all you've phoned me for then you're wasting your time.'

'I don't think so. The fact that you're not telling me is answer enough,' he said with a smile in his voice. 'If you had agreed to marry Paul you'd have been quick to ram it down my throat. Congratulations, Kristie—you've done the right thing.'

'Damn you!' she spat.

Another smile from him—a triumphant smile. She could see it in her mind's eye. He would consider her fair game now. Her life would be sheer hell. Unless she succumbed, of course. And it would be so easy to do that. Even thinking about it sent a trail of destruction through her body. 'It's time for me to go home,' she said tersely. 'Is that all you've phoned me for?'

'What are you thinking, Kristie?' he asked in a low, seductive voice. 'You sound panic stricken. Are you afraid that you might do the unthinkable and let yourself actually like me?'

'Never!'

'Never is a long time. And we've already got through one barrier.'

'Which I deeply regret,' she riposted. 'There certainly won't be a repeat.'

'Mm, I wonder.'

The way he said it, suggesting that he'd enjoy trying and would undoubtedly find her easy prey, created further unwanted sensations. Because she knew beyond any shadow of doubt that she would be unable to resist him if he made a full-scale attack on her senses. Radford Smythe *was* irresistible. There, she'd admitted it. She'd fallen for him.

Heaven help her.

'I hear my mother's invited you to dinner tonight. It's a pity I won't be there.'

'Maybe that's the very reason she invited me,' suggested Kristie. 'Maybe she knows that I don't like you.'

'My mother thinks everyone should fall in love with me. I'm her blue-eyed boy, didn't you know that?'

Kristie gave a mirthless laugh. 'It's natural she'd have a biased view—mothers always do.' She did herself. She thought Jake was the most gorgeous, intelligent little boy there ever was. There was no one to beat him. It didn't matter that he was adopted; she loved him as if he were her own child.

'I'll be back by the weekend. Enjoy yourself tonight.'

'I'll do my best.'

'I'll be thinking of you,' he added on a soft growl.

And she would be thinking what a relief it was that he wasn't joining them. Except that the conversation would be sure to touch on him. There would really be no escape. His presence would be felt whether he was there or not. She slammed down the phone and was fuming as she walked to the car. She really ought not to have accepted Peggy's invitation.

Normally, when she was driving, she kept her mobile phone switched on in case Chloe needed to get in touch with her. But she was so disturbed by her conversation with Radford that she forgot. When she arrived home she found an empty house—and a hastily scribbled note from Chloe to say that Jake had had an accident and been taken to hospital.

Kristie's heart panicked as she raced back to her car. What kind of an accident? Oh, God, please, please, don't let anything happen to him, she prayed.

CHAPTER FOURTEEN

RADFORD felt pleased after he had finished talking to Kristie. She wasn't going to marry Paul after all. He felt on top of the world, fairly dancing around his London apartment. She might still try to keep her distance but there was hope now where there had been none before.

Later he was having dinner with a client but for the moment he could devote all his thoughts to the woman he loved. He only had to think about her to feel an arousal. Especially when he pictured her stunning naked body. She was incredibly beautiful—so slender, so perfectly formed, with skin as soft as thistledown. If it hadn't been for that photograph of Tarah he would have made love to her. It would, he felt, have been a turning point in their relationship.

He wondered then, as he had at the time, whether Kristie knew who he was. There had been an odd inflection in her voice when she'd asked him whether he recognised Tarah. And if she did know why hadn't she mentioned it?

When he took his shower later he was still thinking about her. It would give him a great deal of pleasure to melt her resistance. He was looking forward to it immensely.

A little red light blinked at him from the telephone, telling him he had missed a call. Perhaps tonight's engagement was off? He wouldn't mind because he could sit here thinking about Kristie, planning how he would woo her. The mere thought of it gave him immense pleasure.

He pressed the button. 'Radford, pick up the phone.' It was his mother, impatient as usual to speak with him, hating having to talk to a machine. 'I've just had a call from Chloe, Kristie's friend. Jake's in hospital. I thought you'd want to know.'

His heart leapt into his throat and he immediately phoned his mother back. But she couldn't tell him anything more. 'Something about an accident. I don't know exactly. But if I hear anything I'll—'

'I'm on my way,' cut in Radford at once. 'Kristie will need someone with her. Which hospital is it?'

Kristie was out of her mind with worry. Jake was in surgery and there was nothing she could do but wait. Chloe was in floods of tears. 'It's all my fault,' she kept saying. 'I'll never forgive myself, never.'

When Kristie arrived at the hospital it had taken her ages to get any sense out of Chloe. The girl kept sobbing uncontrollably, beside herself with worry and guilt and Kristie had to shout at her to make her stop and tell her what had happened.

'I picked Jake up from school as usual,' she said tremulously. 'We were almost home when he saw the Browns' new little puppy in their garden. He let go my hand and raced across the road before I could stop him. He didn't even look.'

There were more sobs before she could go on.

'I saw the car and I yelled at Jake, but it was too late. The driver didn't stand a chance of stopping. Jake looked like a rag doll as he was flung in the air.' Chloe buried her face in her hands, her shoulders heaving as she relived that fateful moment. 'He didn't move. I was so scared—I thought he was dead.' She couldn't go on then, her throat was choked with emotion and the tears wouldn't stop. 'Oh, God, Kristie, what have I done? I am so sorry.'

Tears streamed down Kristie's cheeks too but she tried

to be strong for Chloe's sake. 'Don't blame yourself. It could have happened to me.' Jake adored the little dog and at times like that, no matter how often he'd been told not to run across the road without checking for traffic, he would forget. All he'd be interested in was the puppy.

Suddenly she remembered that she was supposed to be dining at the Mandervell-Smythes' and she gave Chloe the task of phoning Peggy and explaining. It was something for the girl to do and for a few minutes took her mind off the terror of what had happened. Nevertheless they were both still clinging to each other and crying when one of the doctors came to find them. He smiled reassuringly. 'Which one of you is Jake's mother?'

'I am,' answered Kristie, standing up. 'How is he?'

'We've just finished operating. You have nothing to worry about—he'll pull through.'

He would never know what a relief it was to hear him say that. Kristie felt like kissing him. 'Is he badly hurt?' Chloe had been unable to tell her anything.

'He's very bruised, naturally, and he has a broken arm, but he also ruptured his spleen, which was our main concern. He lost a lot of blood and he'll need a top up, but other than that he'll do fine. He's a very lucky young boy. I suggest you both go and have a cup of tea.'

'Can I see him?' A drink was the furthest thought from her mind.

'As soon as we get him settled in ITU. I'll come and find you myself.' He laid a reassuring hand on Kristie's shoulder. 'No more tears now.'

She smiled weakly and thanked him, and she and Chloe headed for the cafeteria. The coffee was strong and bitter and, although she was still desperately worried it stopped her from shaking.

The tears started again though when she saw Jake. He

was asleep, so still and pale and tiny and vulnerable, that it was all she could do not to throw herself down beside him and hug him and hug him and will some of her strength into him. Thank God he was alive. She'd had all sorts of visions as she had raced to the hospital, even while she'd sat waiting for news. In fact, the relief of seeing him made her legs buckle and Chloe was the one to slide her a chair.

She lost track of time as she sat at his bedside holding his hand, stroking his brow, trying to ignore all the tubes that were fixed to his tiny body. He was constantly monitored and checked and every time the nurse came Kristie asked if he was all right and was reassured that everything was as it should be.

Kristie sent Chloe home. There was nothing she could do and Kristie had listened to enough apologies. It was while she was whispering to Jake that she loved him and would he please hurry and wake up so that she could talk to him that she felt a hand on her shoulder.

Looking up, she saw Radford and for the first time ever she was pleased to see him. He was someone solid she could depend on. She stood up and, as his arms came about her, she buried her head in his shoulder, tears flowing again, but tears of relief this time. She didn't have to bear this alone.

Radford pulled up a chair and sat beside Kristie, holding her hand, murmuring soothing words, not really knowing what he was saying, or even caring. His main concern was Kristie. He'd stood a few moments watching her before he had made his presence known and his heart had gone out to her. She'd looked so fragile, so afraid, willing her life into this battered little boy.

Daylight was filtering into the room when Jake woke. They had both sat watching him for a very long time, talk-

ing quietly. Kristie had explained what had happened and
he'd expressed his concern. And all the time Jake lay there
pale and lifeless, only the machine that monitored him telling them that he was alive.

Then the boy's eyes slowly opened. 'Mummy,' he whispered.

'Darling.' Mindful of his injuries, Kristie carefully
hugged him.

'I love you, Mummy.'

'I love you too, sweetheart.'

'I'm tired.' And he drifted back to sleep.

'He's going to be all right,' she said with a relieved
smile.

Radford nodded. 'And now that you know, don't you
think you ought to go home and get some sleep yourself?'

Kristie shook her head very definitely. 'Not until he's
properly awake and I know for certain.'

'So let's go and get some coffee.' She looked desperately
tired and very pale too. He took her arm as she got to her
feet and he didn't let it go as they walked to the cafeteria.
It wasn't yet open but there was a hot drinks machine
nearby and they sat on the corridor chairs with their plastic
cups cradled in their hands.

'How did you know about Jake?' asked Kristie.

'My mother phoned and told me.'

'And you drove all the way from London just to be with
me?'

He nodded. 'It was the least I could do. I couldn't let
you suffer alone. I bet Chloe's not feeling too happy?' He
didn't tell her that he'd nearly had an accident too. In his
desperation to be with her he'd been driving far too fast,
had only come to his senses when he'd almost hit a car
that had swerved in front of him on the motorway.

'She can't stop apologising. It's why I sent her home. It's not her fault. Kids will be kids.'

'That's very magnanimous of you. Are you sure she deserves it?' If it had been his child he'd have throttled the woman.

'So long as Jake's OK I can't really lay the blame on her.'

'And you'll carry on employing her?'

'Of course. Jake loves her. The ideal solution would be for me to give up work myself and look after Jake full time, but needs must. I can't live on fresh air.'

'If you married me you wouldn't need to work again.' Dammit, he hadn't meant to say that. Not in this place, not at this time. What the hell was he thinking of? He felt her go tense beside him. 'I'm sorry. That was uncalled for. Forget I said it.' But he wouldn't forget. He would say it again one day, when Jake was better, when he felt the time was right.

'Let's go and see if Jake's awake,' she said quietly.

A nurse stood by the bed, checking the blood that was steadily dripping into Jake, and she smiled as they approached. 'Your little man's fully awake, dying to see his mummy and daddy.'

'I'm not the father,' said Radford.

'Oh, well, whoever you are I'm sure he'll be pleased to see you,' responded the nurse cheerfully. 'He's doing well.'

Radford smiled as he watched Kristie give her son a big kiss. The bond between them was unmistakable. Such tenderness, such love. Would he ever experience that? He turned his head away, feeling an unexpected lump in his throat. The nurse had gone and he busied himself looking at all the equipment, giving Kristie a moment or two alone with her son. The label on the blood caught his attention and for a second it surprised him. AB negative. Very rare.

He was AB positive himself and he understood that two positives made a negative. He looked at Kristie. 'Your blood group must be rare too. Something else we have in common.'

She glanced at him and shook her head and turned her attention quickly back to Jake.

He frowned. Something didn't add up here. 'What are you saying?'

This time when she glanced at him there was a haunted expression in her eyes and a look of guilt on her face and for a moment he couldn't understand what was wrong. Then he looked at Jake—and he saw what he should have seen clearly before. He saw Tarah, not Kristie.

He looked at Kristie again and there was nothing of Jake in her. Could this, therefore, be Tarah's child and Kristie had taken him in when her sister had died? And if that was the case, who was the father? Did it, could it, be *his* son? His heart leapt into his throat. No, no, it had to be some other man's. Tarah hadn't been pregnant when their affair had ended. But the blood groups? Was it too much of a coincidence? The time span was right. Perhaps she had been pregnant and hadn't told him. And Kristie's stricken expression suddenly said it all.

She had been watching him, seeing the thoughts flood through his mind, seeing realisation dawn, and she turned away with a cry of despair.

But he said nothing in front of Jake. He waited until the boy had drifted to sleep again then he took Kristie outside into the corridor. 'You and I have to talk,' he said grimly. 'Jake's my son, isn't he?'

Kristie looked anywhere but into his eyes and he took her by the shoulders and forced her to face him. 'Isn't he?'

She nodded uncomfortably.

His suspicions confirmed, Radford felt a most peculiar

pang in his stomach. He couldn't even begin to describe it. He let her go and turned away, then he turned back again just as quickly. 'My son!' he rasped. 'And you never told me. God in heaven, woman, why?'

He was disappointed in her. She had shattered both his trust and the love that had been growing inside him. Tarah had let him down, and now Kristie too. What had she hoped to gain from it? He couldn't begin to understand her reasoning. She hadn't even let on that she knew who he was. Why?

Because she'd wanted to keep Jake to herself, that was why. She was one of those possessive women who couldn't bear to share. Like Tarah! Tarah had been possessive. She had hated it when he had so much as looked at another girl. He felt truly crushed.

'Why, Kristie?' He needed to hear it from her own lips.

'Because he's mine now,' she shrieked, becoming suddenly furiously alive. 'I adopted him. He's nothing to do with you.' He had never seen her so incensed. Her eyes had darkened dramatically and were fiercely beautiful.

'How can you say that?' His thick brows beetled across his forehead. 'He's very much my son, and I think the law would agree with me.' He wanted Jake—he wanted him with a passion that surprised him. From being a man who couldn't care less about children he had become an enraged father all in one fell swoop. This was his own flesh and blood and belonged with him. Kristie could go to hell.

'It was the law who let me adopt him,' she pointed out. 'He's been mine since he was a few hours old, and if you think you're going to—'

'What do you mean, a few hours?' he cut in, feeling a cold chill steal down his spine.

'Tarah died shortly after he was born. She never even

got to hold him. So he's mine, and I shall see to it that you never get your hands on him.'

This was getting out of control, and a hospital corridor was no place to argue. He needed time to think. 'I'm going home to get washed and changed,' he said. 'I suggest you do the same. I'll speak to you again later.'

Outside the hospital Radford took several deep, steadying breaths. His whole world had been turned upside down in a matter of minutes. He was a father. Jake was his son. It was beyond comprehension. He wondered whether Kristie would ever have told him. He was disappointed in her, deeply disappointed. How could she have been so cruel?

It was hard to believe that all along she had known who he was, and yet he still couldn't understand why she hated him so much. Or perhaps it wasn't hatred—perhaps it was because she had thought he would take Jake off her if he ever found out, and so she'd tried to keep him at arm's length. What she hadn't taken into account was the fact that she might be attracted to him. She could deny it as much as she liked but her body told a different story. And he didn't think it was pure lust because Kristie didn't strike him as being that type of person.

But this had nothing to do with their current dilemma. She had let him down. He was hurt that she had kept the knowledge to herself. They were two for a pair, these sisters. Tarah had shattered his trust all those years ago and Kristie had done the same now. Dammit, why did he always fall for the wrong type? Why couldn't he see through them? Was he doomed never to get married?

But the fact was that he now had a son and he intended to fight Kristie tooth and nail for custody of him. To hell with the fact that she'd adopted him—there had to be a way round it.

When he got home he told his concerned mother about Jake's injuries, but not about his discovery. That could wait. He had a lot of thinking to do first.

Kristie didn't go home; she stayed with Jake. She was petrified now that she would lose him. Her worst nightmare was being realised. The law would be on Radford's side, he'd said. Would it? Could he take Jake off her? She didn't know and her ignorance was her biggest fear.

Chloe came back and when she saw Kristie's pale, strained face she insisted that she go home and get some rest. 'I'll sit with Jake. I won't let anything else happen to him, I promise.'

Kristie reluctantly agreed. She'd had no sleep for twenty-four hours and was on the verge of collapse. Coupled with Radford finding out about Jake, she felt drained of every possible emotion. But what if he came back while she was absent? What if he'd already set the law into motion? Her mind spun out of control. She heard Chloe cry out, felt her legs give way, and the next thing she knew she was sitting in a chair and a nurse was offering her a glass of water.

'What happened?' she croaked as she took a sip of the cool liquid.

'You fainted. You haven't eaten or slept for the last twenty-four hours. You must go home now and go to bed.'

'But Jake,' she protested. She was scared of leaving him.

'Jake will be all right. He's having the very best of attention.'

'You won't leave him alone?' They didn't know that Radford might come along and kidnap him. And she was being fanciful. He couldn't do anything while Jake was in this state.

The nurse smiled. 'Of course we won't leave him. Besides, your friend's here. Your son likes Chloe, doesn't he?

And there's your boyfriend as well. I expect he'll be back soon.'

Kristie closed her eyes. Boyfriend! Enemy would be more like it. She didn't want him anywhere near Jake. And yet how could she stop him? He had as much right as she had. Possibly more. It hurt her to even think that, but Jake was his flesh and blood after all.

Chloe said now, 'You don't look fit to drive, Kristie. I'll run you home and then come straight back.'

'No!' She almost screeched the word, and both Chloe and the nurse looked at her in surprise. 'I can drive myself. I'll be OK. I want you to stay with Jake. He'll be scared when he wakes up if neither of us are here.'

She saw the nurse look at Chloe over the top of her head and lift her brows. They clearly both thought she was being neurotic, which she probably was. But with just cause. She finished the water and stood up. She felt slightly unsteady but not enough to stop her walking out of the hospital and driving home. 'I'll see you in a few hours, Chloe,' she said. 'Keep a close watch on Jake and ring me if there's a problem, anything at all.'

'There won't be,' Chloe assured her, but Kristie knew better. There was one very big problem—and his name was Radford Smythe.

Radford woke with a much clearer head. He'd sat up for hours thinking about Jake before finally falling asleep, but now he had everything sorted in his mind.

Discovering that he had a son had been the biggest shock of his life; more so than when he'd found out that Tarah was dead. And he couldn't think how it had happened because he and Tarah had always taken the utmost care. Besides, he'd never wanted children—he'd seen enough of his cousin's two unruly boys to put him off them for life.

But then he'd met Jake, and a more well-behaved or better mannered boy he couldn't have wished to meet. It made him think that maybe it wouldn't be so bad to be a father after all. Perhaps with Kristie as the mother? What a thought that had been. He'd imagined himself marrying her and them having either a brother or sister for Jake.

It had been nothing short of miraculous discovering that Jake was his own flesh and blood. The feelings it evoked were impossible to put into words. He felt—what did he feel? Amazed, for one thing—truly amazed. Exhilarated as well. He had created another human being—a living, loving human being. But also he was angry that he hadn't been told. He could have gone his whole life and never found out. It didn't bear thinking about.

But he was no longer angry with Kristie. She had done what she had thought best. Had she been a scheming woman, which was his first harsh thought, she would have hit him for a financial contribution to Jake's upbringing years ago. As it was, she had struggled to bring him up alone—and had done a very good job of it. Now it was up to him to help her.

And the best solution all round, as far as he could see, was to marry Kristie. That way they would both be happy. The three of them would be happy. Jake would have a father as well as a mother and the family would be complete.

It might take a little while for her to agree to his offer, but even she would surely see that it was by far the best solution. There would be no heartache for either of them. He couldn't wait to put his proposition to her.

But on his arrival at the hospital he found only Chloe. 'Kristie's gone home,' she said. 'She fainted and the nurse insisted she go and get something to eat and then try to sleep.'

Radford's first instinct was to go to her, but he made himself stay and chat to Chloe and Jake for a few minutes. Jake, he was pleased to see, was looking much better. He had colour in his cheeks now and it made Radford's heart swell to look at him and realise that this was his very own son. He wanted to tell Jake, but this wasn't the moment. Soon he would, though; soon they would be a proper father and son. He couldn't wait for that moment.

'I'll go and see how Kristie is,' he said after a while.

'Maybe you ought to take my key,' volunteered Chloe, 'in case she's asleep. It wouldn't be right to wake her. She was so exhausted when she left here.'

He smiled. 'A good idea.' In more ways than one. There was always the chance that Kristie wouldn't let him in, especially after the way he'd threatened her with the law. He was sorry for that now. It had been a heat of the moment thing. He hadn't been able to understand why she hadn't told him and his blood had boiled.

He knocked softly on the door when he arrived at the house but there was no answer and so he turned the key in the lock and walked in. Kristie was nowhere to be seen. He looked through the kitchen window into the garden but she wasn't there either. He called her name and slowly began to mount the stairs, but before he reached the top she appeared before him. She still had the same clothes on as before and she stood staring down at him, arms akimbo, face furious. 'What are you doing here? How did you get in?'

'Chloe lent me her key. I didn't want to bang on the door and wake you.'

'If you thought I might be asleep why did you come?' she retorted. 'You have no right creeping into my house and—'

'I was concerned about you. Chloe said that you'd fainted

and I wanted to make sure you were all right.' He climbed the last steps and halted in front of her. She looked so tired and pale and worried that he wanted to hold her tight and assure her that everything was going to be all right.

'You mean that you've come to tell me you're claiming Jake,' she yelled, her eyes over-bright, her cheeks suddenly flaming. 'Over my dead body. Jake's mine and he's staying mine.'

'Kristie, I'm not going to take him away from you,' he said gently.

'You're not?' She looked surprised. 'Then why—'

'Am I here?' he cut in. 'Because I have the perfect solution. But first of all I want to apologise for the way I spoke to you. I was totally out of order. You've no idea how much of a shock it was to discover that Jake is my son. And when that had sunk in all I wanted was to claim him as mine.'

She looked briefly ashamed.

'But then I realised that it wouldn't be fair on you. You've treated him as your own all these years. You've grown to love him and—'

'He is mine,' she maintained. 'In every sense of the word.'

'I realise that's how you must think, but listen to it from my side. Jake is my flesh and blood. He is my son, whichever way you look at it.' He saw the panic begin to rise. 'And no, I am not going to take him off you; I have a much better idea. And not one that's new to me either. I want you to marry me, Kristie.'

CHAPTER FIFTEEN

RADFORD waited with bated breath for Kristie's answer. To him, getting married was the perfect solution—the only solution. They were compatible in so many ways. And now that she knew she needn't fear that he would take Jake off her, what other reason would she have for saying no?

And yet she did say it. And she didn't mince her words. 'If you think I'd marry a man like you then you don't know yourself very well,' she stormed. 'Just look at the way you treated my sister. Do you really think I'd put myself in the same position? I know what would happen if we did get married. Give it a few months and you'd chuck me out on the dirt pile the same way as you did Tarah—then you'd claim Jake as your own.'

Radford was aghast by Kristie's outburst. He hadn't a clue what she was talking about. What had Tarah said to make Kristie feel like this? 'What are you suggesting?' he asked, a deep frown darkening his brow. 'I didn't—'

'No, of course you didn't do anything, did you?' she cut in furiously. 'You didn't end your relationship simply because you thought she was getting too serious, did you? You didn't end it because you were scared she wanted a family? Oh, no, you wouldn't admit to that.' She was fairly bouncing on her feet now. 'And now that you've discovered you do have a child, then you want him, and you're prepared to go to any lengths to get him. How two-faced is that? Damn you, Radford. Damn you to hell.'

There was something seriously wrong here and he intended to get to the bottom of it. 'Are you suggesting that Tarah told you I was the one to end our relationship?'

'I am.' She folded her arms across her chest and looked at him haughtily. 'She was distraught.'

'Tarah lied.' He tried to keep calm but in reality he was raging inside and he knew it wouldn't be long before he let it all out.

'Oh, you'd say that, wouldn't you,' she snapped. 'Now that she's no longer here to defend herself. What a coward you are. Why won't you admit the truth?'

'It is the truth,' he bellowed, his patience finally running out. 'Tarah was the one to put an end to things. As a matter of fact, she was never the perfect sister that you seem to think. I could tell you a hundred and one things she had wrong with her, but you wouldn't believe me, would you? Blood's thicker than water and all that.' Tarah had been jealous and possessive, but despite that he had loved her and had thought she had loved him. It had come as a shock when she had finished with him.

'And you're Mr Perfect, are you?' Kristie spat, her eyes over-bright, her whole body shaking with rage. 'You killed my sister, do you realise that? If you hadn't got her pregnant she'd never have died. I hate you from the bottom of my heart. Go, now, because I'm very tempted to push you down the stairs and put an end to your life too.'

So this was the reason she had been so hostile towards him. Poor Kristie, how she had suffered. But he knew that nothing he could say at this moment would help matters. 'Maybe I should go.' He breathed in deeply through his nose, his chest rising, his eyes never leaving hers. 'But this isn't the end of our conversation. I still think that getting married is the wisest decision. I'll leave you to think about it. It's either me and Jake, or nothing at all.'

*   *   *

Kristie watched Radford going back down the stairs—she watched with hatred in her eyes and dread in her heart. Not only had she got a sick son to worry about, but the very real fear that she would have him taken off her.

And what was that Radford had said about Tarah dumping him? He had to be lying; he simply did. Tarah wouldn't have told her own sister an untruth; she'd have no reason to. She'd been heartbroken when she had phoned and said that Radford had finished with her. There'd have been no tears if she'd been the one to end their relationship.

But she hadn't got time to think about this now. She must go back to the hospital—Jake would be asking for her. She hadn't slept much—a few short minutes at a time, that was all. It was impossible.

Downstairs she found Chloe's key on the hall table and she slipped it into her pocket. At least it meant that he couldn't sneak up on her again. She'd been scared half to death when she had heard him climbing the stairs; she'd thought it was a burglar, that perhaps in her distress she'd left the front door open.

And as for his suggestion that they get married—was he insane? They both knew his only reason was so that he could get hold of Jake. Kristie didn't take into account the fact that he'd asked her once before; that went completely out of her mind. All she knew was that he wanted Jake and that he'd go to any lengths to get him.

She spent the rest of the day at the hospital, fearful that Radford might put in a further appearance, mightily relieved when he didn't. And that evening she went home with Chloe. She wanted to stay, desperately. She was so afraid of what Radford might do, but in reality she knew that he couldn't do very much, not with Jake attached to so many machines. It would be inhuman to take him away.

Jake wanted Flopsy, his bunny rabbit. It was a soft toy

he'd long outgrown but he wanted it now. Kristie had stored it in the loft with a lot of other toys he no longer used, and it was while she was looking for it that she came upon a box she'd brought back from her sister's flat in London. It contained personal items that she'd not had the heart to look at at the time and she'd forgotten all about them. Now, she decided, might be a good idea to go through them.

But it was long after Chloe had gone to bed before she felt able to do so. Memories had resurrected themselves today. Her conversation with Radford had upset her and she'd said things she didn't mean, like wanting to push him down the stairs. When she said it she had meant it, but not now. He hadn't known Tarah was pregnant when they split up. She couldn't, in all honesty, lay the blame on him. Even though she had done so all these years.

So what had caused her change of heart? Was it because she had fallen in love with him? Because she had, there was no doubt about it. It wasn't something that she'd wanted to happen—the feelings had crept up on her unawares and, if she was honest with herself, she would rather she didn't feel anything. It would make things so much easier if she still hated him—because she felt very sure that she was going to have a fight on her hands where Jake was concerned.

She went cold all over every time she thought about Jake and the near miss he'd had. He could so easily have been killed. Her whole life would have been ruined because he *was* her life.

When she finally opened the box the first thing Kristie picked up was a photograph of Tarah and Radford. They were both laughing, having clearly set the camera to take the picture automatically. Kristie had done that with herself and Jake many times and it was always a mad scramble to get into position in time.

Tarah looked so happy, her head resting on Radford's shoulder, his arm around her. They were a perfect couple and Kristie found it hard to believe that Tarah would have ended their relationship. Why had she done that? Why would she have lied? What had really happened? Would she ever find out?

There were more photographs, some of Tarah on her own, posing, pouting, flirting, being typically outrageous Tarah, and some taken again with Radford. A few were of Radford on his own. Kristie studied these, wondering what the odds were against her meeting the man who had been her sister's lover. A man who lived over a hundred miles away. And, what was more amazing, she had fallen in love with him.

It was a preposterous thought, one that had dawned on her slowly over the last few days. He aroused her sexually, yes, but that was all, she had kept telling herself. She didn't like him in any other sense. They'd done nothing but fight since they'd met. How could it be love?

She tucked the thought away and looked at some more photographs. There were a few of Tarah with her husband, the man who had cheated on her. He was good-looking too, though not as tall as Radford, and he had blond hair. Kristie had never truly liked him.

Tarah's taste in men hadn't been the same as hers, another reason why it was hard to accept that she had fallen in love with Radford. It couldn't be love. Love didn't stand a chance, feeling as she did about him.

Kristie put the box on one side and went into the kitchen to make herself a cup of coffee. And remembered the time she and Radford had stood here doing exactly the same thing. Heavens, there were memories of him everywhere.

She went to bed without looking at anything else in the box. They would wait for another time. She wished she could do the same with her thoughts of Radford. Why couldn't she push them to one side too? Why did they keep intruding? Because, she told herself severely, he's a part of your life now whether you wish it or not. Jake has bound you irrevocably to him.

Jake was sufficiently improved the next day to be moved out of intensive care to a children's ward. It did Kristie's heart good to see him chatting and laughing and she didn't feel quite so bad about leaving him. Radford didn't put in an appearance at all, much to her relief, although she was told that he'd telephoned several times.

As on the night before, Kristie waited until Chloe had gone to bed before she pulled out Tarah's box. There were some beautiful pieces of jewellery, some of which she had never seen before. Were they presents from Radford? Kristie's heart sank. There she went again, thinking of him. What did it matter who they were from? Except that she might have worn some of them herself, but not if they'd been given to her by Jake's father; not in a million years. And she had no way of knowing unless she asked him, which she had no intention of doing.

At the very bottom of the box were Tarah's diaries. When she'd originally found them Kristie had been surprised because she hadn't even known that her sister kept a diary, and as she glanced through them now she felt guilty. It was like invading her privacy.

There was the break-up of her marriage—heart-rending stuff. Tarah had poured every ounce of grief into these tear-stained pages and Kristie's eyes felt moist as she read them. Her sister had put on such a brave face at the time. Kristie herself hadn't known how much she was suffering.

Suddenly Radford's name sprang out from the page.

Their first meeting. Her instant love for him. Her euphoria at having found a man she felt she could spend the rest of her life with. For months the ecstasy continued, but then the pages became smudged with tears again, everything was not going as it should.

He doesn't want children, he hates them. And he doesn't want me any more. I've seen him out with another girl. He says it's a new author but I can tell he's excited about her. I'm fed up of playing second fiddle.

The writing became more and more illegible as her tears washed away whole sentences, but Kristie managed to decipher the important words.

It's all over. He's finished with me.

So bang went Radford's declaration that Tarah had been the one to end their affair. Here was the proof. Kristie slammed the diary shut but she was too incensed now to go to bed. She wanted to speak to Radford, to confront him, and she didn't want to wait.

But of course she had to. It was almost midnight, far too late to phone him, but first thing tomorrow, she promised herself, before she went to the hospital she would ring him and tell him exactly what she thought of him and his idea of them getting wed. Not that she'd even entertained such a thing; it was a ludicrous suggestion. He'd only made it because he wanted Jake, and if he thought she couldn't see through that then he was being particularly insensitive.

In the event, Kristie didn't have to phone him; he turned up on her doorstep at half past eight the following morning. Chloe looked pleased and excited as she showed Radford into the living room where Kristie was doing some work on her computer. Chloe thought he was God's gift and would like nothing better than for the two of them to fall in love. At least she knew nothing about Radford being Jake's father, thought Kristie, or she would never have given her a minute's peace. She would have thought they were destined for each other.

'What are you doing here?' was her first blunt question as she stood up to face him. He looked awfully good in a sky-blue shirt and pale chinos. And, despite the fact that she resented every inch of him, she couldn't ignore the sudden bump of her heart.

His eyebrows rose. 'Now is that any way to greet the father of your child?'

'Shh!' Kristie looked anxiously at the doorway. 'Chloe doesn't know.'

Radford lifted his wide shoulders in an indifferent shrug. 'She'll find out soon enough.'

'Not from me, she won't.'

'Why? When we're married it will become common knowledge.' His smile held all the pleasure of a predatory animal.

'And is that why you're here?' she demanded. 'To see what my answer is? Well, I'll tell you. It's no. You don't stand a cat in hell's chance.'

His eyes glittered and narrowed on to her face. 'Is that a wise decision?'

Kristie glared. 'That sounds like a threat. I can assure you, Mr—'

'And I can assure you, Kristie,' he cut in swiftly, 'that I'll do everything within my power to get Jake. Marriage would be the simplest and least painful option but if that's out of the question then prepare yourself for battle.'

CHAPTER SIXTEEN

'OF COURSE it's out of the question,' Kristie declared fiercely. 'Why would I want to marry a liar?'

'I beg your pardon?' Radford's frown bit even deeper into his forehead.

'You lied,' she accused. 'You said that Tarah had finished with you.'

'Yes.'

'Well, I have proof that she didn't. You were the one who ended the affair.'

'Oh, yes?' The brows lifted now into his hairline.

'Yes! I've found her diaries—it's all there.'

'Then your sister was lying.'

'To her diary?' she asked incredulously. 'I don't think so.'

'Let me tell you a few things about your sister,' he said. 'Maybe you didn't know her as well as you thought.'

Kristie shot him a scornful glance. 'Nonsense. Until she moved to London we were inseparable. I know everything there is to know about Tarah.'

Radford took her hand and led her to the settee. 'Sit down and listen.'

'I will not sit down,' she fumed, snatching her hand away. 'This is my house; you have no right taking over.' But he was, whether she wanted him to or not. In truth he was taking over her body. The mere touch of his hand had set her senses sizzling and it was wrong. How could she feel like this about a man who was trying to take Jake away from her? How could she love such a man?

171

'Then we'll talk standing up.'

His grey eyes were steady on hers and she felt herself being pulled inexorably into their depths. She felt her whole body being taken over. This was madness, sheer madness. She shook her head and sank on to the settee—anything to break eye contact. This is your enemy, she told herself fiercely. Don't ever forget that.

Radford spoke quietly. 'I loved Tarah. When I first met her I thought I had found the girl I wanted to marry. She moved in with me. We had a lot of good times together, but then the true Tarah began to emerge.'

Kristie frowned. 'What do you mean, the true Tarah?'

'Your sister was a very possessive woman.'

'You mean she didn't like you taking other girls out,' flashed Kristie, bouncing back to her feet. She wasn't going to allow this man to say things about her sister that weren't true. 'Don't forget I've read her diary; it's all there.'

'Tarah wouldn't listen to the truth,' he told her, his mouth grim at the memories. 'She put her own interpretation on events. I was never unfaithful to her but she wasn't convinced. She wanted me to account for every second of my time. I had a third degree every evening when I arrived home. She became neurotic about it. I even caught her spying on me when I took an author out to lunch.'

Kristie couldn't accept this. He was lying; he had to be, to save his own face.

'Your sister had a split personality,' he went on. 'On the surface she was every man's dream, but the other side of her proved to be a nightmare. I'm sorry to say that, and I don't expect you to believe me, but—'

'No, I don't,' she spat. 'I'll show you her diary. You'll soon see that—'

He stopped her quickly. 'I don't want to see it.'

'Because you're afraid?'

'Because I think we ought to carry on with this discussion some other time, when you've had a chance to digest and think about what I've said. It might even be a good idea to read her diary again to make sure you weren't mistaken.' He turned towards the door. 'Perhaps I'll see you at the hospital?' he asked over his shoulder.

'Jake doesn't need you,' she flung. 'He's out of intensive care now—he's recovering well.'

'Yes, I know,' he said, swinging round to look at her.

Kristie frowned.

'I visited him last night after you'd left.'

Sheer cold horror filled her body. It would be easy for him to kidnap Jake now that he wasn't under scrutiny every minute of the day. What was she to do? Was she never going to get a minute's peace again for fear of this man?

'You surely didn't think I was going to ignore my son? I know you didn't want me there—it's why I chose to visit later. At least he was pleased to see me. I think we're developing quite a bond.' And with that parting shot he headed out of the door.

Kristie sat down before her legs buckled. A bond! Damn! What was she to do?

Marry the guy, suggested her conscience.

But I can't.

Why not?

Because he's a liar and he killed my sister.

Now you're overreacting. I thought you loved him?

I do.

Then what's your problem? Sort it out with him. Don't make a mistake you'll regret for the rest of your life.

Would she regret it? Kristie didn't know. The way she was thinking at this moment, no. But later, when she'd calmed down, when she'd had time to think rationally, what then? She shook her head. Why had life become so complicated?

All the time she was at the hospital Kristie kept looking over her shoulder for Radford. Even Jake asked where he was. 'I like him, Mummy,' he said. 'He's kind. He bought me this car.'

It was an exact replica of Radford's own car, and if Jake had told her once that Radford had given it to him he'd told her a hundred times. She was fed up with hearing it. 'He's a busy man, Jake. You can't expect him to keep visiting you.'

'Why? He can come when he finishes work. Don't you like him, Mummy?'

There must have been something in her voice. Jake was a sensitive little soul, always picking up on her moods. 'Of course I like him.' But even to her own ears it didn't sound convincing.

It wasn't until later, when she got home, that thoughts of Tarah slipped back into Kristie's mind. She sat with a glass of wine and let her thoughts wander. Chloe had gone out, thankfully, because after Radford's visit that morning she'd plied her with questions, all of which Kristie had refused to answer.

And as she leaned back and closed her eyes memories of long ago returned. Times when she and her sister were teenagers and Tarah had been in the throes of first love. She had once flown in a rage at Kristie and had accused her of trying to take her boyfriend off her, whereas Kristie had done no such thing. She'd spoken to the boy, yes, but that had been all.

There had been other occasions too when Tarah had developed irrational jealousy, moments that Kristie had completely forgotten about until now. She'd also been extremely possessive about her clothes or her jewellery, never letting Kristie borrow anything but often taking something belonging to her sister without even asking.

But Kristie had dismissed all this—sibling rivalry was part of growing up as far as she was concerned. She hadn't dreamt for one minute that Tarah had still behaved in such a manner. Could it be that Radford was right and she was wrong? But the diary? Tarah wouldn't have lied to her diary.

Urgently now, Kristie fetched it and settled back into her seat. It didn't take her long to find the page she was looking for and it took her even less time to realise that she had read into it what she had wanted to read. It was barely legible because of Tarah's tears, but she was just able to make out that it was her sister who had finished with Radford and not the other way round.

Tears filled her own eyes then and fell on the page to join those of her sister. It was a deeply emotional moment and she felt as though a release valve had been opened inside her and all the resentment and hatred that she had felt for Radford was freeing itself and flying away into infinity.

She felt sorry for her sister, sorry that she hadn't been with her at the time because then maybe Tarah would never have felt the need to lie. But grateful to Radford for insisting that she look at Tarah's diary again. *He* wasn't a liar! A smile lit her face. He was a good, honourable man who had treated her sister fairly and she owed him a huge apology.

The next two weeks in the diary were blank. Clearly Tarah had been too upset to write anything more. But then came the news:

I'm pregnant. I've finally got the better of Radford. I've got something of his that he can never take away from me.

Instead, thought Kristie sadly, Tarah's life had been taken away from her.

For the rest of the evening she felt unutterably sad, and when she went to the hospital the next day she found Radford there talking to Jake. Not that she said anything in front of her son. He was delighted to have his two favourite people visiting him at the same time.

'Mummy, Radford's brought me another car. Look, a red one. It's a Porsche.'

'You're a very lucky boy,' she told him. 'I hope you thanked him properly.'

'I did, didn't I?' asked Jake, looking up trustingly at Radford.

'You certainly did, son.'

Kristie cringed. Son! And this time he meant it. And the hardest thing was that Jake was getting attached to Radford. He'd be asking next whether he could be his daddy since Paul had disappeared from the scene. She'd actually tried ringing Paul because she felt sad that they'd parted, but he was never in and never returned her messages. And, in all honesty, it didn't surprise her. He needed to get on with his life.

When it was time for Jake to have his lunch Radford suggested they go out somewhere to eat too. 'You look as though you've been starving yourself,' he said.

How could she eat when so much was going on in her life? And she certainly didn't feel like eating now, not with Radford anyway. But she had no choice. He took her elbow and led her from the ward. 'We'll be back later, son,' he called cheerfully.

In his car Kristie's body reacted instantly to his and she knew that it would be foolish to continue fighting him now that she knew the truth. He was right—marriage was the perfect solution, both from Jake's point of view and her own. But could she be really sure that she would be doing the right thing? Wasn't Radford's main aim to get his hands on Jake? Except that he had hinted at marriage before he'd found out about his son. It was all so confusing.

They went to a hotel for their meal—Radford had booked a private dining suite. She glanced round at the elegant room, where a table for two was set near the window overlooking a lake. At the other end were plump easy chairs and a couch. 'You had this planned all along?'

'We needed somewhere to talk and not be disturbed.'

It was the 'not be disturbed' bit that made Kristie's heart flutter liked a trapped butterfly. She waited until their orders were taken and their pre-dinner drinks brought to them before she said quietly, 'I re-read Tarah's diary.'

'You did?' he asked, sipping his iced water.

'Mmm, yes,' she mumbled, not happy at having to confess to being wrong. She had perched on the edge of the couch, a fatal mistake, she realised, when Radford sat beside her.

'And?'

'You were right—she was the one who ended your affair. The page was tear-stained; it was an easy mistake.'

'So do I get an apology?' he asked with a twinkle in his eye.

Kristie was relieved to see he wasn't angry with her and she nodded. 'I truly am sorry. I should never have doubted you.'

'I guess it was natural that you would take your sister's side,' he said with a faint shrug. 'But I would never lie to you, Kristie.'

'I know that now,' she said quietly. 'I was so sure that you were the bad guy in all of this that I wouldn't have believed you if you'd sworn on the bible. Can you ever forgive me?'

'It might take a little while,' he said, but he was smiling and Kristie knew that he was teasing. She felt incredibly happy all of a sudden.

'I'm glad we've sorted it out,' she said, with the strongest urge to kiss him. Even during her periods of intense hatred she had wanted him. It was a feeling she'd buried and tried to forget, but now it rushed to the surface as though it had suddenly been mercifully released.

'I think we should drink to it.' He raised his glass. 'To a new understanding.'

'A new understanding,' she replied, wondering where that understanding was going to lead.

'What are you thinking?' Radford had seen differing emotions chase across her face. They had changed from relief to terror, which wasn't exactly what he had been hoping for. Now that she had discovered he wasn't a total reprobate he had expected a little more warmth from her. In fact, he was hoping that today would be a turning point in their relationship.

The passion was in her, he knew that; she had been so ready for him the day he had discovered she was Tarah's sister. And feelings like that didn't just go away—it wasn't something she could turn on and off at will. It was a matter now of trying to resurrect those feelings, of showing her that he cared. Perhaps he ought to tell her that he loved her so that she wouldn't think his sole reason for wanting to marry her was Jake.

There was no doubt that discovering Jake was his son had changed the way he thought about things; it had given him a new insight into life. He had a fearsome duty now. It was an awesome feeling to be responsible for someone so young. He had to be a role model for Jake, guide him through life. There were so many different aspects to think about. And he wanted Kristie at his side as he did so. She'd done such a good job so far in bringing him up that he had nothing but admiration for her.

'Jake's recovering well,' he said and was surprised to see her look suddenly fearful. 'Isn't he?' His heart stopped for a moment. 'Is there something I should know?'

'You're not having him,' she declared fiercely.

So he was right. She still thought he intended to take Jake off her. Admittedly he'd made threats but they'd all been empty ones. What he really wanted was both of them—Jake and Kristie, and he felt quietly confident that he could persuade her to marry him. If not—well, it didn't bear thinking about. Yes, he would want Jake, but he wouldn't want to hurt Kristie in the process. So they'd have to strike a deal. Hopefully, though, it would never come to that.

'I don't intend to take him off you, Kristie,' he said softly. 'How could I do that when you've made him your own?'

There was faint hope in her eyes. 'But you said—'

'I know what I said and it was wrong of me. I want us to share him, Kristie. I want you to marry me.' And, as she opened her mouth to protest, 'Please listen.'

She took a quick gulp of her wine.

'I love you, Kristie. I fell in love with you long before I knew about Jake. Probably from the first moment I met you. If it wasn't love then it was something very akin to it. Finding out what you've done for Jake, for your sister, has served only to strengthen my feelings. You're the most selfless woman I've ever met. I'm proud to love you.'

He remained silent for a moment, trying to judge her reaction. She gave nothing away. Looking at him with her huge green eyes, her expression sad almost. His heart swelled with love and he couldn't help himself. He gathered her to him, not kissing her, simply holding her against his heart.

She neither struggled nor relaxed but he could feel the pulsing beat of her. 'My sweet, Kristie,' he murmured, stroking her hair. 'I know you still have your doubts. I know you think of Tarah and the way you believed I'd treated her. It makes sense now, how much you were against me from the beginning. And I know you still perhaps think I want to take Jake from you, but nothing is further from the truth. I want us to be a family, a real family. Jake is my biological son but he's your son too in every sense of the word. He'd be happy if we married. But if you say yes, and I'm desperately hoping you will, then it must be for all the right reasons. This will be a partnership for life.'

Slowly he felt her relax, and then equally as slowly she lifted her mouth to his. Her first voluntary kiss. He felt as though he'd been given the moon and the stars and the sun all rolled into one, but he was careful to keep the kiss gentle, to take only what was offered. 'Is this your answer?' he asked gruffly. 'Is this your way of saying yes?'

'Yes,' she whispered shyly against his mouth.

Lord, she tasted so sweet, smelled so intoxicating, that he couldn't help himself. His arms tightened and his lips ground against hers in a kiss so suddenly possessive that she couldn't mistake his meaning.

Neither of them heard the door to their private room open, or the waiter silently close it again. Time and place had lost all meaning and it was a long, long time before either of them withdrew.

When they did, Kristie made one last appeal. 'It will work, won't it? You won't let me down?'

'Never,' came his strong response. 'You are my perfect woman. For all time. I love you dearly.'

'And I love you too,' she admitted. 'If I'm honest, it didn't take me long to realise that you were not the ogre Tarah painted. Although, naturally, I wouldn't admit it,' she added with a rueful smile. 'I fought for so long against my feelings. You've no idea. And now I'm tired of fighting.'

'I think we should get married straight away,' he said.

'But your sister? We can't take her excitement away from her. We must wait.'

'There you go again, thinking of others before yourself. What a sweet-natured girl you are. How incredibly lucky I am to have found you. Flick's wedding isn't until next June. I can't possibly wait that long. I want to get married now, today, tomorrow, as soon as is humanly possible. And I don't even need you to co-ordinate it—I'll make all the arrangements myself.'

'We must at least wait until Jake's better,' she insisted.

'Of course. Shall we tell him? Shall we go now?' He jumped up and pulled her to her feet.

'But our lunch?'

'Forget lunch. This is all I need.' And he kissed her again thoroughly. He was the world's happiest man.

EPILOGUE

'KRISTIE ELIZABETH SWIFT, do you take this man—'

Kristie was on cloud nine, as she had been ever since agreeing to marry Radford. She gazed into his grey eyes now, answering the Reverend's questions automatically, thinking of nothing except the fact that in a matter of minutes, seconds even, she would become Radford's wife.

All her angst had gone, all her fears, all her hatred; she was deeply in love. It was three weeks since Radford had asked her to marry him, and three weeks had never gone so quickly. His mother had been surprised, though very pleased. Felicity hadn't been surprised at all and was happy for them. She didn't even mind that they had pipped her to the post.

And Jake. Jake had been over the moon. He couldn't quite believe his good luck in finding a father. A real father. He was too young to take it all in but a real father was good enough for him.

'I now pronounce you man and wife.'

Kristie's attention was brought back to the present. This was it. This was the moment she had been waiting for.

'You may kiss the bride.'

And Radford did. Thoroughly. Right there in front of all their guests. Kristie was still on her cloud. She didn't want the kiss to stop in case she woke up and found it was all a dream. But it wasn't a dream. They held hands and they walked down the aisle, and she looked stunningly beautiful in her slender, elegant white wedding dress.

Jake walked behind, his arm still in a sling, but as proud

as Punch in his page-boy suit. 'This is my mummy and daddy,' he said to everyone in the congregation as he walked past. 'My real daddy.'

Everyone smiled benevolently. There were distant cousins of Kristie, an aunt and an uncle, and Chloe and other friends, but mostly they were Radford's relations. Felicity was at the back of the church in her wheelchair and she beamed as they reached her. 'Well done, brother,' she said. 'About time too.'

'Only because I've been waiting for the right lady,' he returned with a grin.

'And now you've found her don't let her go,' she warned.

'Have no fear; she's far too precious for that.' He looked down at Kristie and smiled tenderly. 'Is this day as perfect for you as it is for me?'

'More than perfect,' she told him softly. He looked truly gorgeous in his grey morning suit with a green and blue waistcoat which matched Jake's outfit exactly. As handsome a man as she could wish to meet anywhere and she wondered how she had managed to resist him for so long.

The reception was being held at his family home, with a firm of caterers brought in to do the honours. And, true to his word, Radford hadn't allowed Kristie to do a thing. He had organised it all himself, with perhaps a little help from his mother.

They were postponing their honeymoon until Jake's arm was better because Kristie wanted to be with him when he had the cast taken off. They had talked about where they would live. Radford thought they should both move into his rooms in his mother's house until he found a place for them somewhere nearer to London. He had told her that she could bring Chloe with her to help look after Jake. And so tonight that was where they would be sleeping and Kristie couldn't wait for their guests to go.

The room was enormous and decorated in dark manly colours, but it didn't detract from Kristie's happiness. She had at last found true peace. Accepting that Tarah had been the guilty party had been a hard thing to do, and she was deeply sorry that her sister had made some mistakes but not sorry that she had met Radford. Despite their rocky start, she was confident that the rest of their lives would be one big honeymoon. She loved him more deeply than she had ever imagined possible. And she said this to him now that they were finally alone.

'And I love you too, my darling,' he said as he pulled her close against him. 'More than words can say.'

She lifted her mouth eagerly for his kiss and suddenly there was no time for words. With a smile on his face and hunger in his eyes he undressed her. She wanted to do the same to him but he couldn't wait. He tore his clothes off with indecent haste and, picking her up, he carried her to his bed.

'Now, my sweet darling, I will make you truly mine.'

Kristie had no complaints as he began a slow exploration of her body. It sent every possible kind of desire screaming through her. She wanted him to hurry up and make love to her, but at the same time she luxuriated in the feelings he was managing to arouse.

There was not one inch of her that didn't pulse beneath his touch, and she could feel the heat of his body too beneath her fingertips, his hair-roughened skin, the hard muscles. Lord, he was all man. And he was hers! What a glorious thought. Hers for all time, wasn't that what he'd said? Without a doubt she would love him for ever.

'You are so beautiful, so intoxicatingly beautiful,' he muttered as his mouth closed over hers, as his body brushed against her sensitive breasts, as his fingers worked their magic in the most private part of her.

Kristie had to force air into her lungs and she wrapped her legs around him as he slowly entered her, riding with him, lifting her hips, exhilarating in every thrust he made. It was all and more than she had hoped for. Her surrender was absolute and complete.

She had never before reached such a pinnacle of ecstasy and her cries mingled with his when they climaxed at almost the same time. Their bodies shuddered and came to a slow and gradual stillness. He lay with his arm draped over her, one breast captured, his eyes closed, and Kristie lay looking at him, at this man she loved from the bottom of her heart.

'Maybe we've created another baby,' she said quietly.

The hand on her breast tightened and one eye opened. 'Would you mind?'

'Mind?' she echoed. 'I'd be delirious. Jake needs a brother.'

'Or maybe even a sister? Or perhaps one of each?' His other eye opened and he pushed himself up on one elbow. 'For a man who didn't like children I've suddenly become very fond of them. In fact—' he said, tweaking her nipple, and sending a fresh rush of sensations through her '—I think I want to spend the rest of my life making babies with you.'

Kristie grinned. 'No, sir, two's your limit, but—I have nothing against you spending the rest of your life making love to me. Would you like to do it again—now?'

And, of course, Radford said yes.

On sale 3rd August 2007

*An Italian toyboy, a marriage of convenience,
five adorable babies, and a love lost and found…*

THE ITALIAN'S WIFE BY SUNSET *by Lucy Gordon*

The Rinucci brothers are back! Della's affair with sexy
toyboy Carlo wasn't meant to last, but this is one Italian
determined to win himself a bride…

REUNITED: MARRIAGE IN A MILLION *by Liz Fielding*

Belle's perfect life and gorgeous husband are the envy
of many. But underneath, the truth of their marriage
of convenience is tearing them apart in this first of the
stunning ***Secrets We Keep*** trilogy.

HIS MIRACLE BRIDE *by Marion Lennox*

Shanni doesn't 'do' family, but when she is faced with *five*
little babies to care for – and one extremely handsome helper
– she begins to change her mind…

BREAK UP TO MAKE UP *by Fiona Harper*

Nick and Adele thought their marriage was over – until a
romantic evening by a twinkling fire shows them that the
wonderful thing about breaking up…is making up!

Available at WHSmith, Tesco, ASDA, and all good bookshops
www.millsandboon.co.uk

Blaze

On sale 3rd August 2007

IF YOU COULD READ MY MIND...
by Jeanie London

What if your lover knew your every fantasy? Michael Landry has discovered he can read his wife's mind. And now he knows her secret desires, he knows *just* how to rekindle their spark!

MINUTE BY MINUTE
by Jo Leigh

Meg Becker thinks Alex Rosten is the perfect online boyfriend – clever, sexy and five thousand miles away! But he's sent her a ticket to a gorgeous island resort. Can their virtual fantasies live up to reality?

MIDNIGHT TOUCH
by Karen Kendall

Blue-blooded Kate Spinney is branching out on her own when she meets the raw, sexy Alejandro Torres, who seems determined to take her on a sexual adventure she'll never forget...

MY ONLY VICE
by Elizabeth Bevarly

Rosie Bliss has a *big* thing about the police chief. But when she propositions him, his hands say yes, while his mouth says no. Lucky for Rosie she's hard of hearing...

THE ROYAL HOUSE OF NIROLI

...International affairs, seduction and passion guaranteed

Volume 1 – July 2007
The Future King's Pregnant Mistress by Penny Jordan

Volume 2 – August 2007
Surgeon Prince, Ordinary Wife by Melanie Milburne

Volume 3 – September 2007
Bought by the Billionaire Prince by Carol Marinelli

Volume 4 – October 2007
The Tycoon's Princess Bride by Natasha Oakley

8 volumes in all to collect!

THE ROYAL HOUSE OF NIROLI

*...International affairs, seduction
and passion guaranteed*

Volume 5 – November 2007
Expecting His Royal Baby by Susan Stephens

Volume 6 – December 2007
The Prince's Forbidden Virgin by Robyn Donald

Volume 7 – January 2008
Bride by Royal Appointment by Raye Morgan

Volume 8 – February 2008
A Royal Bride at the Sheikh's Command by Penny Jordan

8 volumes in all to collect!